HIGHER
ALGEBRA
FOR THE UNDERGRADUATE

1964

HIGHER
ALGEBRA
FOR THE UNDERGRADUATE

SECOND EDITION

The late
MARIE J. WEISS

Professor of Mathematics
Newcomb College, Tulane University

Revised by
ROY DUBISCH

Professor of Mathematics
University of Washington

John Wiley & Sons, Inc., New York • London

Preface

In preparing the second edition of *Higher Algebra for the Undergraduate*, I have tried to preserve the organization and spirit of this very teachable text. I have, however, made a large number of minor changes in the interests of clarity and correctness; and a few major changes to provide a better coverage of the basic ideas of elementary abstract algebra.

Among the more significant changes are the following:

1. Many constructive and explicit illustrations of the definitions have been inserted.

2. The number of exercises has been increased by over 40%. Some of the added exercises are additional simple ones in sections where I felt they were needed, but others are more difficult problems designed to challenge the better student.

3. Motivational material has been added before the appearance of unfamiliar constructions (e.g., the negative integers).

4. All technical terms introduced are now italicized for easy identification.

5. References have been brought up to date.

6. A section on ordered integral domains has been added to Chapter 4, and a section on automorphisms of fields to Chapter 9. (The latter section provides a natural introduction to the further study of modern Galois theory.)

7. Probably the most important change is the almost complete rewriting of Chapter 6, "Matrices over a Field." This chapter has been replaced by two: Chapter 6 is now entitled "Vectors and Matrices," and Chapter 7 is now "Systems of Linear Equations."

These new chapters include such previously omitted topics as linear independence and dependence of vectors, the inner product of vectors, and the concept of basis and dimension of a vector space (considered as a set of n-tuples over a field). This portion of the revision is certainly in line with the current trend of more linear algebra at the undergraduate level.

ROY DUBISCH

Seattle, Washington
October 15, 1961

Contents

I The Integers

1 · THE POSITIVE INTEGERS

The mathematical symbols first encountered by everyone are those of the positive integers: $1, 2, 3, \cdots$. These are often called the *natural numbers*. Their properties are familiar to all, and we shall list them systematically. It is not our purpose to develop these properties from a minimum number of hypotheses and undefined terms but rather to list those laws and properties that have long been familiar to the student and to use them as a characterizing definition of the positive integers.

The familiar operations on the positive integers are those of addition and multiplication; that is, for every pair of positive integers a, b we know what is meant by the sum $a + b$ and the product ab and that the sum and product are again positive integers. The fact that the sum and product of any two positive integers are again positive integers is often expressed by saying that the set of positive integers is *closed* under addition and multiplication. As is well known, the positive integers $a, b, c, \cdots$ obey the following laws governing these operations:

The commutative law
    for addition $\qquad\qquad\qquad a + b = b + a,$
    for multiplication $\qquad\qquad\qquad ab = ba.$

The associative law
    for addition $\qquad\qquad a + (b + c) = (a + b) + c,$
    for multiplication $\qquad\qquad a(bc) = (ab)c.$

The distributive law $\qquad\qquad a(b + c) = ab + ac.$

1

For example, $2 + 3 = 5 = 3 + 2$; $2 \cdot 3 = 6 = 3 \cdot 2$; $2 + (3 + 4) = 2 + 7 = 9$ and, also, $(2 + 3) + 4 = 5 + 4 = 9$; $2(3 \cdot 4) = 2 \cdot 12 = 24$ and, also, $(2 \cdot 3)4 = 6 \cdot 4 = 24$; $2(3 + 4) = 2 \cdot 7 = 14$ and, also, $2 \cdot 3 + 2 \cdot 4 = 6 + 8 = 14$.

Many other properties of the positive integers may now be established on the basis of the properties just stated. For example, we sometimes call the distributive law, $a(b + c) = ab + ac$, the *left-hand* distributive law and may establish the *right-hand* distributive law,

$$(b + c)a = ba + ca.$$

For, using in turn the commutative law for multiplication, the left-hand distributive law, and the commutative law for multiplication again, we have $(b + c)a = a(b + c) = ab + ac = ba + ca$.

An illustration of a system in which some of these laws do not hold can be given by arbitrarily defining an addition and a multiplication for positive integers as follows: Denote the new addition by $\oplus$ and the new multiplication by $\odot$. Let $a \oplus b = 2a$ and $a \odot b = 2ab$, where $2a$ and $2ab$ denote the results of ordinary multiplication. Then

$$
\begin{aligned}
& b \oplus a = 2b, \qquad b \odot a = 2ba, \qquad a \oplus (b \oplus c) = a \oplus 2b = 2a, \\
& (a \oplus b) \oplus c = 2a \oplus c = 4a, \qquad a \odot (b \odot c) = a \odot 2bc = 4abc, \\
& (a \odot b) \odot c = 2ab \odot c = 4abc, \qquad a \odot (b \oplus c) = a \odot 2b = 4ab, \\
& \qquad (a \odot b) \oplus (a \odot c) = 2ab \oplus 2ac = 4ab.
\end{aligned}
$$

Note that the commutative and associative laws fail for addition but hold for multiplication. Are there two distributive laws in this system?

Exercises

1. Reduce the left-hand side of the following equalities to the right-hand side by using successively one associative, commutative, or distributive law:

    a. $(3 + 5) + 6 = 3 + (5 + 6)$.   b. $1 + 5 = 5 + 1$.
    c. $2(3 \cdot 5) = (2 \cdot 3)5$.   d. $2(3 \cdot 5) = 5(2 \cdot 3)$.
    e. $6(8 + 4) = 4 \cdot 6 + 6 . 8$.   f. $6(8 \cdot 4) = (4 \cdot 6)8$.
    g. $3(7 + 5) = 5 \cdot 3 + 7 \cdot 3$.   h. $5(6 + 3) = 3 \cdot 5 + 5 \cdot 6$.
    i. $6(5 \cdot 3) = (3 \cdot 6)5$.   j. $4 \cdot 6 + 7 \cdot 4 = 4(7 + 6)$.
    k. $a[b + (c + d)] = (ab + ac) + ad$.
    l. $a[b(cd)] = (bc)(ad)$.   m. $a[b(cd)] = (ab)(cd)$.
             n. $(ad + ca) + ag = a[(g + c) + d]$.

2. Determine whether the operations $\oplus$ and $\bigcirc$ for positve integers x, y defined as follows obey the commutative, associative, and distributive laws:

    a. $x \oplus y = x + 2y$, $x \bigcirc y = 2xy$.   b. $x \oplus y = xy$, $x \bigcirc y = x + y$.
    c. $x \oplus y = x + y^2$, $x \bigcirc y = xy^2$.   d. $x \oplus y = 2(x + y)$, $x \bigcirc y = 2xy$.
    e. $x \oplus y = x^2 + y^2$, $x \bigcirc y = x^2y^2$.

2 · FURTHER PROPERTIES

Some further properties of the positive integers will be listed. Note that the positive integer 1 is the only positive integer such that $1 \cdot a = a$, for every positive integer a. We say that 1 is an *identity* for multiplication. Again the following *cancellation* laws for addition and multiplication hold:

1. If a, b, and x are positive integers and $a + x = b + x$, then $a = b$.
2. If a, b, and x are positive integers and $ax = bx$, then $a = b$.

Moreover, for any two positive integers a and b, either $a = b$, or there exists a positive integer x such that $a + x = b$, or there exists a positive integer y such that $a = b + y$, and only one of these alternatives hold. For example, if $a = 2$ and $b = 2$, $a = b$; if $a = 2$ and $b = 3$, $2 + 1 = 3$; if $a = 3$ and $b = 2$, $3 = 2 + 1$.

From these alternative relations between two positive integers, we can define *inequalities*. If a, b, and x are positive integers such that $a + x = b$, we write $a < b$ (read a less than b) and $b > a$ (read b greater than a). Thus $2 < 3$ and $3 > 2$ since $2 + 1 = 3$. Hence, for any two positive integers, we have the following mutually exclusive alternatives—either $a = b$, or $a < b$, or $a > b$—and we have established an *order relation* between any two positive integers. From the above definition, we may prove the familiar properties of inequalities for positive integers:

1. If $a < b$ and $b < c$, then $a < c$.
2. If $a < b$, then $a + c < b + c$.
3. If $a < b$, then $ac < bc$.

For example, if $a < b$ and $b < c$, then there exist positive integers x and y such that $a + x = b$ and $b + y = c$. Then $(a + x) + y = a + (x + y) = c$ and, since $x + y$ is a positive integer, $a < c$.

Exercises

1. Prove that, if a, b, and c are positive integers and $a < b$, then $a + c < b + c$.
2. Prove that, if a, b, and c are positive integers and $a < b$, then $ac < bc$.
3. Prove that, if a, b, c, and d are positive integers, $a < b$, and $c < d$, then $a + c < b + d$.

3 · FINITE INDUCTION

We come now to the last important property of the positive integers that will be discussed. This property will enable us to make proofs by the method known as *finite induction* or *mathematical induction*.

Postulate of Finite Induction

A set S of positive integers with the following *two* properties contains *all* the positive integers:

1. The set S contains the positive integer 1.
2. If the set S contains the positive integer k, it contains the positive integer $k + 1$.

This postulate is used to prove certain propositions that involve positive integers. The proof is said to be made by finite induction.

First Method of Proof by Finite Induction

Let $P(n)$ be a proposition that is defined for every positive integer n. If $P(1)$ is true, and if $P(k + 1)$ is true whenever $P(k)$ is true, then $P(n)$ is true for all positive integers n.

The proof is immediate by the postulate of finite induction. For consider the set S of positive integers for which the proposition $P(n)$ is true. By hypothesis it contains the positive integer 1 and the positive integer $k + 1$ whenever it contains the positive integer k. Hence the set S contains all the positive integers.

EXAMPLE. Let the power a^n, where n is a positive integer, be defined as follows: $a^1 = a$, $a^{k+1} = a^k \cdot a$. Prove that $(ab)^n = a^n b^n$.

If $n = 1$, we have $(ab)^1 = ab = a^1 b^1$ by the definition. Assume that this law of exponents holds for $n = k$: $(ab)^k = a^k b^k$. Then $(ab)^k(ab) = (ab)^{k+1}$ by definition, and $(ab)^k(ab) = (a^k b^k)(ab)$ by assumption. Applying the associative and commutative laws to the right-hand side of the last equality and using the definition, we have $(ab)^k(ab) = (a^k a)(b^k b) = a^{k+1} b^{k+1}$, which was to be proved. Hence this law of exponents is true for all positive integers n.

Closely allied to the postulate of finite induction is the *well-ordering principle*: In every nonempty set of positive integers there is a smallest positive integer. This principle can be proved from the postulate of finite induction.* We use this principle to establish the

Second Method of Proof by Finite Induction

Let $P(n)$ be a proposition defined for every positive integer n. If $P(1)$ is true, and if, for each m, $P(m)$ is true whenever $P(k)$ is true for all positive integers $k < m$, then $P(n)$ is true for all positive integers n.

Let S be the set of positive integers for which $P(n)$ is false. If S is not empty, it will contain a smallest positive integer m. Note that $m \neq 1$, for

---

* For a proof see H. Eves and C. V. Newsom, *An Introduction to the Foundations and Fundamental Concepts of Mathematics*, New York, Rinehart & Co., 1958; or E. Landau, *Foundations of Analysis*, p. 13, New York, Chelsea Book Co., 1951.

by hypothesis $P(1)$ is true. Hence, for all positive integers $k < m$, $P(k)$ is true. From our induction hypothesis we then have $P(m)$ true, but m is in the set S. Hence the set S is empty.

Exercises

Prove by finite induction for all positive integers n.
1. Use the definition given in the above example to prove the following laws:

   a. $1^n = 1$.   b. $a^m a^n = a^{m+n}$.   c. $(a^m)^n = a^{mn}$.

2. $4 + 8 + 12 + \cdots + 4n = 2n(n + 1)$.
3. $3 \cdot 6 + 6 \cdot 9 + 9 \cdot 12 + \cdots + 3n(3n + 3) = 3n(n + 1)(n + 2)$.
4. $6 \cdot 1^2 + 6 \cdot 2^2 + 6 \cdot 3^2 + \cdots + 6n^2 = n(n + 1)(2n + 1)$.
5. $3 \cdot 1 \cdot 2 + 3 \cdot 2 \cdot 3 + 3 \cdot 3 \cdot 4 + \cdots + 3n(n + 1) = n(n + 1)(n + 2)$.
6. Prove the following theorems by finite induction.

   a. $1 \leq n$ for all positive integers n.
   b. If h and k are any positive integers such that $h < k + 1$, then $h \leq k$.
   c. If m is any positive integer, then there is no positive integer n such that $m < n < m + 1$.

4 · SUMMARY

For the sake of reference we shall now list the properties of the positive integers which fully characterize them. They may be used as a set of postulates for the positive integers.

The system of positive integers has the following properties:

1. The set of positive integers is closed under the two operations addition and multiplication. These operations obey the commutative, associative, and distributive laws.

2. The positive integer 1 has the property $1 \cdot a = a$ for every positive integer a.

3. The cancellation laws hold. If a, b, and x are positive integers:

   i. If $a + x = b + x$, then $a = b$.
   ii. If $ax = bx$, then $a = b$.

4. For any two positive integers a and b, either $a = b$, or there exists a positive integer x such that $a + x = b$, or there exists a positive integer y such that $a = b + y$, and only one of these alternatives hold.

5. The postulate of finite induction holds.

5 · THE INTEGERS

We are familiar with the fact that, given any two positive integers a and b, we cannot always find a positive integer x such that $a + x = b$. This unsatisfactory state of affairs was remedied long ago by the introduction of the negative integers and zero to make up the system of integers. Rather than assuming the properties of integers, however, we will define integers in terms of positive integers and operations with integers in terms of operations with positive integers. Thus we will be able to establish the properties of integers on the basis of the properties of the positive integers. To do this, we consider pairs of positive integers such as (2, 1), (1, 2), etc. We will define equality, addition, and multiplication of such pairs in such a fashion that, for example, the pairs equal to $(a + x, a)$ will behave very much like $(a + x) - a = x$, and the pairs equal to $(a, a + x)$ will behave very much like $a - (a + x) = -x$.

This is the motivation for our considerations. Let us now proceed with a formal treatment of the symbols (a, b), where a and b are positive integers.

Definition of Equality

The equality $(a, b) = (c, d)$ holds if and only if $a + d = b + c$. Although this is not the ordinary concept of equality, as identity, we shall show that it has the usual properties of equality.

Theorem 1.   The equality (a, b) = (c, d) *is:*

1. *Reflexive:* (a, b) = (a, b).
2. *Symmetric: if* (a, b) = (c, d), *then* (c, d) = (a, b).
3. *Transitive: if* (a, b) = (c, d) *and if* (c, d) = (e, f), *then* (a, b) = (e, f).

These properties are readily proved from the definition of equality and the properties of the positive integers. Since $a + b = b + a$, property 1 holds. If $a + d = b + c$, then $c + b = d + a$ and property 2 holds. In property 3 we wish to prove that $a + f = b + e$, given that $a + d = b + c$ and $c + f = d + e$. Now $(a + d) + f = (b + c) + f = b + (c + f) = b + (d + e)$. Thus $(a + f) + d = (b + e) + d$, and, hence, by the cancellation law for positive integers, $a + f = b + e$.

Any relation between pairs of elements, such as the above equality of pairs of positive integers, that is reflexive, symmetric, and transitive is called an *equivalence relation*. Note that this equivalence relation or equality separates the set of pairs of positive integers into mutually exclusive classes of pairs such that any two members of a class are equivalent or equal, whereas members from different classes are nonequivalent or unequal. An *integer* is defined to be a class of equivalent pairs. Thus, for example, we will later define the integer 2 as the class of all pairs equivalent to (3, 1) and the integer -2 as the class of all pairs equivalent to (1, 3). Note that, conceptually, there is a difference between the positive integer 2 and the integer 2. We will return to this point later but, for the moment, we continue with the formal treatment of integers as classes of pairs of positive integers.

Definition of Addition and Multiplication

We define* the sum

$$(a, b) + (c, d) = (a + c, b + d)$$

and the product

$$(a, b) \cdot (c, d) = (ac + bd, ad + bc).$$

These definitions of the sum and the product of two pairs (a, b) and (c, d) are really definitions of the sum and product of the class of pairs containing (a, b) and the class of pairs containing (c, d). For we can substitute any pair $(a', b') = (a, b)$ and any pair $(c', d') = (c, d)$ in the above definitions and obtain a sum pair

$$(a' + c', b' + d') = (a + c, b + d)$$

and a product pair

$$(a'c' + b'd', a'd' + b'c') = (ac + bd, ad + bc).$$

For example, if $(a', b') = (a, b)$ and $(c', d') = (c, d)$, we have $a' + b = b' + a$, $c' + d = d' + c$, and hence

$$(a' + c') + (b + d) = (b' + d') + (a + c).$$

Consequently,

$$(a', b') + (c', d') = (a' + c', b' + d') = (a + c, b + d).$$

By a slightly more involved manipulation, we can also prove that $(a', b') \cdot (c', d') = (a, b) \cdot (c, d)$. Thus the definitions of sum and product of two pairs (a, b) and (c, d) determine two classes of pairs, the sum and product classes, which are determined by the classes containing (a, b) and (c, d). We have thus defined the sum and product of two integers.

It is easily proved that addition and multiplication of integers obey the commutative, associative, and distributive laws. For example, the distributive law can be proved as follows:

$$
\begin{aligned}
(a, b) \cdot [(c, d) + (e, f)] &= (a, b) \cdot (c + e, d + f) \\
&= (a[c + e] + b[d + f], a[d + f] + b[c + e]) \\
&= ([ac + bd] + [ae + bf], [ad + bc] + [af + be]) \\
&= (ac + bd, ad + bc) + (ae + bf, af + be) \\
&= (a, b) \cdot (c, d) + (a, b) \cdot (e, f).
\end{aligned}
$$

---

* Our motivation for these definitions, of course, lies in the identities of elementary algebra: $(a - b) + (c - d) = (a + c) - (b + d)$ and $(a - b)(c - d) = (ac + bd) - (ad + bc)$.

Note that in the above proof we used not only the definitions of the new addition and multiplication but also the associative, commutative, and distributive properties of the positive integers. The proofs of the other laws are left to the student.

Exercises

1. Prove that addition of integers is commutative.
2. Prove that multiplication of integers is commutative.
3. Prove that addition of integers is associative.
4. Prove that multiplication of integers is associative.

6 · THE NUMBER ZERO

Now let us investigate more closely the pairs (a, b) with respect to the order relation between the positive integers a and b. Recall that either $a = b$, or $a > b$, or $a < b$. Thus any pair (a, b) may be written either as (a, a), or $(x + b, b)$, or $(a, x + a)$.

We consider first the properties of the pairs (a, a). We note that $(a, a) = (b, b)$. Moreover, if $(a, a) = (b, c)$, then $b = c$, for, by the definition of equality, $a + c = a + b$. Thus the pairs in which both positive integers are equal determine a class that may be represented by the pair (a, a) but that is independent of the particular integer a. We shall call this class the integer zero, and we shall represent it by any pair in which both positive integers are equal.

Properties of Zero

For every pair (x, y),
$$(x, y) + (a, a) = (x, y)$$
and
$$(x, y) \cdot (a, a) = (a, a).$$

These two properties follow immediately from the definitions for
$$(x, y) + (a, a) = (x + a, y + a) = (x, y)$$
and
$$(x, y) \cdot (a, a) = (ax + ay, ax + ay) = (a, a).$$

The first property listed is often characterized by saying that zero is an *identity for addition*.

7 · THE POSITIVE INTEGERS AS A SUBSET OF THE INTEGERS

We now need to define a *one-to-one correspondence* between two sets of symbols. We say that there is a one-to-one correspondence between the elements of a set A and the elements of a set B if the elements of the two sets can be paired so that to each element of A there corresponds one and only one element of the set B and if each element of B is the correspondent or image of one and only one element of A. For example, there is a one-to-one correspondence between the set of chairs in a classroom and the set of students in the classroom if there is a chair for each student and if there is a student for each chair.

Now consider the pairs $(x + b, b)$. We note that $(x + b, b) = (x + c, c)$. Moreover, $(x + b, b) = (y + c, c)$ only if $x = y$. Hence only one distinct integer is represented by all the pairs $(x + b, b)$, where x is fixed and b is any positive integer. Thus we may set up a one-to-one correspondence between the classes represented by the pairs $(x + b, b)$ and the positive integers as follows. We shall denote the correspondence by writing

$$(x + b, b) \leftrightarrow x.$$

Thus to each class represented by $(x + b, b)$, where x is fixed, we assign the positive integer x, and to each positive integer x we assign the class represented by $(x + b, b)$. Now if

$$(x + b, b) \leftrightarrow x \qquad \text{and} \qquad (y + c, c) \leftrightarrow y,$$

then

$$(x + b, b) + (y + c, c) = (x + y + b + c, b + c) \leftrightarrow x + y*$$

and

$$(x + b, b) \cdot (y + c, c) =$$
$$(xy + xc + by + bc + bc, xc + by + bc + bc) \leftrightarrow xy.$$

Such a one-to-one correspondence in which addition and multiplication are preserved is called an *isomorphism*. Thus we see that the classes of pairs (a, b) for which $a > b$ may be regarded as merely different symbols for the positive integers, for they have exactly the same properties as the positive integers. For example, then, the positive integer 2 corresponds to the class of all pairs equivalent to $(2 + 1, 1) = (3, 1)$. We now see that, although the positive integer 2 is not identical with the integer 2, we do have positive integer 2 $\leftrightarrow$ integer 2.

To summarize, we have proved the following theorem.

Theorem 2. The classes of pairs (a, b), *with a > b, are isomorphic to the positive integers.*

---

* To save space we shall no longer indicate the use of the associative law for addition for positive integers by means of parentheses. The meaning of $a + b + c$ is now clear.

Exercises

1. Let A be the set of positive integers and B the set of even positive integers. Is the correspondence $n \longleftrightarrow 2n$ for n a positive integer a one-to one correspondence? Is it preserved under addition? Under multiplication?

2. Let A be the set of integers and B be the set of positive integers. Is the correspondence $n \longleftrightarrow n^2$ for n an integer a one-to-one correspondence? Is is preserved under addition? Under multiplication?

3. Prove that the class of pairs (a, b) with $a \geq b$ is not isomorphic to the positive integers.

8 · THE NEGATIVE INTEGERS

So far then we have introduced by means of our new symbols (a, b) only one essentially new number, namely zero. The third type of pairs (a, b), with $a < b$, then, represent numbers other than zero and the positive integers. They may be written in the form $(a, x + a)$, and as in the case of the pairs $(x + b, b)$ only one distinct class or integer is represented by the pairs $(a, x + a)$, where x is fixed and a is any positive integer. We shall call these classes of pairs *negative integers*. For example, -2 may be defined as the class of all pairs equivalent to $(1, 2 + 1) = (1, 3)$.

Thus we have extended our number system. Since a subset of the classes of pairs of positive integers may be identified with the positive integers, we say that the positive integers have been *embedded* in the system of integers. Moreover, we may now find a solution x in the system of integers for the equation $a + x = b$, where a and b denote integers. We first prove the following cancellation laws.

Theorem 3.   *If* $(a, b) + (c, d) = (a, b) + (e, f)$, *then* $(c, d) = (e, f)$. *If* $(x, y) \cdot (a, b) = (x, y) \cdot (c, d)$ *and* $(x, y) \neq (z, z)$, *then* $(a, b) = (c, d)$.

The cancellation law for addition is easily proved by using the cancellation law for positive integers. We are given $(a + c, b + d) = (a + e, b + f)$. Hence $a + c + b + f = b + d + a + e$. Thus $(c + f) + (a + b) = (d + e) + (a + b)$, $c + f = d + e$, and we have $(c, d) = (e, f)$.

To prove the cancellation law for multiplication, suppose first that (x, y) represents a negative integer and let $y = x + z$. Then $(x, x + z) \cdot (a, b) = (x, x + z) \cdot (c, d)$. Performing the multiplication, and using the definition of equality and finally the cancellation laws for positive integers, we have the desired result $b + c = a + d$. The proof when (x, y) represents a positive integer is similar.

Theorem 4.   *The equation* $(a, b) + (x, y) = (c, d)$ *has a unique solution.*

Note that $(a, b) + (c + b, d + a) = (a + c + b, b + d + a) = (c, d)$.

Hence $(c + b, d + a)$ is a solution. Now let (u, v) be any solution. Then $(a, b) + (c + b, d + a) = (a, b) + (u, v)$, and, by the cancellation law for addition, we have $(u, v) = (c + b, d + a)$.

The solution $(x, y) = (c + b, d + a)$ is known as the *difference*, $(c, d) -$ (a, b), and the operation of forming this difference is called *subtraction*. In particular, the solution (x, y) of the equation $(a, b) + (x, y) = (z, z)$ is $(z, z) - (a, b) = (z + b, z + a) = (b, a)$. It will be denoted by $-(a, b)$, and $-(a, b)$ is known as the *additive inverse* of (a, b).

Now that we have established the basic properties of the integers, it is no longer necessary to utilize the notation of pairs of positive integers. We write 0 for the class of pairs equivalent to $(1, 1)$, $+1$ for the class of pairs equivalent to $(2, 1)$, -1 for the class of pairs equivalent to $(1, 2)$, etc. As an additional abbreviation we write 1 for $+1$, 2 for $+2$, etc., and, if any integer is denoted by y, we denote its additive inverse by $-y$. Thus, if $y = +2$, $-y = -2$, whereas if $y = -2$, $-y = +2$.

We have seen that the operations of addition and multiplication of integers are commutative and associative, and that multiplication is distributive with respect to addition. The cancellation law for addition holds as it did for positive integers. The cancellation law for multiplication holds with a slight modification: if a, b, and x are integers, $ax = bx$ implies $a = b$ only if $x \neq 0$.

Many of the familiar properties of the integers may now be proved by using representatives from the classes defining the integers. For example, to prove that, if y is any integer, $-(-y) = y$ we let (a, b) represent y. Then $-(a, b) = (b, a)$ represents $-y$ and $-(b, a) = (a, b)$ represents $-(-y)$. Hence $-(-y) = y$.

Exercises

1. Complete the proof of Theorem 3.
2. Prove the following statements for integers x, y, and z:

a. $(-x)(-y) = xy$.
b. $(-x)y = x(-y) = -(xy)$.
c. $-(x + y) = (-x) + (-y)$.
d. $-(x - y) = (-x) + y$.
e. $x(y - z) = xy - xz$.
f. $(x - y) + (y - z) = x - z$.

3. Prove that the negative integers are not isomorphic to the positive integers.
4. Prove: If x and y are integers and $xy = 0$, then $x = 0$ or $y = 0$.
5. Prove by induction for positive integers n:

a. $1 + 3 + \cdots + (2n - 1) = n^2$.
b. $1 + 5 + \cdots + (4n - 3) = n(2n - 1)$.
c. $1^3 + 3^3 + \cdots + (2n - 1)^3 = n^2(2n^2 - 1)$.
d. $2 + 2^2 + 2^3 + \cdots + 2^n = 2(2^n - 1)$.
e. $1 \cdot 2 + 2 \cdot 2^2 + 3 \cdot 2^3 + \cdots + n \cdot 2^n = (n - 1)2^{n+1} + 2$.

9 · INEQUALITIES

We now define inequalities between integers in terms of the positive integers. The integer a is said to be *less than* the integer b or the integer b is said to be *greater than* the integer a if and only if $b - a$ is a positive integer. We write $a < b$ or $b > a$. Thus, for example, $-5 < -3$ and $-3 > -5$ because $-3 - (-5) = 2$ is a positive integer. The following properties of inequalities of integers can be proved from the definition:

1. If $a < b$ and $b < c$, then $a < c$.
2. If $a < b$, then $a + c < b + c$.
3. If $a < b$ and $c > 0$, then $ac < bc$.
4. If $a < b$ and $c < 0$, then $ac > bc$.

For example, if $a < b$ and $b < c$, then $b - a$ and $c - b$ are positive integers. Hence $(b - a) + (c - b) = c - a$ is a positive integer and it follows that $a < c$.

Absolute Value

For a given integer a, either $a = 0$, or $a > 0$, or $-a > 0$. Thus we define the absolute value of a: $|a| = 0$, or a, or $-a$, according as $a = 0$, $a > 0$, or $-a > 0$. The two properties of absolute value that we shall need are

$$|a| \cdot |b| = |ab| \qquad \text{and} \qquad |a + b| \leq |a| + |b|,$$

and they may easily be proved by a consideration of the various possibilities for a and b as positive or negative integers or zero. As an example, we shall prove the second inequality. If a and b are both positive or both negative, or if at least one is zero, we easily see that the equality sign holds. If a is positive and b is negative, we have $|a| = a$ and $|b| = -b$. Then, if $a + b$ is negative, $|a + b| = -(a + b)$. But, since a is positive, $-(a + b) = -a - b < a - b = |a| + |b|$. If $a + b$ is nonnegative, $|a + b| = a + b$, and $a + b < a - b$. We merely interchange the roles of a and b if a is negative and b is positive.

Exercises

1. Prove that, if a, b, and c are integers, then:
   a. If $a < b$, then $a + c < b + c$.
   b. If $a < b$ and $c > 0$, then $ac < bc$.
   c. If $a < b$ and $c < 0$, then $ac > bc$.

2. Prove that $|a| \cdot |b| = |ab|$ for all integers a and b.

3. If x and y are integers such that $xy = 1$, prove that either $x = y = 1$ or $x = y = -1$.

4. Prove by induction that for all positive integers $n > 1$, $n^3 + 1 > n^2 + n$.
5. Prove by induction that for all positive integers n, $2^n > n$.

10 · DIVISION OF INTEGERS

We have seen that the set of integers is closed with respect to addition, subtraction, and multiplication. However, the set of integers is not closed with respect to division, defined as follows:

Definition of Division
An integer a is said to be divisible by an integer b if there exists an integer c such that $a = bc$. We write $b \mid a$, and say that b is a *divisor* of a and a is a *multiple* of b.

We note that the relation of divisibility is reflexive and transitive. For $a \mid a$ and, moreover, if $a \mid b$ and $b \mid c$, then integers x and y exist such that $ax = b$ and $by = c$, so that $(ax)y = a(xy) = by = c$ and $a \mid c$.

Associates
Two nonzero integers a and b are called associates if both $a \mid b$ and $b \mid a$. Since $a = bc$ and $b = ad$, $a = adc$. By the cancellation law for multiplication $dc = 1$, and hence $d = 1$ or -1 and $c = 1$ or -1. Thus the only associates of a are a and $-a$.

Units
An associate of the integer 1 is called a unit. Hence the only units are 1 and -1.

Primes
A nonzero integer p is a prime if it is neither 1 nor -1 and if its only divisors are $1, -1, p$, and $-p$.

Exercises

1. Find the divisors of 24.
2. List the first 15 positive primes.
3. Find the positive prime divisors of 112.
4. Prove: If $a \mid b$ and $a \mid c$, then $a \mid (b + c)$.
5. If $b \mid a$ and $a \neq 0$, then $|b| \leq |a|$.
6. If $b \mid a$ and $|a| < |b|$, then $a = 0$.
7. Prove the following by induction for all positive integers n:

   a. $8^n - 3^n$ is divisible by 5.
   b. $3^{2n+2} - 8n - 9$ is divisible by 64.
   c. $9^n - 8n - 1$ is divisible by 64.
   d. $7^{2n} - 48n - 1$ is divisible by 2304.

11 · GREATEST COMMON DIVISOR

Theorem 5.   The Division Algorithm.   Given two integers a *and* b *with* b > 0, *there exists a unique pair of integers* q *and* r *such that* a = bq + r, *where* $0 \leq r < b$.

To motivate the proof, consider the integers displayed on a line where all of the possible multiples, bq, of b form a set of equally spaced points on the line as shown below:

Certainly, the point representing a must fall in one of the intervals determined by these points. Suppose that it falls in the interval between bq and $b(q + 1)$ (exclusive of the right-hand point). Then $a - bq = r$, where r represents a length shorter than the whole length of the interval and, hence, $0 \leq r < b$ as asserted.

We now proceed to develop an algebraic proof based on this geometric point of view. Thus we consider the set of integers $a - bx$. It contains at least one nonnegative integer, namely $a - (-|a|)b$. For if $b > 0$, $b \geq 1$ and $-|a|\, b \leq -|a| \leq a$. Thus the set contains either zero or a smallest positive integer. Let this smallest nonnegative integer be $r = a - bq$. Now $r \geq 0$, and, if $r \geq b$, then $0 \leq r - b = a - bq - b = a - (q + 1)b < r$, contrary to the choice of r. Thus the existence of the desired integers r and q has been established. The integer r is called the *remainder*, and the integer q the *quotient*. To prove the uniqueness of q and r we assume that there is a second set of integers q' and r' such that $a = bq' + r'$, where $0 \leq r' < b$. Then $bq' + r' = bq + r$, and $r' - r = (q - q')b$, which says that b divides $r' - r$. But $|r' - r| < b$. Hence $r' - r = 0$, and, since $b \neq 0$, $q' - q = 0$.

Greatest Common Divisor

An integer d is called a greatest common divisor of two integers a and b if $d \mid a$ and $d \mid b$, and, if c is any common divisor of a and b, $c \mid d$. It is easy to see that, if either a or b is zero, then the nonzero integer is a greatest common divisor. If both a and b are zero we define zero to be the greatest common divisor. Further note that, according to the definition, any two greatest common divisors of two nonzero integers must be associates. Hence, if two nonzero integers a and b have a greatest common divisor, they have a positive greatest common divisor, which we shall denote by (a, b) and call the g.c.d.; for example, $(9, 12) = 3$.

Theorem 6.   The euclidean algorithm.   Any two nonzero integers a *and* b *have a positive greatest common divisor.*

The proof will also give us a method for finding the greatest common divisor. Since any two greatest common divisors of a and b are associates, it may be assumed that both a and b are positive. Write $a = bq + r$, $0 \leq r < b$. If $r = 0$, then b is the g.c.d. of a and b. If $r \neq 0$, we prove that $(a, b) = (b, r)$. Let $d = (a, b)$ and $d' = (b, r)$. Now d divides a and b, and hence d divides $a - bq = r$ and is a common divisor of b and r. Thus $d \mid d'$. Similarly, d' divides b and r, and, thus, d' divides $bq + r = a$ and is a common divisor of a and b. Hence $d' \mid d$. Therefore $d = d'$, and we have reduced the problem of finding the greatest common divisor of a and b to that of finding the greatest common divisor of b and r.

Now apply the division algorithm to b and r, obtaining $b = rq_1 + r_1$, $0 \leq r_1 < r$. If $r_1 = 0$, r is the g.c.d. of b and r. If $r_1 \neq 0$, $(b, r) = (r, r_1)$, and the problem of finding the g.c.d. of b and r has been reduced to that of finding the g.c.d. of r and r_1. Continuing in this manner, we obtain the following equalities:

$$
\begin{array}{ll}
a = bq + r, & 0 < r < b, \\
b = rq_1 + r_1, & 0 < r_1 < r, \\
r = r_1 q_2 + r_2, & 0 < r_2 < r_1, \\
r_1 = r_2 q_3 + r_3, & 0 < r_3 < r_2, \\
\cdot \ \cdot \ \cdot \ \cdot \ \cdot \ \cdot \ \cdot \ \cdot & \cdot \ \cdot \ \cdot \ \cdot \ \cdot \ \cdot \\
r_j = r_{j+1} q_{j+2} + r_{j+2}, & 0 < r_{j+2} < r_{j+1}.
\end{array}
$$

Since the r_j form a decreasing set of nonnegative integers, there must exist an r_{n+1} equal to zero. Hence

$$
\begin{array}{ll}
r_{n-2} = r_{n-1} q_n + r_n, & 0 < r_n < r_{n-1}, \\
r_{n-1} = r_n q_{n+1}.
\end{array}
$$

Now $(a, b) = (b, r) = (r, r_1) = \cdots = (r_{n-1}, r_n) = r_n$. Thus the greatest common divisor of a and b is r_n.

Theorem 7.   If $d = (a, b)$, *there exist integers* m *and* n *such that* $d = ma + nb$.

This theorem can be proved by expressing the successive remainders r_j, obtained by the euclidean algorithm, in terms of a and b as indicated below:

$$
\begin{aligned}
r &= a - bq = a + (-q)b, \\
r_1 &= b - rq_1 = b - (a - bq)q_1 = (-q_1)a + (1 + qq_1)b, \text{ etc.}
\end{aligned}
$$

A general proof can be made by induction. Denote r by r_0 and q by q_0. Now assume that $r_j = m_j a + n_j b$, where m_j and n_j are integers, for all nonnegative integers $j < k$. We have checked that this equation holds for $j = 0$ and $j = 1$. Then we have

$$r_k = r_{k-2} - r_{k-1}q_k \text{ (by the euclidean algorithm)}$$
$$= m_{k-2}a + n_{k-2}b - (m_{k-1}a + n_{k-1}b)q_k \text{ (by our induction hypothesis)}$$
$$= (m_{k-2} - m_{k-1}q_k)a + (n_{k-2} - n_{k-1}q_k)b,$$

and our proof is completed. Thus r_n can be expressed as a linear function of a and b with integral coefficients.

EXAMPLE. Find the g.c.d. of 595 and 252, and express it in the form $252m + 595n$. We have

$$595 = 2 \cdot 252 + 91,$$
$$252 = 2 \cdot 91 + 70,$$
$$91 = 1 \cdot 70 + 21,$$
$$70 = 3 \cdot 21 + 7,$$
$$21 = 3 \cdot 7.$$

Hence $(252, 595) = 7$. To find m and n it is convenient to begin with the last nonzero remainder. Thus (underlining the remainders and 252 and 595 to keep track of them):

$$7 = \underline{70} - 3 \cdot \underline{21}$$
$$= \underline{70} - 3(\underline{91} - 1 \cdot \underline{70}) = 4 \cdot \underline{70} - 3 \cdot \underline{91}$$
$$= 4(\underline{252} - 2 \cdot \underline{91}) - 3 \cdot \underline{91} = -11 \cdot \underline{91} + 4 \cdot \underline{252}$$
$$= -11(\underline{595} - 2 \cdot \underline{252}) + 4 \cdot \underline{252} = 26 \cdot \underline{252} + (-11)\underline{595}.$$

We note that m and n are not unique. For example,

$$7 = (26 + 595)252 - (11 + 252)595 = 621 \cdot 252 + (-263)595.$$

Exercises

1. Find $(294, 273)$, and express it in the form $294m + 273n$ in two ways.
2. Find $(163, 34)$, and express it in the form $163m + 34n$ in two ways.
3. Find $(6432, 132)$, and express it in the form $132m + 6432n$.
4. Find $(3456, 7234)$.
5. Prove that, if $m > 0$, $(ma, mb) = m(a, b)$.
6. Prove that $[(a, b), c] = [a, (b, c)] = [(a, c), b]$.
7. Prove that if $(a, m) = (b, m) = 1$, then $(ab, m) = 1$.
8. Prove that if $(a, c) = d$, $a \mid b$, and $c \mid b$, then $ac \mid bd$.

12 · PRIME FACTORS

Theorem 8. If p *is a prime and if* p $\mid$ ab, a *and* b *integers, then* p $\mid$ a *or* p $\mid$ b.

Since p is a prime its only divisors are ± 1 and $\pm p$. Therefore, if p does not divide a, the g.c.d. of a and p is 1. By the previous theorem there exist integers m and n such that $1 = ma + np$. Now $b = mab + npb$. Since p is a factor of the right-hand side of this equation, it divides b by definition, and the theorem is proved.

Corollary. If p *is a prime and divides the product of integers* $a_1 a_2 \cdots a_n$, *then* p *divides one of the integers* a_i.

Repeated application of the preceding theorem gives this result immediately.

DEFINITION. If $(a, b) = 1$, the two integers a and b are said to be *relatively prime*.

Theorem 9. If $(a, b) = 1$ *and if* b $\mid$ ac, *then* b $\mid$ c.

The proof is similar to the proof of the preceding theorem, for by hypothesis there exist integers m and n such that $1 = ma + nb$, and hence $c = mac + nbc$.

Theorem 10. Unique factorization theorem for integers. Every integer a, $|a| > 1$, *can be expressed as a unit times a product of positive primes. This representation is unique except for the order in which the prime factors occur.*

Let a be the integer to be factored. If a is a prime, the integer has been represented according to the theorem. Therefore, let a be *composite*, i.e., neither a unit nor a prime. Now assume the theorem true for all integers less than $|a|$. Since a is composite, $|a| = |b| \cdot |c|$, where $|b|$ and $|c|$ are integers less than $|a|$. Hence, by the induction hypothesis, $|b| = p_1 p_2 \cdots p_s$ and $|c| = q_1 q_2 \cdots q_t$, where p_i and q_j are positive primes. Thus

$$|a| = |b| \cdot |c| = p_1 p_2 \cdots p_s q_1 q_2 \cdots q_t,$$

and it remains to be proved that the representation is unique except for the order in which the prime factors occur. Suppose there were a second factorization $|a| = p_1' p_2' \cdots p_v'$. Then $p_1' p_2' \cdots p_v' = p_1 p_2 \cdots p_s q_1 q_2 \cdots q_t$. Now by the previous corollary p_1' divides one of these primes, say p_1; and hence $p_1' = p_1$. Thus

$$p_2' p_3' \cdots p_v' = p_2 \cdots p_s q_1 \cdots q_t.$$

Reapplying the same reasoning to these equal products a finite number of times, we obtain $v = s + t$ and thus a unique factorization of $|a|$ and hence of a.

Note that the theorem does not exclude the occurrence of equal primes. Hence we may write the integer

$$a = \pm p_1^{a_1} p_2^{a_2} \cdots p_n^{a_n}, \text{ where } 1 < p_1 < p_2 < \cdots < p_n,$$

and we have proved that the exponents a_i as well as the primes are uniquely determined.

Exercises

1. Illustrate the unique factorization theorem for the integers 576, -321, and 5244.
2. What can you conclude about the g.c.d. of a and b if integers x and y exist such that $ax + by = 1$? if $ax + by = 3$?
3. If $d = (a, b)$, $a = a_1 d$, $b = b_1 d$, then $(a_1, b_1) = 1$.
4. If $(a, b) = 1$, and $a \mid c$ and $b \mid c$, then $ab \mid c$.
5. Prove that $2m^2 = n^2$ is an impossible equation in integers when $(m, n) = 1$.
6. If $(a, b) = 1$, then $(a + b, a - b) = 2$ or 1.
7. If $(c, d) = 1$, then $(c^n, d) = 1$, where n is a positive integer.
8. Prove that the number of primes is infinite. *Hint:* Assume that the number of primes is finite and form their product $p_1 p_2 \cdots p_n$. Then consider the integer $p_1 p_2 \cdots p_n + 1$.
9. Show that $2^{2n} + 1$ is divisible by 5 for n a positive odd integer.
10. Show that $2^{2n} - 1$ is divisible by 5 for n a positive even integer.

13 · CONGRUENCES

DEFINITION.   Two integers a and b are said to be *congruent modulo a positive integer m* if and only if there exists an integer k such that $a - b = km$.   Note that this definition merely says that m divides $a - b$. We write $a \equiv b$ (mod m), and call m the *modulus* of the congruence.   For example, $7 \equiv 15$ (mod 4), for $7 - 15 = 4(-2)$.

Theorem 11.   The relation, congruent modulo m, *is:*

1. Reflexive: a $\equiv$ a *(mod* m).
2. Symmetric: if a $\equiv$ b *(mod* m)*, then* b $\equiv$ a *(mod* m).
3. Transitive: if a $\equiv$ b *(mod* m) *and* b $\equiv$ c *(mod* m)*, then* a $\equiv$ c *(mod* m).

These properties follow immediately from the definition of a congruence. For example, we can prove transitivity as follows: Since $a - b = km$ and $b - c = nm$, we obtain $a - c = (k + n)m$ by addition, which is the result desired.

From this theorem we may expect that congruences behave in many respects like equalities.   The following three theorems illustrate this similarity.

Theorem 12.   If a $\equiv$ b *(mod* m)*, then* a $+$ x $\equiv$ b $+$ x, *and* ax $\equiv$ bx *(mod* m) *for all integers* x.

The proofs are again immediate from the definition and are left to the student.

Theorem 13.   If a $\equiv$ b *and* c $\equiv$ d *(mod* m)*, then* a $+$ c $\equiv$ b $+$ d, a $-$ c $\equiv$ b $-$ d, *and* ac $\equiv$ bd *(mod* m).

Each of these statements can be proved directly from the definition. However, the last is proved more simply by using the second part of Theorem 12 and the transitive property of congruences as follows: $ac \equiv bc$ and $bc \equiv bd \,(\mathrm{mod}\ m)$, and therefore $ac \equiv bd \,(\mathrm{mod}\ m)$.

Theorem 14. *If* ca $\equiv$ cb *(mod* m*) and* d $=$ (c, m), *so that* m $=$ dw, *then* a $\equiv$ b *(mod* w*).*

Now $c = dv$ and $m = dw$, where $(v, w) = 1$. Moreover, $dw \mid c(a - b)$ and hence $w \mid v(a - b)$. Thus, since $(v, w) = 1$, $w \mid (a - b)$. If $d = 1$, we obtain the following theorem:

Theorem 15. *If* ca $\equiv$ cb *(mod* m*) and* (c, m) $= 1$, *then* a $\equiv$ b *(mod* m*).*

A useful alternative definition of congruence is incorporated in the following theorem.

Theorem 16. a $\equiv$ b *(mod* m*) if and only if* a *and* b *leave the same remainder when divided by* m.

If $a \equiv b \,(\mathrm{mod}\ m)$, then $b - a = km$. Let $a = mq + r$, $0 \le r < m$. Now $b = a + km = mq + r + km = (q + k)m + r$, which states that r is the remainder when b is divided by m. On the other hand, if $a = mq + r$ and $b = mq_1 + r, 0 \le r < m$, then $a - b = (q - q_1)m$ and $a \equiv b \,(\mathrm{mod}\ m)$.

Thus any integer a is congruent modulo m to its remainder r. Hence, by the transitive property of congruences, we may substitute r for a in any congruence modulo m. For example, if $313x \equiv 7 \,(\mathrm{mod}\ 10)$, then $3x \equiv 7 \,(\mathrm{mod}\ 10)$ is an equivalent statement, for $313 \equiv 3 \,(\mathrm{mod}\ 10)$, and $313x \equiv 3x \,(\mathrm{mod}\ 10)$.

Exercises

1. Complete the proof of Theorem 11.
2. Prove Theorem 12.
3. Complete the proof of Theorem 13.
4. Find the least positive integers modulo 7 to which the integers 22, 312, and $22 \cdot 312$ are congruent.
5. Find the least positive integer modulo 11 to which the product $3 \cdot 7 \cdot 13 \cdot 515 \cdot 23$ is congruent.
6. Find the least positive integers modulo 5 to which the powers 3^2, 3^3, 3^4, 3^{10} are congruent.
7. Find the least positive integer modulo 7 to which 10^{515} is congruent.
8. If $14x \equiv 2 \,(\mathrm{mod}\ 8)$, quote theorems that enable us to write $7x \equiv 1 \,(\mathrm{mod}\ 4)$, $6x \equiv 2 \,(\mathrm{mod}\ 8)$, and $3x \equiv 1 \,(\mathrm{mod}\ 4)$.
9. If m is an integer, then $m^2 \equiv 0$ or $1 \,(\mathrm{mod}\ 4)$.
10. Recall that any positive integer may be expressed as follows:

$$a_n 10^n + a_{n-1} 10^{n-1} + \cdots + a_1 10 + a_0,$$

where the a_i are integers 0 through 9. Hence show that, if a positive integer is divisible by 9, the sum of its digits is divisible by 9.

14 · THE LINEAR CONGRUENCE

We shall now discuss the linear congruence $ax \equiv b \pmod{m}$. Note that, if x_1 is a solution, i.e., $ax_1 \equiv b \pmod{m}$, then any other integer $x_2 \equiv x_1 \pmod{m}$ is also a solution, for we have $ax_2 \equiv ax_1 \equiv b \pmod{m}$. We usually take integers in the interval $0 \leq x < m$ as representatives of the solutions.

Theorem 17. The congruence ax $\equiv$ b *(mod* m) *has a solution if and only if the greatest common divisor* d *of* a *and* m *divides* b. *If* d *divides* b, *the congruence has exactly* d *incongruent solutions modulo* m.

Let $ax \equiv b \pmod{m}$ have a solution x_1. Then $ax_1 - b = km$, and $d = (a, m)$ necessarily divides b. Now given that d divides b, we seek solutions of the congruence. Since $d = (a, m)$, there exist integers x_1 and y_1 such that $ax_1 + my_1 = d$. Now $b = b_1 d$, and multiplying the linear expression for d by b_1 we have $a(x_1 b_1) + m(y_1 b_1) = db_1 = b$. Thus $x_1 b_1$ is a solution of the congruence $ax \equiv b \pmod{m}$.

It remains to be proved that there are d incongruent solutions modulo m. Now $m = m_1 d$, and $a = a_1 d$. Hence a solution x of the congruence $ax \equiv b \pmod{m}$ is also a solution of the congruence $a_1 x \equiv b_1 \pmod{m_1}$, and conversely. Any two solutions of $a_1 x \equiv b_1 \pmod{m_1}$ are congruent modulo m_1. For, let x_0 and x_1 be any two solutions. Then $a_1 x_0 \equiv b_1 \equiv a_1 x_1 \pmod{m_1}$, and, since $(a_1, m_1) = 1$, $x_0 \equiv x_1 \pmod{m_1}$. Hence all the incongruent solutions modulo m of $ax \equiv b \pmod{m}$ are found among the integers $x_0 + km_1$. We wish to show that the set of integers $x_0 + km_1$ contains exactly d incongruent integers modulo m, whose representatives are $x_0, x_0 + m_1, x_0 + 2m_1, \cdots, x_0 + (d-1)m_1$. First, these representatives are all incongruent modulo m, for, if $x_0 + r_1 m_1 \equiv x_0 + r_2 m_1 \pmod{m}$, where $r_1 < d$ and $r_2 < d$, then $r_1 m_1 \equiv r_2 m_1 \pmod{m}$ and $r_1 \equiv r_2 \pmod{d}$; but $|r_1 - r_2| < d$, and hence $r_1 = r_2$. Next, any integer $x_0 + km_1$ is congruent to one of the above representatives, for $k = qd + r$, where $0 \leq r < d$, and $x_0 + km_1 = x_0 + (qd + r)m_1 \equiv x_0 + rm_1 \pmod{m}$.

In solving any linear congruence, first note how it may be simplified by using all the properties of congruences that have been developed. For example, $x + 50 \equiv 39 \pmod{7}$ is equivalent to $x + 1 \equiv 4 \pmod{7}$, and hence $x \equiv 3 \pmod{7}$. Again, if $235x \equiv 54 \pmod{7}$, then $4x \equiv 5 \pmod{7}$, and hence $x \equiv 3 \pmod{7}$. Again, if $29x \equiv 5 \pmod{34}$, then $-5x \equiv 5 \pmod{34}$ and $x \equiv -1 \pmod{34}$.

The congruence $35x \equiv 5 \pmod{14}$ is an example of a linear congruence without a solution, for $(35, 14) = 7$, and 7 does not divide 5. On the other hand, $35x \equiv 14 \pmod{21}$ has exactly 7 incongruent solutions modulo 21. In this case we divide through by 7, obtaining the congruence $5x \equiv 2 \pmod{3}$, which has 1 as its least positive solution. Hence representatives of the 7 incongruent solutions of $35x \equiv 14 \pmod{21}$ in the interval $0 \leq x < 21$ are 1, 4, 7, 10, 13, 16, and 19.

If the modulus is a large number, the greatest common divisor process enables us to find a solution as was shown in the proof of the general theorem. For example, in the congruence $11x \equiv 2 \pmod{317}$, $(317, 11) = 1$, and we find by solving for the remainders in the greatest common divisor process that $1 = 5(317) + 11(-144)$. Then $2 = 10(317) + 11(-288)$, and -288 is a solution. We take the least positive solution 29 as a representative solution.

Exercises

Find the incongruent solutions of the following congruences.

1. $x - 3 \equiv 2 \pmod{5}$.   2. $2x + 1 \equiv 4 \pmod{5}$.
3. $2x + 1 \equiv 4 \pmod{10}$.   4. $3x \equiv 2 \pmod{7}$.
5. $51x \equiv 32 \pmod{7}$.   6. $13x \equiv 10 \pmod{28}$.
7. $273x \equiv 210 \pmod{588}$.   8. $66x \equiv 8 \pmod{78}$.
9. $104x \equiv 16 \pmod{296}$.   10. $1183x \equiv 481 \pmod{533}$.
11. $572x \equiv 412 \pmod{516}$.   12. $45x \equiv 24 \pmod{348}$.
13. Prove that, if p is a prime and $c \not\equiv 0 \pmod{p}$, then $cx \equiv b \pmod{p}$ has a unique solution modulo p.
14. Find integers x and y such that $313x + 45y = 17$.
15. Prove that, if $(m_1, m_2) = 1$, then the congruences $x \equiv b \pmod{m_1}$ and $x \equiv c \pmod{m_2}$ have a common solution x and that any two solutions are congruent modulo $m_1 m_2$.

15 · RESIDUE CLASSES

Recall that any relation between pairs of elements that is reflexive, symmetric, and transitive is called an equivalence relation. Hence congruent modulo m is an equivalence relation between pairs of integers. Any equivalence relation between the elements of a set separates the elements into mutually exclusive classes of elements such that any two elements of a class are equivalent and elements from different classes are not equivalent. Thus we separate the integers into classes modulo m, putting into the same class all those integers that are congruent modulo m. We obtain m classes, for any integer is congruent modulo m to its remainder, and there are m remainders $0, 1, 2, \cdots, m - 1$. These classes, called *residue classes modulo m*, are the m sets of integers $km, km + 1, km + 2, \cdots, km +$

$m - 1$, where k runs through all the integers. Denote these classes by $C_0, C_1, C_2, \cdots, C_{m-1}$, respectively. For example, if $m = 3$, C_0 is the set of all integers divisible by 3; C_1 is the set of all integers that have a remainder of 1 when divided by 3; and C_2 is the set of all integers that have a remainder of 2 when divided by 3.

Addition and multiplication of these residue classes can be defined as follows: The sum $C_i + C_j$ is the class that contains the sum of an integer from C_i and an integer from C_j. The product $C_i C_j$ is the class that contains the product of an integer from the class C_i by an integer from the class C_j. Thus, in our previous example, $C_0 + C_0 = C_0$; $C_0 + C_1 = C_1$; $C_0 + C_2 = C_2$; $C_1 + C_1 = C_2$; $C_1 + C_2 = C_0$; $C_2 + C_2 = C_1$; $C_0 C_0 = C_0 C_1 = C_0 C_2 = C_0$; $C_1 C_1 = C_1$; $C_1 C_2 = C_2$; and $C_2 C_2 = C_1$.

Note that these sums and products are unique, for, if a_i and a_i' are any two integers from C_i, and if a_j and a_j' are any two integers from C_j, then, since $a_i \equiv a_i'$ and since $a_j \equiv a_j'$, $a_i + a_j \equiv a_i' + a_j'$ and $a_i a_j \equiv a_i' a_j'$ (mod m). From these definitions we can easily prove that addition and multiplication of residue classes obey the commutative, associative, and distributive laws. The proofs are left to the student.

Exercises

1. For the modulus 6:
    a. Calculate $C_2 C_3$, $(C_4 C_5) C_1$, $C_4 (C_2 + C_3)$, $C_4 C_3 + C_4 C_2$.
    b. Find solutions C_x of the equations $C_2 + C_x = C_0$, $C_5 C_x = C_1$, $C_i + C_x = C_j$.
    c. Has the equation $C_3 C_x = C_2$ a solution?
    d. If $C_3 C_x = C_3 C_y$, can we conclude that $C_x = C_y$?
2. Answer the same questions for the modulus 7.
3. For the arbitrary modulus m find a solution C_x of the equation $C_i + C_x = C_j$.
4. For the arbitrary modulus m, has the equation $C_i C_x = C_j$ always a solution C_x?
5. Prove: $C_i C_j = C_0$ implies $C_i = C_0$ or $C_j = C_0$ if and only if the modulus m is a prime.
6. Prove that:
    a. The addition of residue classes is commutative.
    b. The multiplication of residue classes is commutative.
    c. The addition of residue classes is associative.
    d. The multiplication of residue classes is associative.
    e. The multiplication of residue classes is distributive with respect to addition.

16 · POSITIONAL NOTATION FOR INTEGERS

A direct application of the congruence properties of integers is the method used to represent any integer. Recall that any integer is represented by means of a signed sequence of the ten symbols 0, 1, 2, 3, $\cdots$, 9, (i.e., the remainders modulo 10). This representation is obtained in the following way. Let a be a positive integer. By means of the division algorithm the integer a may be written in the form $a = 10q_0 + r_0, 0 \leq r_0 < 10$. If $q_0 = 0$, r_0 is the symbol used for a. If $q_0 > 0$, reapply the division algorithm to q_0, obtaining $q_0 = 10q_1 + r_1, 0 \leq r_1 < 10$. If $q_1 = 0$, $a = 10r_1 + r_0$, and the symbol for a is r_1r_0. If $q_1 > 0$, $q_1 = 10q_2 + r_2, 0 \leq r_2 < 10$. If $q_2 = 0$, $a = 10(10r_2 + r_1) + r_0 = 10^2r_2 + 10r_1 + r_0$, and the symbol for a is $r_2r_1r_0$. If $q_2 > 0$, the process is repeated. Since the q_i form a decreasing set of nonnegative integers, the process must cease in a finite number of steps. Thus

$$a = 10^n r_n + 10^{n-1}r_{n-1} + \cdots + 10r_1 + r_0,$$

and the symbol for a is $r_n r_{n-1} \cdots r_1 r_0$. This representation is unique, for at each stage the quotients and remainders are unique. Negative integers are obviously represented in the same way, but they are preceded by a minus sign.

It is evident that the above process does not depend upon the particular integer 10, called the base. Any other positive integer m (except 1) can be used as a base, and the integer a can be represented by a sequence of the m symbols representing the m remainders modulo m. For example, the base 3 might be used, and an integer can then be represented by means of the symbols 0, 1, 2. Since 15 can be written as $1 \cdot 3^2 + 2 \cdot 3 + 0$, its symbol written with the base 3 is 120. The rules for addition and multiplication hold, but, of course, new tables must be learned if the computations are to be carried out with dispatch. The addition and multiplication tables for the base 3 are:

+	0	1	2
0	0	1	2
1	1	2	10
2	2	10	11

×	0	1	2
0	0	0	0
1	0	1	2
2	0	2	11

EXAMPLE. Let 120 and 121 be integers written with the base 3. Find their sum and product.

Sum

$$120 = 1 \cdot 3^2 + 2 \cdot 3 + 0$$
$$121 = 1 \cdot 3^2 + 2 \cdot 3 + 1$$
$$1011 = 2 \cdot 3^2 + 4 \cdot 3 + 1 = 3 \cdot 3^2 + 1 \cdot 3 + 1$$
$$= 1 \cdot 3^3 + 0 \cdot 3^2 + 1 \cdot 3 + 1$$

Product

$$120 = 1 \cdot 3^2 + 2 \cdot 3 + 0$$
$$121 = 1 \cdot 3^2 + 2 \cdot 3 + 1$$

120	$1 \cdot 3^2 + 2 \cdot 3 \ \ + 0$	$=$	$1 \cdot 3^2 + 2 \cdot 3 + 0$
1010	$2 \cdot 3^3 + 4 \cdot 3^2 + 0 \cdot 3$	$= 1 \cdot 3^4 + 0 \cdot 3^3 + 1 \cdot 3^2 + 0 \cdot 3$	
120	$1 \cdot 3^4 + 2 \cdot 3^3 + 0 \cdot 3^2$	$= 1 \cdot 3^4 + 2 \cdot 3^3 + 0 \cdot 3^2$	

$$22{,}220 = \qquad\qquad\qquad\qquad 2 \cdot 3^4 + 2 \cdot 3^3 + 2 \cdot 3^2 + 2 \cdot 3 + 0$$

Exercises

1. Find the symbol for 26 using in turn the base 2, 3, 4, 5, 9, and 12.
2. What number is represented by the symbol 333 if it is interpreted as a number written with the base 4? With the base 5? With the base 9?
3. Make an addition and multiplication table for the base 5. Find the sum and product of 23 and 34 if these symbols represent numbers written with the base 5.
4. A druggist has only the five weights of 1, 2, 4, 8, and 16 ounces, respectively, and a two-pan balance (weights may be placed in either pan). Show that he can weigh any amount up to 31 ounces.
5. Prove that the sum of the digits of any multiple of 9 is itself divisible by 9.

2 The Rational, Real, and Complex Numbers

1 · THE RATIONAL NUMBERS

It has been seen that the set of integers is not closed with respect to division. We shall now define *rational numbers* and the addition and multiplication of rational numbers. It will turn out that addition and multiplication of rational numbers obey the commutative, associative, and distributive laws. In addition, however, the set of nonzero rational numbers is closed with respect to division. Just as we constructed the integers by using pairs of positive integers, we shall in a similar way construct the rational numbers by using pairs of integers. The pair of integers will be denoted by a/b, with $b \neq 0$.

Definition of Equality

$a/b = c/d$ if and only if $ad = bc$. Note that this equality is not an identical equality, but it is a relation which is obviously reflexive and symmetric and is easily proved to be transitive. Hence it is an equivalence relation, and we can separate the pairs of integers into classes, putting into the same class all those pairs that are equal. A rational number is defined to be a class of equal pairs, and we shall represent a rational number by any pair of integers belonging to the class defining it.

We shall now examine these classes. Note that $ma/mb = a/b$, for all integers m not zero. Further, if the g.c.d. of a and b is m, so that $a = a_1 m$ and $b = b_1 m$, then $a/b = a_1/b_1$. Now if $(a, b) = 1$, the equality $a/b = c/d$ gives us $ad = bc$, and hence $c = ma$ and $d = mb$. Thus members of the same class are all of the form ma/mb, where m is any integer not zero. In practice we usually replace a/b, if $d = (a, b) > 1$, by its equal, a_1/b_1, where $a = a_1 d$ and $b = b_1 d$. Thus the class containing a/b may be represented by a_1/b_1, where $(a_1, b_1) = 1$.

Definition of Addition

$$\frac{a}{b} + \frac{c}{d} = \frac{ad + bc}{bd} .$$

Definition of Multiplication

$$\frac{a}{b} \cdot \frac{c}{d} = \frac{ac}{bd} .$$

From our previous discussion we see that the addition and multiplication of pairs really define an addition and multiplication of classes of pairs, for if each pair is replaced by a pair equal to it we obtain a pair that belongs to the class of the sum or the product. Hence the sum and product of rational numbers has been defined.

It is easily verified by using the above definitions that the addition and multiplication of rational numbers obey the commutative, associative, and distributive laws. For example, the distributive law,

$$\frac{a}{b}\left(\frac{c}{d} + \frac{e}{f}\right) = \frac{a}{b} \cdot \frac{c}{d} + \frac{a}{b} \cdot \frac{e}{f},$$

can be verified as follows:

$$\frac{a}{b}\left(\frac{c}{d} + \frac{e}{f}\right) = \frac{a}{b}\left(\frac{cf + de}{df}\right) = \frac{acf + ade}{bdf}$$

and

$$\frac{a}{b} \cdot \frac{c}{d} + \frac{a}{b} \cdot \frac{e}{f} = \frac{ac}{bd} + \frac{ae}{bf}$$

$$= \frac{acbf + aebd}{b^2 df}$$

$$= \frac{acf + aed}{bdf} .$$

Identity for Addition

Since $a/b + 0/1 = a/b$ for every a/b, we say that $0/1$ is an identity for addition.

Additive Inverse

Since $a/b + (-a)/b = (ab - ab)/b^2 = 0/1$, we say that $(-a)/b$ is an additive inverse of a/b.

Identity for Multiplication

Since $(a/b)(c/c) = a/b$, we say that c/c is an identity for multiplication.

Cancellation Laws for Addition and Multiplication

The student can verify that the cancellation laws for addition and multiplication hold, i.e., (1) if $a/b + c/d = a/b + e/f$, then $c/d = e/f$, and (2) if $(a/b)(c/d) = (a/b)(e/f)$, $a/b \neq 0/1$, then $c/d = e/f$.

Division

A pair a/b is divisible by c/d if a pair x/y exists such that $a/b = (x/y)(c/d)$. It is easily seen that $(ad)/(bc)$ is such a pair unless $c = 0$. If $c = 0$, then $a = 0$, and x/y is any pair. Thus any rational number is divisible by any nonzero rational number, and the set of nonzero rational numbers is closed under the so-called *rational operations*: addition, subtraction, multiplication, and division.

Exercises

1. Prove that the addition of rational numbers obeys the commutative and associative laws.
2. Prove that the multiplication of rational numbers obeys the commutative and associative laws.
3. Prove the cancellation law for addition for rational numbers.
4. Prove the cancellation law for multiplication for rational numbers.

2 · THE INTEGERS AS A SUBSET OF THE RATIONAL NUMBERS

We shall show that the subset of classes of pairs consisting of those classes of pairs which are of the form $a/1$ is isomorphic to the integers. A one-to-one correspondence can be set up as follows: Let the class represented by $a/1$ correspond to the integer a, and conversely let the integer a correspond to this class. Now if

$$\frac{a}{1} \leftrightarrow a \qquad \text{and} \qquad \frac{b}{1} \leftrightarrow b,$$

then

$$\frac{a}{1} + \frac{b}{1} = \frac{a+b}{1} \leftrightarrow a+b \qquad \text{and} \qquad \frac{a}{1} \cdot \frac{b}{1} = \frac{ab}{1} \leftrightarrow ab.$$

Since addition and multiplication are preserved under this one-to-one correspondence, this subset of classes is isomorphic to the set of integers. Since abstractly these two sets of entirely different entities are alike, we use them as if they were identical, and in practice we replace the symbol for a rational number of this subset by the symbol for an integer.

3 · THE REAL NUMBERS

It is evident that the rational numbers are not sufficient to meet ordinary needs. For example, the hypotenuse x of a right triangle each of whose legs is of unit length cannot be represented by a rational number, for its square is 2. If a rational number p/q, with $(p, q) = 1$, existed such that $p^2/q^2 = 2$, then $p^2 = 2q^2$, but we have seen (Exercise 5, p. 18) that such an equation has no solution in integers. To meet such obvious needs the real numbers are constructed from the rational numbers. No postulational approach to the real numbers will be given, and no proofs will be given that the real numbers obey the same laws of algebra that the rational numbers do. We shall merely describe how to obtain sequences of rational numbers that are approximations to the real numbers.

We need to recall the meaning of the decimal notation for rational numbers. The number 3.12, for example, means

$$3 + \frac{1}{10} + \frac{2}{10^2}.$$

In general the sequence of integers $b.a_1a_2 \cdots a_n$, where $a_1, a_2, \cdots, a_n$ are remainders modulo 10, means

$$b + \frac{a_1}{10} + \frac{a_2}{10^2} + \cdots + \frac{a_n}{10^n},$$

whereas the notation $b.a_1a_2 \cdots a_n \cdots$ means that the decimal does not consist of a finite sequence of digits. Now any rational number can be converted into a decimal. For example, $32/5 = 6.4$. By the division algorithm we have $32 = 6 \cdot 5 + 2$, and so 6 is the integral part of the decimal representation. Now multiply the remainder by 10, and we have $20 = 5 \cdot 4$. Four is therefore the first and final digit after the decimal point. Similarly we find that $1/7$ can be represented by the infinite *repeating* decimal $0.142857142857 \cdots$.

To convert any nonintegral rational number c/d into a decimal we proceed in the same way. For convenience assume c and d positive. We have $c = db + r_0$, where $0 < r_0 < d$, and b is the integral part of c/d. Then $10r_0 = da_1 + r_1$, where $0 \le r_1 < d$. Since $r_0 < d$, $10r_0 = da_1 + r_1 < 10d$, and hence $a_1 < 10$. Thus a_1 is the first digit after the decimal point. If $r_1 = 0$, $c/d = b + a_1/10 = b.a_1$; but if $r_1 \ne 0$, we continue, obtaining $10r_1 = a_2d + r_2$, where $0 \le r_2 < d$. Thus $c/d = b + a_1/10 + a_2/10^2 + r_2/10^2d$. If $r_2 \ne 0$, we have a decimal approximation $b.a_1a_2$ to c/d; but if $r_2 = 0$, we have an exact representation of c/d as a finite decimal. Thus we may continue in this fashion obtaining any desired accuracy. If the rational number is not represented by a finite decimal, it is easily seen that the digits in the decimal part must repeat, for there are only a finite number of remainders modulo d. It can also be proved that any infinite repeating decimal represents a rational number. Such a proof involves the notion of a limit in some form or another and, hence, falls somewhat outside the province of algebra. The following example, however, may help to convince the student of the plausibility of our statement. Consider the repeating decimal $x = 0.141414 \cdots$. Then $100x = 14.141414 \cdots = 14 + 0.141414 \cdots = 14 + x$. Thus, $99x = 14$ and $x = 14/99$.

To return to the problem of constructing a number x to represent the hypotenuse of the above right triangle, we proceed as follows: We approximate to x, which as usual we shall denote by $\sqrt{2}$, by rational numbers, and we shall use the decimal notation. Now 2 lies between 1^2 and 2^2 and therefore between two consecutive terms of the sequence

$$(1.0)^2, (1.1)^2, (1.2)^2, \cdots, (1.9)^2, 2^2.$$

We find $(1.4)^2 < 2 < (1.5)^2$. Thus 2 lies between two consecutive terms of the sequence

$$(1.40)^2, (1.41)^2, (1.42)^2, \cdots, (1.49)^2, (1.50)^2,$$

and we find that $(1.41)^2 < 2 < (1.42)^2$. We may continue this process as long as we please, obtaining an approximation to $\sqrt{2}$ by means of decimals to any degree of accuracy desired. We say that $\sqrt{2}$ is represented by the infinite (nonrepeating) decimal $1.4142 \cdots$.

The real numbers may be said to consist of the finite and infinite decimals, and we shall now interpret this definition geometrically. Represent the integers by points on a line as follows: Take two arbitrary points, labeling one 0 and the other 1. The distance between these two points is taken as the unit length, and we lay off unit intervals on the line labeling the points in the customary manner:

The rational numbers, as we learn from elementary geometry, can also be laid off as points on this line. However, the rational numbers do not exhaust the points on the line, for we can lay off the hypotenuse of a right triangle whose legs are of unit length, and, as we have seen, this point cannot be represented by a rational number. Since there are numbers other than rational numbers which can be represented by points on the line, we extend our number system to include these numbers, and we assume that there is a one-to-one correspondence between the real numbers and the points on a line. The points that do not correspond to rational numbers, we say, correspond to *irrational* numbers, and our system of real numbers consists of the rational and irrational numbers.

It remains to show that to each point on the line there corresponds a uniquely determined decimal, finite or infinite. We do this in the following way. Let P be any point on the line. If it lies between two integral points i and $i + 1$, we say that it belongs to this interval. On the other hand, if it lies on a division mark i, it belongs to both intervals $(i - 1, i)$ and $(i, i + 1)$. We shall say arbitrarily that it belongs to the right-hand interval $(i, i + 1)$, and, in the further divisions that we shall make, we shall also take the right-hand interval if the point P lies on a division mark. Now let P belong to the interval $(i, i + 1)$. Divide this interval into ten equal parts by the points of division $i + 1/10, i + 2/10, \cdots, i + 9/10$, and label these subintervals $0, 1, 2, \cdots, 9$ from left to right. The subinterval a_1 then has the end points $i + a_1/10$ and $i + (a_1 + 1)/10$. Let P belong to this subinterval. Divide this subinterval again into ten equal parts and say that P belongs to the new subinterval a_2, where a_2 is one of the integers $0, 1, 2, \cdots, 9$. Then P belongs to the subinterval whose end points are

$$i + \frac{a_1}{10} + \frac{a_2}{10^2} \quad \text{and} \quad i + \frac{a_1}{10} + \frac{a_2 + 1}{10^2}.$$

If we continue this process t times, P will belong to the subinterval whose end points are

$$i + \frac{a_1}{10} + \frac{a_2}{10^2} + \cdots + \frac{a_t}{10^t}$$

and

$$i + \frac{a_1}{10} + \frac{a_2}{10^2} + \cdots + \frac{a_t + 1}{10^t}.$$

Now, of course, these end points may be written as $i.a_1 a_2 \cdots a_t$ and $i.a_1 a_2 \cdots a_t + 1/10^t$. We say that $i.a_1 a_2 \cdots a_t$ is an approximation to the number representing P. If this process is continued indefinitely, we obtain the infinite decimal $i.a_1 a_2 \cdots a_t \cdots$, which we say is the real number corresponding to P.

In our method of finding a decimal representation of P, we arbitrarily chose the right-hand interval in each case. We could, of course, have chosen the left-hand interval. This accounts for the two representations, for example, of 2, namely, $2.0000 \cdots$ and $1.999 \cdots$.

It is evident that we need not have chosen the base 10 in our representation. For example, we could have divided each interval into five equal parts. Thus, if we had chosen the base 5, the positional representation of 1/3 would have been $0.1313 \cdots$, meaning $1/5 + 3/5^2 + 1/5^3 + 3/5^4 + \cdots$.

Exercises

1. Prove that $\sqrt{3}$ is an irrational number.
2. Find a decimal approximation to $\sqrt{7}$ to three decimal places by the method used to find an approximation to $\sqrt{2}$.
3. Express 2/9 as a repeating decimal.
4. Express 3/11 as a repeating decimal.
5. Express the repeating decimal $0.343434 \cdots$ as a fraction.
6. Express the repeating decimal $1.259259 \cdots$ as a fraction.
7. Write 2/3 with the base 5 and with the base 6.
8. Write 0.425 with the base 7.
9. Write 0.312 with the base 9.

4 · THE COMPLEX NUMBERS

The equation $x^2 + 2 = 0$ has no solution x that is a real number, for the square of every real number is positive or zero. The desire to have solutions for such equations led to the further extension of the number system, namely, the complex numbers. We shall define the complex numbers in terms of the real numbers. This is in contrast to the usual approach in elementary algebra where complex numbers are introduced by a consideration of the square root of -1, and the implication is given that there is something quite mysterious going on. (This feeling is intensified by the use of the epithet "imaginary"!) Here we will define the complex numbers as ordered pairs of real numbers and see that they are just as "real" as the integers which were defined as ordered pairs of natural numbers or the rational numbers which were defined as ordered pairs of integers. In the next section we will relate, in an obvious fashion, our pairs (a, b) to the customary notation $a + bi$.

Definition

A *complex number* is an ordered pair of real numbers denoted by (a, b).

Definition of Equality

Two complex numbers (a, b) and (c, d) are equal if and only if $a = c$ and $b = d$. Note that this is an identical equality

Definition of Addition

$(a, b) + (c, d) = (a + c, b + d)$.

Definition of Multiplication

$(a, b) \cdot (c, d) = (ac - bd, ad + bc)$.

It will be left to the student to verify that addition and multiplication of complex numbers obey the commutative, associative, and distributive laws.

Identity for addition

Since $(a, b) + (0, 0) = (a, b)$, an identity for addition is $(0, 0)$.

Additive Inverse

Since $(a, b) + (-a, -b) = (0, 0)$, we have $(-a, -b)$ as an additive inverse of (a, b). We define $-(a, b) = (-a, -b)$ and $(a, b) - (c, d) = (a, b) + (-c, -d)$.

Identity for Multiplication

Since $(a, b) \cdot (1, 0) = (a, b)$, $(1, 0)$ is a unity element or an identity for multiplication.

Cancellation Laws

The cancellation law for addition is readily proved from the definitions of equality and sum. The cancellation law for multiplication may be put into the more easily proved equivalent form $(a, b) \cdot (c, d) = (0, 0)$ implies $(a, b) = (0, 0)$ or $(c, d) = (0, 0)$. To prove this law, suppose $(c, d) \neq (0, 0)$. Then we have $(ac - bd, ad + bc) = (0, 0)$. Hence $ac - bd = 0$, $ad + bc = 0$, and hence $b(c^2 + d^2) = 0$. Thus $b = 0$, and $a = 0$. The student should prove that the two forms of the cancellation law for multiplication are equivalent.

Division

It is easy to show that the solution (x, y) of the equation $(a, b) = (x, y) \cdot (c, d)$, where $(c, d) \neq (0, 0)$, is given by $x = (ac + bd)/(c^2 + d^2)$ and $y = (bc - ad)/(c^2 + d^2)$. Thus we find that division except by zero is always possible and that the set of nonzero complex numbers is closed under the rational operations.

Exercises

1. Prove that the addition of complex numbers obeys the commutative and associative laws.
2. Prove that the multiplication of complex numbers obeys the commutative and associative laws.
3. Prove that the multiplication of complex numbers distributes over addition.
4. Prove the cancellation law for addition for complex numbers.
5. Prove that, if $(a, b)(c, d) = (0, 0)$ implies that $(a, b) = (0, 0)$ or $(c, d) = 0$, then $(a, b)(x, y) = (c, d)(x, y)$, with $(x, y) \neq (0, 0)$ implies that $(a, b) = (c, d)$, and conversely.
6. Prove that the equation $(a, b) = (x, y) \cdot (c, d)$, where $(c, d) \neq (0, 0)$ has the unique solution (x, y) where $x = (ac + bd)/(c^2 + d^2)$ and $y = (bc - ad)/(c^2 + d^2)$.

7. Prove that there is a *unique* identity for addition of complex numbers.
8. Prove that there is a *unique* identity for multiplication of complex numbers.
9. Prove that every complex number has a *unique* additive inverse.

5 · THE REAL NUMBERS AS A SUBSET OF THE COMPLEX NUMBERS

We may set up an isomorphism between the subset of complex numbers of the form $(a, 0)$ and the real numbers a as follows: Let $(a, 0) \leftrightarrow a$. Now if

$$(a, 0) \leftrightarrow a \qquad \text{and} \qquad (b, 0) \leftrightarrow b,$$

then

$$(a, 0) + (b, 0) = (a + b, 0) \leftrightarrow a + b,$$

and

$$(a, 0) \cdot (b, 0) = (ab, 0) \leftrightarrow ab.$$

We shall now introduce the most common notation for the complex number (a, b), namely, $a + bi$. Let the complex number $(0, 1)$ be denoted by i. Then $i^2 = (0, 1) \cdot (0, 1) = (-1, 0)$, which corresponds to the real number -1. Furthermore, $(a, 0) \cdot (0, 1) = (0, a)$ and $(a, b) = (a, 0) + (0, b) = (a, 0) + (0, 1) \cdot (b, 0)$. Now we replace $(a, 0)$ by its correspondent real number a and $(b, 0)$ by its correspondent real number b and write (a, b) symbolically as $a + bi$. When we use the notation $a + bi$ we carry out addition and multiplication as for addition and multiplication of first-degree polynomials in i but we replace i^2, where it occurs, by -1. Thus, $(2 + 3i) + (1 + 4i) = 3 + 7i$ and $(2 + 3i)(1 + 4i) = 2 + 11i + 12i^2 = -10 + 11i$. Obviously, we have an isomorphism between the couples (a, b) and the symbols $a + bi$ for, if $(a, b) \leftrightarrow a + bi$ and $(c, d) \leftrightarrow c + di$, then

$$(a, b) + (c, d) = (a + c, b + d) \leftrightarrow (a + c) + (b + d)i,$$

and

$$(a, b) \cdot (c, d) = (ac - bd, ad + bc) \leftrightarrow (ac - bd) + (ad + bc)i.$$

From now on we shall use the customary notation $a + bi$, in which a and b are real numbers, for a complex number. If $b = 0$, we say that the number $a + 0i$, or simply a, is a real number. If $a = 0$ and if $b \neq 0$, the complex number is called a *pure imaginary* number.

The complex number $a - bi$ is called the *conjugate* of the complex number $a + bi$, and we note that $(a - bi)(a + bi) = a^2 + b^2$ is a non-negative real number. We can easily express the quotient $(a + bi)/(c + di)$ as a complex number by multiplying numerator and denominator by $c - di$, obtaining $(ac + bd)/(c^2 + d^2) + i(bc - ad)/(c^2 + d^2)$. *Note:* $\sqrt{-1}$ is also a symbol for i.

Exercises

1. Show that the subset of complex numbers of the form $(0, b)$ is not isomorphic to the real numbers.
2. Write the following numbers in the form $a + bi$: $1 - 2\sqrt{-2}$, $1/i$, $1/(1 + i)$, $(2 + 3i)/(1 + 4i)$, $(2 - \sqrt{-3})(3 + 2i)$, 2, i^3, i^4, i^{10}.
3. Show that $i^n = 1, -1, i, -i$ according as n is an integer congruent to 0, 2, 1, or 3 modulo 4.

6 · GEOMETRIC REPRESENTATION OF COMPLEX NUMBERS

Complex numbers may be represented by points in a plane. Let (x, y) be the rectangular cartesian coordinates of a point P in the plane. We say that the point P represents the complex number $x + yi$. Thus to each point in the plane we can attach a complex number, and every complex number represents a point in the plane. It is evident that real numbers correspond to the points on the x-axis and that pure imaginary numbers correspond to points on the y-axis. For this reason the x-axis is often called the axis of reals, and the y-axis the axis of imaginaries.

It is also useful to use polar coordinates. Let (ρ, θ) be the polar coordinates of a point P whose rectangular coordinates are (x, y), and restrict ρ to a positive number or zero. We recall that $\rho = \sqrt{x^2 + y^2}$, $x = \rho \cos \theta$, $y = \rho \sin \theta$, and $\tan \theta = y/x$. Now ρ is called the *absolute value* or *modulus* of the complex number $x + yi$, and θ is called the *angle* or *amplitude*. For example, the absolute value of the complex number $1 - i$ is $\sqrt{2}$, and its angle is $315°$. Hence $1 - i = \sqrt{2}(\cos 315° + i \sin 315°)$. In the general case, $x + yi = \rho (\cos \theta + i \sin \theta)$, where ρ is the absolute value and θ is the angle.

The student must not fall into the error of reading off the angle or the absolute value of a complex number incorrectly when he encounters an expression that is similar to, but not identical with, the standard form of a complex number written in polar coordinates. For example, the angle of the complex number $2(\sin 30° + i \cos 30°)$ is not $30°$ but $60°$, for this number must be written as $2[\cos (90° - 30°) + i \sin (90° - 30°)]$ in order to be in standard form. Again $-2(\cos 60° + i \sin 60°)$ has 2 as its absolute value but $240°$ as its angle, for

$$-2(\cos 60° + i \sin 60°) = 2[\cos (180° + 60°) + i \sin (180° + 60°)].$$

In the representation of a complex number in polar coordinates, we note that, although the absolute value is uniquely determined, the angle is determined only to within integral multiples of $360°$ or, in radian measure, to within integral multiples of 2π. Hence *two complex numbers are equal if and only if their absolute values are equal and if their angles differ by multiples of* 2π. It is also useful to note that the conjugate of the number $\rho(\cos\theta + i\sin\theta)$ is $\rho[\cos(-\theta) + i\sin(-\theta)] = \rho(\cos\theta - i\sin\theta)$.

Exercises

1. Plot the following complex numbers: $2 + 2i, -1 - i, -2, 2i, (1 + i)/(1 - i)$, $(2 - 2i)/i$.
2. Find the angle and absolute value of each of the following numbers: $3(\cos 20° + i\sin 20°), -3(\cos 20° + i\sin 20°), 3(\cos 20° + i\sin 20°)$, $3(\sin 20° + i\cos 20°), 2(\cos 60° - i\sin 60°), 2(-\cos 60° + i\sin 60°)$.
3. Find the angle and absolute value of each of the numbers in Exercise 1 and the numbers $-1 + \sqrt{3}i$ and $i/(-1 - \sqrt{3}i)$. Write these numbers in polar form.

7 · DE MOIVRE'S THEOREM

The product and quotient of two complex numbers when written in polar form give us some interesting results. Let

$$z_1 = \rho_1(\cos\theta_1 + i\sin\theta_1) \quad \text{and} \quad z_2 = \rho_2(\cos\theta_2 + i\sin\theta_2).$$

Then

$$z_1 z_2 = \rho_1\rho_2[\cos\theta_1\cos\theta_2 - \sin\theta_1\sin\theta_2 + i(\sin\theta_1\cos\theta_2 + \cos\theta_1\sin\theta_2)]$$
$$= \rho_1\rho_2[\cos(\theta_1 + \theta_2) + i\sin(\theta_1 + \theta_2)].$$

Similarly

$$\frac{z_1}{z_2} = \frac{\rho_1(\cos\theta_1 + i\sin\theta_1)}{\rho_2(\cos\theta_2 + i\sin\theta_2)} \cdot \frac{(\cos\theta_2 - i\sin\theta_2)}{(\cos\theta_2 - i\sin\theta_2)}$$

$$= \frac{\rho_1}{\rho_2}[\cos(\theta_1 - \theta_2) + i\sin(\theta_1 - \theta_2)].$$

Thus we have the following theorem.

Theorem 1. The absolute value of the product of two complex numbers is the product of their absolute values, and the angle of the product is the sum of their angles. The absolute value of the quotient of two complex numbers is the quotient of their absolute values, and the angle of the quotient is the angle of the numerator minus the angle of the denominator.

Theorem 2. De Moivre's theorem. If n *is a positive integer*

$$[\rho(\cos\theta + i\sin\theta)]^n = \rho^n(\cos n\theta + i\sin n\theta).$$

This formula is an immediate extension of the formula for a product. It is left to the student to prove it by induction.

Exercises

1. Prove Theorem 2.
2. Write $1/[\rho(\cos \theta + i \sin \theta)]$ in polar form.
3. Prove that $[\rho(\cos \theta + i \sin \theta)]^{-n} = \rho^{-n}[\cos (-n\theta) + i \sin (-n\theta)]$, where n is a positive integer.
4. What is the geometric locus of a complex number a) of fixed absolute value, b) of fixed angle?
5. Find the polar form of AB, A/B, A^2/B, and $1/A$, if $A = 2(\cos 30° + i \sin 30°)$ and $B = 4(\cos 50° + i \sin 50°)$.
6. Write the numbers $A = \sqrt{3} - i$, $B = -\sqrt{3} - i$, $C = -\sqrt{3} + i$ in polar form. Find the angle and absolute value of each of the following: A^2, B^2/AC.
7. Find the value of $(1 + i)^6$ by first writing $1 + i$ in polar form and then applying De Moivre's theorem. Write your final answer in the form $a + bi$. Similarly calculate $(1 - \sqrt{3}i)^5$.
8. Since $(\cos \theta + i \sin \theta)^3 = \cos 3\theta + i \sin 3\theta$, use the binomial theorem to find the value of $\cos 3\theta$ and $\sin 3\theta$ as functions of θ.

8 · THE nth ROOTS OF A COMPLEX NUMBER

We seek the solutions z of the equation $z^n = A$, where n is a positive integer and A a complex number. This problem is easily solved by using polar coordinates. Let $z = \rho(\cos \theta + i \sin \theta)$ and $A = r(\cos \phi + i \sin \phi)$. Then $z^n = A$ becomes

$$\rho^n(\cos n\theta + i \sin n\theta) = r(\cos \phi + i \sin \phi).$$

Recalling that two complex numbers are equal if and only if their absolute values are equal and their angles differ by integral multiples of 2π, we have $\rho^n = r$ and $n\theta = \phi + 2k\pi$, k being an integer. Hence $\rho = r^{1/n}$, the positive real nth root of r, and $\theta = \phi/n + 2k\pi/n$. There will be as many different values of z as there are angles $\phi/n + 2k\pi/n$, which are not coterminal. It is easily seen that these angles are not coterminal for the values $k = 0, 1, 2, \cdots, (n - 1)$, for the difference of any two of them is less than 2π. For k any integer we write $k = nq + m$, with $0 \leq m < n$ and see that the angle $\phi/n + 2k\pi/n$ is coterminal with the angle $\phi/n + 2m\pi/n$. Thus there are exactly n distinct values of z given by

$$r^{1/n}[\cos (\phi/n + 2k\pi/n) + i \sin (\phi/n + 2k\pi/n)], \qquad k = 0, 1, 2, \cdots, (n - 1).$$

Hence there are exactly n nth roots of a complex number.

EXAMPLE 1.   Find the three cube roots of $8i$.
Write $8i = 8 (\cos \pi/2 + i \sin \pi/2)$. Let $\rho(\cos \theta + i \sin \theta)$ be a cube root. Then $\rho^3(\cos 3\theta + i \sin 3\theta) = 8(\cos \pi/2 + i \sin \pi/2)$, and $\rho^3 = 8$ and $3\theta = \pi/2 + 2k\pi$.

Hence $\rho = 2$, and $\theta = \pi/6 + 2k\pi/3$. The three cube roots of $8i$ are:

$$2\left(\cos\frac{\pi}{6} + i\sin\frac{\pi}{6}\right) = \sqrt{3} + i,$$

$$2\left(\cos\frac{5\pi}{6} + i\sin\frac{5\pi}{6}\right) = -\sqrt{3} + i,$$

$$2\left(\cos\frac{3\pi}{2} + i\sin\frac{3\pi}{2}\right) = -2i.$$

EXAMPLE 2. Find the n nth roots of 1.

These roots are often called the n nth *roots of unity*. Using the notation introduced above, we have $r = 1$, and $\phi = 0$, and hence $\rho = 1$, and $\theta = 2k\pi/n$. Thus the n nth roots of unity are given by $\cos 2k\pi/n + i\sin 2k\pi/n$, $k = 0, 1, \cdots,$ $(n-1)$. Note that by De Moivre's theorem, if we let $R = \cos 2\pi/n + i\sin 2\pi/n$, the n nth roots of unity can be written $R, R^2, R^3, \cdots, R^n$.

Exercises

1. Find the three cube roots of 8 and simplify the answers.
2. Find the three cube roots of 1 and simplify the answers.
3. Find the four fourth roots of 1 and write them in simplified form. Which of these are square roots of 1 ?
4. Find the six sixth roots of 1. Which of these are square roots of 1; which are cube roots of 1 ?
5. Find the three cube roots of -8.
6. Find the two square roots of $(1 + i)/\sqrt{2}$.
7. Find the four fourth roots of $-16i$.

9 · PRIMITIVE nth ROOTS OF UNITY

In Example 2 above we showed that there are exactly n complex numbers whose nth powers are 1, namely the numbers $R = \cos 2\pi/n + i\sin 2\pi/n$, $R^2, R^3, \cdots, R^n = 1$. In the above exercises we noted that some of the fourth roots of 1 were also square roots of 1 and that the sixth roots of 1 contained square roots and cube roots of 1. It is of interest to investigate these matters more closely.

DEFINITION. A number z is a *primitive* nth root of 1 if $z^n = 1$ and if $z^m \neq 1$, when $0 < m < n$.

Theorem 3. *Let* $R = \cos 2\pi/n + i\sin 2\pi/n$. *If* $(k, n) = d$, *then* R^k *is a primitive* n/dth *root of unity*.

Let $k = k_1 d$ and $n = n_1 d$ so that $(k_1, n_1) = 1$. Then $R^k = \cos 2k_1 d\pi/n_1 d + i\sin 2k_1 d\pi/n_1 d = \cos 2k_1\pi/n_1 + i\sin 2k_1\pi/n_1$. Now R^k is an $n_1 = n/d$th root of unity, for $(R^k)^{n_1} = \cos 2k_1\pi + i\sin 2k_1\pi = 1$. Moreover, R^k is a primitive n/dth root of unity, for if $(R^k)^m = 1 = \cos 2k_1 m\pi/n_1 + i \sin 2k_1 m\pi/n_1$, $k_1 m/n_1$ is an integer. Since $(n_1, k_1) = 1$, $n_1 \mid m$. Thus m is a multiple of n_1 and the smallest value of m such that $(R^k)^m = 1$ is n_1.

Corollary 1. R^k *is a primitive* nth *root of unity if and only if* $(k, n) = 1$.

If $(k, n) = 1$, R^k is a primitive $n/1$th = nth root of unity by the theorem. Conversely, if R^k is a primitive nth root of unity and $(k, n) = d \neq 1$, then R^k is also a primitive n/dth root of unity; i.e., $(R^k)^{(n/d)} = 1$, which contradicts our hypothesis that R^k is a primitive nth root of unity.

Corollary 2. *If* U *is any primitive* nth *root of unity and* $(k, n) = d$, *then* U^k *is a primitive* n/dth *root of unity.*

Now $U = R^t$, where $(t, n) = 1$. Hence $U^k = R^{tk}$ and $(tk, n) = d$. Thus we may apply the theorem to R^{tk}.

Corollary 3. *The* n nth *roots of unity include all the* mth *roots of unity if and only if* m *divides* n.

If $m \mid n$, $n = mk$ and $(n, k) = k$. By Theorem 3, R^k is a primitive n/kth $= m$th root of unity. Thus $R^k, R^{2k}, \cdots, R^{mk}$ are all mth roots of unity since $(R^{jk})^m = (R^{km})^j = 1$. Hence all of the mth roots of unity are included among the nth roots. On the other hand, if all the mth roots of unity are included among the nth roots, then the primitive mth root $\cos 2\pi/m + i \sin 2\pi/m = R^v$. By Theorem 3, if $(v, n) = d$, R^v is a primitive n/dth root of unity. Hence $n/d = m$ and $n = md$.

Exercises

1. Find the primitive cube roots of 1.
2. Find the primitive 8th roots of 1.
3. Find the primitive 5th roots of 1.
4. Show that if p is a prime there are exactly $p - 1$ primitive pth roots of 1.
5. How many real nth roots of 1 are there?
6. How many real nth roots of a positive real number are there?
7. How many real nth roots of a negative real number are there?
8. How many primitive p^2th roots of 1 are there if p is a prime?
9. Find the twelve 12th roots of 1. Which of these are primitive square roots, primitive cube roots, primitive fourth roots, primitive sixth roots?
10. If $R = \cos 2\pi/7 + i \sin 2\pi/7$, express R^{-1}, R^{-3}, R^{-15}, as R^k, where $0 < k < 7$.
11. If $\omega = -1/2 + i\sqrt{3}/2$, find the value of $\omega^n + \omega^{-n}$ for all positive integers n.

3 Elementary Theory of Groups

1 · DEFINITION

We shall now begin the study of some of the mathematical systems that belong primarily to the division of mathematics called algebra. In any mathematical system we have, first of all, a set S of elements that we shall denote by $a, b, c, \cdots$ and an equals or equivalence relation between pairs of elements. We have had several examples of such equals relations, namely, ordinary identical equality, the equality used to define integers, the equality used to define rational numbers, and the congruence of integers. In all the algebraic systems to be studied herein, we shall assume without further mention that an equals relation exists.

In addition to elements and an equivalence relation in an algebraic system, we have one or more operations on a pair of elements of the set S to produce a third element of S. Such operations are called *binary operations*. In general a binary operation o on a set of elements S is a rule that assigns to every ordered pair of elements a, b in S a unique element c in S, and we write $a \text{ o } b = c$. The binary operation is well defined if, when either a or b or both a and b are replaced by elements respectively equal to them, c is replaced by an element equal to it. Familiar binary operations are those of addition and multiplication of numbers.

One of the simplest of all algebraic systems is that of a group. We give the following definition.

Postulates for a group. A set S of elements $a, b, c, \cdots$ forms a group with respect to the operation o if the following properties hold:

1. If a and b are in S, then $a \text{ o } b$ is in S (closure).
2. For all a, b, c in S, $a \text{ o } (b \text{ o } c) = (a \text{ o } b) \text{ o } c$ (associative law).

3. There exists in S an element i, called a *left-identity*, such that $i \circ a = a$ for every a in S.

4. For each a in S, the equation $x \circ a = i$ has a solution x in S. The solution x is called a *left-inverse* of a and is denoted by a^{-1}.

The student should note that, while a left-identity i is the same for all elements a in S, a left-inverse of an element a is determined by the given element a; i.e., there is a "universal" left-identity but not a "universal" left-inverse. Although in the following examples and exercises all the group operations obey the commutative law, the student should not conclude that commutivity is demanded by the postulates. If $a \circ b = b \circ a$ for all a, b in the group, the group is called a *commutative* or *abelian* group. Examples of nonabelian groups will be encountered later.

EXAMPLES.   The chief examples of groups that the student has encountered so far are found in the number system.

a. The integers form a group with respect to addition but not with respect to multiplication.

b. The residue classes modulo 3 form a group with respect to addition, and the nonzero residue classes modulo 3 form a group with respect to multiplication.

c. The numbers i, -1, $-i$, and 1 form a group with respect to multiplication.

Exercises

In each of the following exercises check through all the postulates for a group.

1. Do the even integers form a group with respect to addition? Do the odd integers form a group with respect to addition?

*2. Do the positive real numbers form a group with respect to multiplication? Do all the rational numbers form a group with respect to multiplication?

3. Do the positive irrational numbers form a group with respect to multiplication?

4. Let $a \circ b = a - b$, where a and b are integers. Do the integers form a group with respect to this operation?

5. Prove that the nonzero residue classes modulo 5 form a group with respect to multiplication.

6. Prove that the nonzero residue classes modulo 4 do not form a group with respect to multiplication.

7. Show that all integers of the form $3m$, where m is an integer, form a group with respect to addition.

*8. Show that all integral multiples of a fixed integer k form a group with respect to addition.

9. If the residue classes modulo 7 are denoted by the integers 0, 1, 2 , 3, 4, 5, 6, which of the following sets form a group with respect to multiplication: (a) [1,2,4]; (b) [0,1,2,3,4,5,6]; (c) [1,6]; (d) [1,3,4,5,]; (e) [1,2,3,4,5,6]?

10. Show that the fifth roots of unity form a group with respect to multiplication

*11. Show that the n nth roots of unity form a group with respect to multiplication.

12. Show that the residue classes modulo m form a group with respect to addition.
13. Show that the nonzero residue classes modulo p form a group with respect to multiplication if and only if p is a prime.
14. Prove that the residue classes C_a modulo m such that $(a, m) = 1$ form a group with respect to multiplication.

2 · ELEMENTARY PROPERTIES

We now prove some simple theorems directly from the definition of a group. In the theorems that follow ab will mean $a \circ b$, and the binary operation will be called multiplication.

Theorem 1. If a, b, c *are in a group,* ab = ac *implies* b = c.

Multiply the equation $ab = ac$ on the left by a left-inverse a^{-1} of a and apply the associative law, obtaining $(a^{-1}a)b = (a^{-1}a)c$, which gives us $ib = ic$ and finally $b = c$.

Theorem 2. In a group a left-identity element is also a right-identity element, i.e., ia = ai = a *for every* a *in the group.*

Let a^{-1} be a left-inverse of a. Then $a^{-1}(ai) = (a^{-1}a)i = ii = i = a^{-1}a$. Applying Theorem 1, we have $ai = a$. Henceforth we shall drop the qualifying words left and right and use the term identity for i.

Theorem 3. In a group a left-inverse a^{-1} *of an element* a *is also a right-inverse of* a, *i.e.,* a^{-1}a = aa^{-1} = i.

Now $a^{-1}(aa^{-1}) = (a^{-1}a)a^{-1} = ia^{-1} = a^{-1} = a^{-1}i$. Thus by Theorem 1, $aa^{-1} = i$. From now on we shall use the term inverse for a^{-1}.

Corollary. If a, b, c *are elements in a group, then* ba = ca *implies* b = c.

The proof is the same as for Theorem 1, for now we can multiply on the right by an inverse of a and obtain $b = c$.

Theorem 4. If a *and* b *are elements in a group, the equations* ax = b *and* ya = b, *respectively, have unique solutions* x *and* y *in the group.*

We readily see that a solution of $ax = b$ is $a^{-1}b$ and that a solution of $ya = b$ is ba^{-1}, for $a(a^{-1}b) = (aa^{-1})b = ib = b$, and $(ba^{-1})a = b(a^{-1}a) = bi = b$. The solutions are unique, for, if x' and y' are second solutions, then $ax = ax'$ and $ya = y'a$, giving $x = x'$ and $y = y'$.

Corollary 1. The identity element in a group is unique.

The identity is the unique solution of the equation $ax = a$.

Corollary 2.   The inverse of an element in a group is unique.

The inverse a^{-1} of a is the unique solution of the equation $ax = i$.

Corollary 3.   The inverse of a^{-1} *is* a.

The element a is obviously the solution of the equation $a^{-1}x = i$. Hence we observe that $(a^{-1})^{-1} = a$.

Theorem 5.   The inverse of a product is the product of the inverses in the reverse order; i.e., $(ab)^{-1} = b^{-1}a^{-1}$.

For $(b^{-1}a^{-1})(ab) = b^{-1}(a^{-1}a)b = b^{-1}(ib) = b^{-1}b = i$.

Exercises

1. If a, b, c, are elements of a group, prove that the equation $xaxba = xbc$ has a unique solution.
2. Prove that, if x is an element of a group and $xx = x$, then $x = i$, the identity element of the group.
3. In a group with an even number of elements, show that there is an element besides the identity which is its own inverse.
4. Prove that $(ab)(ab) = (aa)(bb)$ for all elements a and b of a group G if and only if G is an Abelian group.
5. Let S be a set of elements a, b, c, $\cdots$ which satisfies postulates 1 and 2 and, in addition, has the property that all equations $xa = b$ and $ay = b$ have solutions x and y in S. Prove that S is a group.

3 · PERMUTATIONS

So far all the binary operations we have encountered have obeyed the commutative law. We shall now define some symbols and find that the rule for combining them does not obey the commutative law.

The operation of replacing each of the n integers $1, 2, \cdots, n$ by one of them so that no two distinct integers are replaced by the same integer is called a *permutation* performed on the integers $1, 2, \cdots, n$. A permutation replaces any arrangement of the n integers by a new arrangement. It is obvious that the n integers merely form a convenient notation for any set of n symbols. We introduce a symbol for a permutation. Let $j_1, j_2, \cdots, j_n$ be any arrangement of the set of integers $1, 2, \cdots, n$. The symbol

$$p = \begin{pmatrix} 1 & 2 & 3 & \cdots & n \\ j_1 & j_2 & j_3 & \cdots & j_n \end{pmatrix}$$

shall mean replace 1 by j_1, replace 2 by j_2, etc., until finally n is replaced by j_n. Such a symbol denotes a permutation. Note that the order of the columns in the symbol is immaterial.

We define the product of two permutations $p \circ q$ or, as we shall write it, pq, as meaning first perform p and then perform q. Thus, if

$$q = \begin{pmatrix} j_1 & j_2 & \cdots & j_n \\ k_1 & k_2 & \cdots & k_n \end{pmatrix},$$

where $k_1, k_2, \cdots, k_n$ are $1, 2, \cdots, n$ in some order,

$$pq = \begin{pmatrix} 1 & 2 & 3 & \cdots & n \\ k_1 & k_2 & k_3 & \cdots & k_n \end{pmatrix}.$$

In general this multiplication is not commutative, for if, for example,

$$p = \begin{pmatrix} 1 & 2 & 3 \\ 3 & 1 & 2 \end{pmatrix} \quad \text{and} \quad q = \begin{pmatrix} 1 & 2 & 3 \\ 1 & 3 & 2 \end{pmatrix},$$

then

$$pq = \begin{pmatrix} 1 & 2 & 3 \\ 2 & 1 & 3 \end{pmatrix} \quad \text{and} \quad qp = \begin{pmatrix} 1 & 2 & 3 \\ 3 & 2 & 1 \end{pmatrix}.$$

However, we may prove that permutation multiplication is associative. Let p and q be the permutations on n symbols given above, and let

$$r = \begin{pmatrix} k_1 & k_2 & \cdots & k_n \\ m_1 & m_2 & \cdots & m_n \end{pmatrix},$$

where $m_1, m_2, \cdots, m_n$ are the integers $1, 2, \cdots, n$ in some order. Using the value of pq already found, we have

$$(pq)r = \begin{pmatrix} 1 & 2 & 3 & \cdots & n \\ m_1 & m_2 & m_3 & \cdots & m_n \end{pmatrix},$$

while

$$qr = \begin{pmatrix} j_1 & j_2 & \cdots & j_n \\ m_1 & m_2 & \cdots & m_n \end{pmatrix} \quad \text{and} \quad p(qr) = \begin{pmatrix} 1 & 2 & \cdots & n \\ m_1 & m_2 & \cdots & m_n \end{pmatrix}.$$

Thus $(pq)r = p(qr)$.

For every arrangement of $1, 2, 3, \cdots, n$ we may write down a different permutation. Since there are $n!$ different arrangements of n symbols, there are $n!$ different permutations on n symbols, which can be written down by inserting in the second row of p the $n!$ different arrangements of $1, 2, \cdots, n$.

Theorem 6. The n! *permutations on* n *symbols form a group with respect to permutation multiplication.*

Since all the permutations on n symbols are included in the set, the set is closed with respect to permutation multiplication. This multiplication has just been proved to be associative. The identity is

$$i = \begin{pmatrix} 1 & 2 & 3 & \cdots & n \\ 1 & 2 & 3 & \cdots & n \end{pmatrix},$$

for it obviously has the property $ip = pi = p$ for any permutation p on the n integers $1, 2, \cdots, n$. Let p be the permutation given above. Then the inverse of p is

$$p^{-1} = \begin{pmatrix} j_1 & j_2 & \cdots & j_n \\ 1 & 2 & \cdots & n \end{pmatrix},$$

for $pp^{-1} = p^{-1}p = i$.

This group is called the *symmetric group* on n symbols and plays an important role in many applications of group theory

Cyclic Notation

It is convenient to write permutations in what is called cyclic notation or in cycles. For example, the permutation

$$s = \begin{pmatrix} 1 & 2 & 3 & 4 \\ 2 & 3 & 4 & 1 \end{pmatrix}$$

may be written simply as (1234). We read the new symbol, called a *cycle*, in cyclical order from left to right as follows: 1 is replaced by 2, 2 is replaced by 3, 3 is replaced by 4, and 4 is replaced by 1. Note that $(1234) = (2341) = (3412) = (4123)$. Again the permutation

$$t = \begin{pmatrix} 1 & 2 & 3 & 4 & 5 \\ 2 & 3 & 1 & 5 & 4 \end{pmatrix}$$

is written (123)(45), and the permutation

$$u = \begin{pmatrix} 1 & 2 & 3 \\ 1 & 3 & 2 \end{pmatrix}$$

is written either as (1)(23) or simply as (23). It is understood that when a symbol is omitted it is replaced by itself. It should now be reasonably clear that any permutation may be written as a product of cycles no two of which have a symbol in common (*disjoint* cycles).

Exercises

✶ 1. Write out the 4! permutations on 4 symbols in the two-rowed notation and in the cyclic notation.

2. Perform the following permutation multiplications: (a) (1245)(32154); (b) (123)(243)(134); (c) (15624)(6321).

3. Find the inverse of each of the products in Exercise 2.

4. Perform the following permutation multiplications:

   a. (243)(13),   b. (4312)(2341),   c. (43)(3421),   d. (431)(231),
   e. (12)(34)(24), f. (132)(1342),   g. (34)(143),   h. (1432)(14),
   i. (1324)(134),   j. (1423)(24),   k. (142)(23),   l. (234)(143).

5. If $a = (123456)$, find a^2, a^3, a^4, a^5, a^6.

6. Show that the six permutations in Exercise 5 form a group with respect to permutation multiplication.

7. Write the following products as products of disjoint cycles: (a) (132)(567)(261)(45); (b) (1234)(67)(1357)(136); (c) (24)(132)(45)(24).

4 · EVEN AND ODD PERMUTATIONS

DEFINITION.   A permutation that displaces only two symbols is called a *transposition*.

Theorem 7.   A cycle of n *symbols can be written as a product of* n − 1 *transpositions.*

This is clear when we exhibit the identity

$$(1234 \cdots n) = (12)(13)(14) \cdots (1n).$$

Hence any permutation can be written as a product of transpositions since each of its cycles can be so written.

A permutation can be written as a product of transpositions in many ways. For example, $(123) = (12)(13)$, and $(123) = (13)(12)(13)(12)$. However, for a given permutation the number of transpositions is always even or always odd. This we prove in the following theorem.

Theorem 8.   Let a permutation p *be written as a product of* a *transpositions and as a product of* b *transpositions. Then* a ≡ b *(mod 2).*

In order to prove this theorem, consider the so-called alternating function A on the n distinct symbols $x_1, x_2, \cdots, x_n$, which is the product of the $n(n-1)/2$ factors $(x_i - x_j)$, $i < j$. Thus

$$A = \prod_{i<j}^{n} (x_i - x_j)$$

$$= (x_1 - x_2)(x_1 - x_3)(x_1 - x_4) \cdots (x_1 - x_n)$$
$$(x_2 - x_3)(x_2 - x_4) \cdots (x_2 - x_n)$$
$$(x_3 - x_4) \cdots (x_3 - x_n)$$
$$\cdots\cdots\cdots\cdots\cdots\cdots$$
$$(x_{n-1} - x_n).$$

Operate on A by the transposition $t = (x_i x_j)$, where $i < j$. Every factor of A that contains neither x_i nor x_j remains unchanged when A is operated on by the permutation t, but the factor $(x_i - x_j)$ of A is changed into its negative. The factors of A containing either x_i or x_j, but not both x_i and x_j, may be grouped into pairs of products $\pm(x_k - x_i)(x_k - x_j)$, where $k \neq i, j$. Such a product remains unchanged when it is operated on by t. Hence when A is operated on by a transposition t it becomes $-A$.

Now operate on A by the permutation p, which can be written as a product of a transpositions and also as a product of b transpositions. Operating on A by p when it is written as a product of a transpositions, we obtain $(-1)^a A$, whereas, operating on A by p when it is written as a product of b transpositions, we obtain $(-1)^b A$. Because p is the same permutation no matter how it is written, $(-1)^a A = (-1)^b A$, which shows that $a \equiv b \pmod 2$.

DEFINITION.   A permutation is called an *even* permutation or an *odd* permutation according as it can be written as a product of an even number or an odd number of transpositions.

Theorem 9.   Of the n! *permutations on* n *symbols* n!/2 *are even permutations and* n!/2 *are odd permutations.*

Of the $n!$ permutations on n symbols let $e_1, e_2, \cdots, e_r$ be the even permutations and $o_1, o_2, \cdots, o_r$ be the odd permutations. Multiply each of these permutations on the left by the transposition t (which is, of course, an odd permutation). The $te_j, j = 1, 2, \cdots, s$ are odd permutations, for each e_j has been multiplied by the one transposition t, whereas the $to_k, k = 1, 2, \cdots, r$ are even permutations, for each o_k has been multiplied by the one transposition t. We now prove that the te_j and the to_k are the $n!$ permutations over again. Since, obviously, no even permutation is ever equal to an odd permutation, we need to prove only that no $te_v = te_w$ when $e_v \neq e_w$, and no $to_v = to_w$ when $o_v \neq o_w$. This follows directly from the cancellation law, for $te_v = te_w$ implies $e_v = e_w$, and $to_v = to_w$ implies $o_v = o_w$. Thus the $te_j, j = 1, 2, \cdots, s$, are the permutations $o_k, k = 1, 2, \cdots, r$, in some order, and hence $s = r = n!/2$.

Exercises

1. Show that the identity is an even permutation.
2. Show that a cycle containing an odd number of symbols is an even permutation, whereas a cycle containing an even number of symbols is an odd permutation.
3. Write each of the 4! permutations on 4 symbols as a product of transpositions. Which are even permutations and which are odd permutations?
4. If p is an even permutation, show that p^{-1} is an even permutation.

5. Prove that the $n!/2$ even permutations on n symbols form a group with respect to permutation multiplication. This group is known as the *alternating group* on n symbols.
6. Prove that every even permutation is a cycle of length three or can be expressed as a product of cycles of length three.

5 · ISOMORPHISM

DEFINITION. An *isomorphism* between two groups G and G' is a one-to-one correspondence $a \leftrightarrow a'$ between the elements a and a' of G and G' respectively such that, if $a \leftrightarrow a'$ and $b \leftrightarrow b'$, then $ab \leftrightarrow a'b'$. In the isomorphism, a' is called the *image* of a.

Note that an isomorphism does not demand that the operation or law of combination for the elements of each group be the same. We have omitted the symbol for the operation in the definition, but, if o is the operation for G and if o' is the operation for G', then the condition for an isomorphism reads $a' \text{ o}' \ b' = (a \text{ o } b)'$.

EXAMPLE. Let G be the multiplicative group of the fourth roots of unity, and let G' be the additive group of the residue classes modulo 4 (whose elements will be denoted by 0, 1, 2, 3 in place of C_0, C_1, C_2, and C_3, respectively). Then we may set up an isomorphism between G and G' in the following two ways:

$$
\begin{array}{cc}
G & G' \\
1 \leftrightarrow 0 \\
i \leftrightarrow 1 \\
-1 \leftrightarrow 2 \\
-i \leftrightarrow 3;
\end{array}
\qquad
\begin{array}{cc}
G & G' \\
1 \leftrightarrow 0 \\
i \leftrightarrow 3 \\
-1 \leftrightarrow 2 \\
-i \leftrightarrow 1.
\end{array}
$$

The number of ways an isomorphism can be established between two groups depends upon the structure of the group. No matter how the isomorphism is set up, however, we should observe the following fact. Write the so-called "multiplication table" for each group G and G'.

G:

×	1	i	-1	$-i$
1	1	i	-1	$-i$
i	i	-1	$-i$	1
-1	-1	$-i$	1	i
$-i$	$-i$	1	i	-1

G':

+	0	1	2	3
0	0	1	2	3
1	1	2	3	0
2	2	3	0	1
3	3	0	1	2

For each isomorphism we see that the two multiplication tables become identical if each symbol of G is replaced by its image in G', and conversely.

Theorem 10.   In an isomorphism between two groups G and G' the identities correspond and if a' *in* G' *is the image of* a *in* G *then the image of* a^{-1} *is* $(a')^{-1}$.

We first prove that the identities correspond. Let i be the identity of G and let i' be the identity of G'. Suppose $i \leftrightarrow a'$ in G' and let x be any element of G and x' its image in G'. Then, since $ix = x$, we have from the definition of an isomorphism, $a'x' = x'$ for any x' of G. Hence a' is an identity for G', and, since the identity is unique, $a' = i'$.

Next prove that inverse elements correspond. Let $a \leftrightarrow a'$ and $a^{-1} \leftrightarrow b'$. Since $a^{-1}a = i$, we have from the definition of an isomorphism, $b'a' = i'$, and, since the inverse of an element is unique, $b' = (a')^{-1}$.

Exercises

1. Set up an isomorphism between the multiplicative group of the fourth roots of unity and the permutation group whose elements are $i = (1)(2)(3)(4)$, (1234), (13)(24), (1432).
2. Is it possible to set up an isomorphism between the multiplicative group of the fourth roots of unity and the permutation group whose elements are $i = (1)$ (2)(3)(4), (12)(34), (13)(24), (14)(23)?
3. Set up an isomorphism between the multiplicative group of the five fifth roots of unity and the permutation group whose elements are $i = (1)(2)(3)(4)(5)$, (12345), (13524), (14253), (15432).
4. Is the multiplicative group of non-zero real numbers isomorphic to the additive group of all real numbers?

6 · CYCLIC GROUPS

Integral Powers of an Element

We shall define integral powers of a group element a. By a^m, where m is a positive integer, we shall mean $a \circ a \circ \cdots \circ a$ to m factors. (If the operation is called addition, we usually denote a^m by $ma = a + a + \cdots a$ (m terms), where it is understood that m is not necessarily a group element and usually is not.) Note that this writing of m factors without parentheses is possible only because a "product" of m factors is independent of the manner in which the factors are grouped. This generalized associative law can be proved by induction from the associative law. Further, we define $a^0 = i$, the identity, and $a^{-m} = (a^{-1})^m$, where m is a positive integer. With these definitions it is easy to prove the following theorem.

Theorem 11.   For any element a *in a group,* (*1*) $a^r \circ a^s = a^{r+s}$, *and* (*2*) $(a^r)^s = a^{rs}$.

First we shall establish (1): For positive integral exponents this law is simply an application of the definition, for $a^r \text{ o } a^s = a \text{ o } a \text{ o } \cdots \text{ o } a$ to $r + s$ factors. From the definition of a^0, (1) holds if one or both exponents are zero. In case $r = -m$, $s = -n$, m and n positive integers, we have

$$
\begin{aligned}
a^r \text{ o } a^s = a^{-m} \text{ o } a^{-n} = (a^{-1})^m \text{ o } (a^{-1})^n \qquad & \text{by definition,} \\
= (a^{-1})^{m+n} \qquad & \text{by (1) for positive exponents,} \\
= a^{-(m+n)} \qquad & \text{by definition,} \\
= a^{r+s}.
\end{aligned}
$$

If $r = -m$ and if $s = n$, where m and n are positive integers, we have, using the definition of negative exponents,

$$ a^r \text{ o } a^s = a^{-m} \text{ o } a^n = a^{-1} \text{ o } a^{-1} \text{ o } \cdots \text{ o } a^{-1} \text{ o } a \text{ o } a \cdots \text{ o } a $$

(m factors a^{-1} and n factors a),

$$
\begin{aligned}
& = a^{n-m}, && m \le n, \\
& = (a^{-1})^{m-n}, && m > n, \\
& = a^{-m+n} = a^{r+s}.
\end{aligned}
$$

Thus all cases have been investigated and (1) holds for all integral exponents.

Now we shall establish (2): It is again obvious that (2) holds if either or both exponents are zero. If $s > 0$, then

$$
\begin{aligned}
(a^r)^s = a^r \text{ o } a^r \text{ o } \cdots \text{ o } a^r \qquad & \text{to } s \text{ factors,} \\
= a^{rs} \qquad & \text{by (1).}
\end{aligned}
$$

If $s = -n$, where n is a positive integer, we have by definition

$$ (a^r)^s = (a^r)^{-n} = [(a^r)^{-1}]^n. $$

Now $(a^r)^{-1}$ is the inverse of a^r and by (1) $a^r \text{ o } a^{-r} = a^0$. Hence, since the inverse of an element is unique, $(a^r)^{-1} = a^{-r}$. Therefore

$$
\begin{aligned}
[(a^r)^{-1}]^n = (a^{-r})^n = a^{-rn} \qquad & \text{by (1),} \\
= a^{rs}.
\end{aligned}
$$

In general, $(ab)^r \ne a^r b^r$. In particular, if $ab \ne ba$, $(ab)^2 \ne a^2 b^2$. For if $(ab)^2 = a^2 b^2$, then $abab = aabb$ and, applying Theorem 1 and the corollary to Theorem 3, we have $ab = ba$.

Definition of a Cyclic Group

Note that the above definitions of the integral powers of a group element a together with Theorem 11 prove that the integral powers of any group element a form a group. A group consisting only of the powers of a single element a is called a cyclic group. Such an element a is called a *generator* of the cyclic group.

Definition of the Order of an Element

An element a in a group is said to be of order n, if n is the least positive integer such that $a^n = i$, the identity. An element a is said to be of order zero if no positive power of a is the identity; i.e., a^0 is the only power of a which is the identity.

Order of a Group

A group consisting of a finite number of elements is called a *finite* group, whereas a group having infinitely many elements is called an *infinite* group. The order of a finite group is the number of its elements. An infinite group is said to have the order zero.

Theorem 12. If a generator a *of a cyclic group* G *is of order zero,* G *is isomorphic to the additive group of integers. If a generator* a *of* G *is of order* n > 0, G *is isomorphic to the additive group of residue classes modulo* n.

We shall prove first that if the order of a is zero no two powers of a are equal. For, if $a^s = a^t$ when $s \neq t$, then $a^s a^{-t} = a^t a^{-t} = i$, and $a^{s-t} = i = a^{t-s}$, and thus, since either $s - t$ or $t - s$ is positive, a positive power of a equals i. Now, since $a^s a^t = a^{s+t}$, the correspondence $a^s \leftrightarrow s$ is an isomorphism, and G is isomorphic to the additive group of integers.

Now we let a be of order $n > 0$, and shall prove that G consists of only n distinct elements. For any integer s, we have $s = nq + r$, where $0 \leq r < n$. Thus any element a^s of G may be written $a^s = a^{nq+r} = a^{nq} a^r = (a^n)^q a^r = i a^r = a^r$. Thus there are at most n distinct elements $a, a^2, \cdots, a^{n-1}, a^n = i$. If $x > y$, where $0 < x < n$ and $0 < y < n$, then $a^x \neq a^y$, for, if $a^x = a^y$, $a^{x-y} = i$; but $0 < x - y < n$, contrary to the definition of the order of a. Thus there are at least n distinct elements. Hence there are exactly n distinct elements $a, a^2, a^3, \cdots, a^{n-1}, a^n = a^0 = i$ in the group. Denoting the residue classes modulo n by $C_0, C_1, C_2, \cdots, C_{n-1}$, we see that the correspondence $a^s \leftrightarrow C_s$ is an isomorphism between the additive group of residue classes modulo n and G, for, if $a^t \leftrightarrow C_t$, then $a^s a^t = a^{s+t} = a^r \leftrightarrow C_s + C_t = C_r$, where $s + t \equiv r \pmod{n}$.

Exercises

1. Show that the following permutations form a group: $i = (1)(2)(3)(4)$, (1234), $(13)(24)$, (1432), (13), (24), $(14)(23)$, $(12)(34)$. Is this group isomorphic to the multiplicative group of the eighth roots of unity? Is the permutation group a cyclic group? Is the multiplicative group of the eighth roots of unity a cyclic group?

2. In the following problems denote the residue classes modulo m by 0, 1, 2, $\cdots$, $m - 1$.

    a. Is the multiplicative group 1, 2, 3, 4, 5, 6 modulo 7 cyclic?

    b. Is the multiplicative group 1, 3, 5, 7, modulo 8 cyclic?

    c. Is the multiplicative group 1, 2, 4, 5, 7, 8 modulo 9 cyclic?

3. Is the additive group of integral multiples of 5 cyclic?

4. Set up an isomorphism in as many ways as possible between the multiplicative group of the sixth roots of unity and the additive group of residue classes modulo 6.

5. How many elements of the cyclic group of order 6 can be used as generators of the group?

6. Show that an abelian group of order 6 which contains an element of order 3 is necessarily a cyclic group.

7. If a cyclic group G is generated by an element a of order m, prove that a^k generates G if and only if $(k, m) = 1$.

8. If a cyclic group G is generated by an element a of order m, find the order of any element a^k of G.

7 · SUBGROUPS

DEFINITIONS. A subset S of elements of a group G that is itself a group is called *a subgroup* of G. The law of combination of the elements is understood to be the same as that for the group itself. The identity alone as well as the group G itself satisfies this definition. Subgroups other than the identity and the group itself are called *proper* subgroups, and we are chiefly interested in these.

Theorem 13. Necessary and sufficient conditions that a subset S *of elements of a group* G *forms a group are (1) if* a *and* b *are in* S, *then* ab *is in* S, *and (2) if* a *is in* S, *then* a⁻¹ *is in* S.

Note that these conditions reduce the number of conditions to be tested from four to two. We prove first that if these conditions hold, the set S forms a group. Conditions (1) and (2) ensure the closure of the set, the presence of the identity in S, and the presence of the inverse of each element a of S in S. The associative law holds because the elements of S are in G. Hence the postulates for a group are satisfied. On the other hand, if the set S forms a group, (1) holds. Now the identity of G is an identity for S. Since S is a group its identity is unique, and hence the identity of S is the identity of G. Moreover, since the inverse of an element in G is unique, the inverse of an element a in S is also the inverse of a in G. Hence (2) holds.

Corollary. A subset S *of a finite group* G *is a subgroup of* G *if and only if* a *and* b *in* S *implies* ab *in* S.

By the theorem, the condition is certainly necessary. Conversely, if the condition is satisfied, (1) of the theorem holds. Furthermore, since G is finite, not all of the powers a, a^2, a^3, $\cdots$ of a in S are distinct, i.e., $a^s = a^t$ for some $s > t$. Then $a^{s-t} = i$, the identity of G. Hence, $a^{s-t-1}a = i$ and a^{s-t-1} in S is the inverse of a. Hence (2) of the theorem is satisfied and S is a subgroup of G.

We shall now determine the subgroups of a cyclic group.

Theorem 14.   A subgroup S of a cyclic group G is cyclic. If a is a generator of G, S is generated by a^m, *where* m *is the least positive integer such that* a^m *is in S. If G is of order zero, the integer* m *is arbitrary and S is isomorphic to the additive group of integral multiples of* m. *If G is of order* n > 0, m *divides* n *and S is of order* n/m.

Let a be a generator of G, and let S be a proper subgroup of G. Because S is a proper subgroup of G, it contains some element a^s and, therefore, also the inverse, a^{-s}, of a^s. Now either s or $-s$ is a positive integer. Hence let m be the least positive integer such that a^m is in S. If a^t is in S, write $t = mq + r$, with $0 \le r < m$. Now $(a^m)^q = a^{mq}$ is in S, and therefore $a^t a^{-mq} = a^{t-mq} = a^r$ is in S. However, $r < m$. Hence $r = 0$ by definition of m and, thus, all elements in S are of the form a^{km}. Thus a^m is a generator of S. If a is of order zero, a^m is a generator of a subgroup for any integer m, and the correspondence $a^m \leftrightarrow m$ is an isomorphism between S and the additive group of integral multiples of m. If a is of order $n > 0$, then $a^n = i$ is in S, and hence $n = mk$. Thus a^m is of order $k = n/m$.

Exercises

1. Select cyclic subgroups of three different orders from the symmetric group on four symbols.
2. Exhibit the proper subgroups in the multiplicative group of the sixth roots of unity.
3. Exhibit the proper subgroups of the additive group of residue classes modulo 12.
4. Set up an isomorphism between the additive group of residue classes modulo 12 and the multiplicative group of the twelfth roots of unity. What roots of unity correspond to the subgroups you have found in Exercise 3?
5. Find the elements of the additive group of residue classes modulo m which can be used as generators of the group.
6. Prove that the elements common to two subgroups S and T of a group G form a subgroup of G. This subgroup consisting of the elements common to S and T is called the *intersection* or *cross cut* of S and T.
7. Show that the following permutations form a group:
   $i = (1)(2)(3)(4)(5)(6)(7)(8)$, $(1234)(5678)$, $(13)(24)(57)(68)$, $(1432)(5876)$, $(1537)(2846)$, $(1735)(2648)$, $(1836)(2745)$, $(1638)(2547)$.
   Find three cyclic subgroups of order 4 of this group.
8. Show that in a group G those elements x such that $xa = ax$ for all a in G form a subgroup of G. This subgroup is called the *center* of G.

8 · COSETS AND SUBGROUPS

We turn now to some properties of groups which will give us further insight into the structure of a group.

DEFINITION.   Let S be a subgroup of G, and let a be any element of G. The collection of elements Sa of G, which consists of the products of each element s of S by the element a of G, is called a *right coset* of S in G. Similarly, the collection of elements aS of G is called a *left coset* of S in G.

Note that according to this definition S itself is both a left coset and a right coset of S in G, for $iS = Si = S$. It is also of interest to point out that in an abelian group the right cosets and the left cosets of a subgroup S coincide, and in this case the qualifying adjectives right and left are omitted.

EXAMPLE 1.   Let G be the *octic* permutation group whose elements are $i = (1)(2)(3)(4)$, $a = (1234)$, $b = (13)(24)$, $c = (1432)$, $d = (13)$, $e = (24)$, $f = (12)(34)$, $g = (14)(23)$, and let S be the subgroup whose elements are i and $d = (13)$. Then the right cosets of S in G are S, Sa, Sc, Se, which respectively consist of the following sets of elements: $i, (13)$; $(1234), (14)(23)$; $(1432), (12)(34)$; (24), $(13)(24)$. Note that $S = Sd, Sa = Sg, Sc = Sf$, and $Se = Sb$. Thus, if we have two equal cosets Sx and Sy, it does not follow that $x = y$ but only that for every element s of S there is an element s' of S such that $sx = s'y$.

EXAMPLE 2.   Let G be the additive group of integers, and let S be the subgroup of integral multiples of 3. In this case the cosets of S are the following sets of integers: $3m, 3m + 1, 3m + 2$. Here, because we use an additive notation for G, we write $S + a$ for a right coset of S instead of Sa. To say that the cosets of S are the sets of integers $3m, 3m + 1$, and $3m + 2$ is simply to assert that, if we add an integer to an integral multiple of 3, the result is either another multiple of 3, a number which is 1 plus a multiple of 3, or a number which is 2 plus a multiple of 3.

We prove the following lemmas and theorems for right cosets, but it should be noted that similar statements and proofs can be made for left cosets.

Lemma 1.   The set of elements Ss, *where* s *is any element of the subgroup* S, *is the subgroup* S.

We write $Ss = S$, meaning that the collection of elements Ss is identical except for order with the elements of S. The elements of the set Ss are in S, and any element s' in S is in Ss, for $s' = (s's^{-1})s$ where $s's^{-1}$ is in S.

Lemma 2.   A one-to-one correspondence may be set up between the elements of a subgroup S *and the elements of a right coset* Sa *of* S *in a group* G.

The correspondence $s \leftrightarrow sa$ is one-to-one, for $sa = s'a$ implies $s = s'$.

Lemma 3.   Two right cosets Sa *and* Sb *of a subgroup* S *in a group* G *either are identical or have no common elements.*

Let x be an element common to Sa and Sb; i.e., $x = sa = sb$. Then $S(sa) = S(s'b)$.   However, $S(sa) = (Ss)a = Sa$ by   Lemma   1,   and similarly $S(s'b) = Sb$.

Note how Example 1 illustrates Lemma 3: $Si \equiv Sd$, $Sa \equiv Sg$, $Sc \equiv Sf$, and $Se \equiv Sb$. On the other hand, S has no elements in common with Sa, Sc, or Se; Sa has no elements in common with S, Sc, or Se, etc.

Theorem 15.   The elements of a group G *can be separated into mutually exclusive right cosets of a subgroup* S *in* G.

Every element a of G belongs to some right coset of S in G, namely the right coset Sa, for this coset contains the element $ia = a$. By Lemma 3 a given element can belong to one and only one right coset of S. Thus we have separated the elements of G into mutually exclusive right cosets of S. We often speak of a as a *representative* of the right coset Sa.

Note that we really have introduced an equivalence relation between the elements of a group by the introduction of right cosets. For suppose that we say that two elements a and b of G are right congruent modulo the subgroup S if $b = sa$, where s is an element of S, and that we write $a \equiv b$ (mod S). Note $a \equiv a$, for $a = ia$. If $a \equiv b$, then $b \equiv a$, for if $b = sa$ then $a = s^{-1}b$. Moreover, if $a \equiv b$ and $b \equiv c$, then $a \equiv c$, for we have $b = sa$, $c = s'b$, and hence $c = s'(sa) = s''a$, It is also of interest to note that, if G is the additive group of integers and if S is the subgroup of integral multiples of a fixed integer m, the concept of the separation of G into cosets of the subgroup S is the same as the separation of the set of integers into residue classes modulo m. Stating that two integers a and b are congruent modulo m is the same as saying that they belong to the same residue class modulo m or the same coset of the subgroup S.

Theorem 16.   Theorem of Lagrange.   The order of a subgroup S *of a finite group* G *is a divisor of the order of* G.

Let g be the order of G and let s be the order of S. Separate the elements of G into right cosets of S, say k in number. By Lemma 2 each right coset contains the same number s of elements. Hence $sk = g$.

Corollary 1.   The order of an element of a group of finite order divides the order of the group.

The proof is immediate when we recall that any element of a group generates a cyclic subgroup of the group.

Corollary 2.   Every group of prime order p *is cyclic.*

The order of the cyclic subgroup generated by an element $a \neq i$ must divide the prime p and hence is of order p itself. Thus the group consists of the powers of the element a.

Corollary 3. Fermat's theorem. If a *is an integer and* p *a prime, then* a$^p \equiv$ a *(mod* p*).*

The multiplicative group of nonzero residues modulo p, where p is a prime, is of order $p - 1$, and 1 is its identity. Thus, for any integer $a \neq 0 \pmod{p}$, $a^{p-1} \equiv 1 \pmod{p}$, and hence $a^p \equiv a \pmod{p}$. The theorem is trivially true if $a \equiv 0 \pmod{p}$.

Exercises

1. Find the left cosets of the subgroup $i = (1)(2)(3)(4)$, $d = (13)$ of the octic permutation group. Are the left cosets the same as the right cosets found in Example 1 ?
2. Separate the elements of the symmetric group on four symbols into right cosets and also into left cosets of the octic group on four symbols.
3. Find all the subgroups of the octic permutation group.
4. Find all the subgroups of the symmetric group on three symbols.
5. Separate the elements of the symmetric group on four symbols into right and left cosets of the subgroup $i = (1)(2)(3)(4)$, $(12)(34)$, $(13)(24)$, $(14)(23)$.
6. Prove that a necessary and sufficient condition that two right cosets Sa and Sb of a subgroup S in a group G be identical is that ab^{-1} be an element of S.
7. What are the possible orders of the subgroups of the symmetric group on four symbols? Find examples of as many subgroups as you can.
8. Prove that the number of right cosets of a finite group is equal to the number of left cosets of the group.

9 · CAYLEY'S THEOREM

To show the intimate relation between permutation groups and finite groups, we shall prove Cayley's theorem.

Theorem 17. Every finite group of order n *is isomorphic to a permutation group on* n *symbols.*

Consider

$$S_j = \begin{pmatrix} s_1 & s_2 & \cdots & s_n \\ s_1 s_j & s_2 s_j & \cdots & s_n s_j \end{pmatrix}$$

for $j = 1, 2, \cdots, n$. Each S_j is then a permutation of the n symbols of the group since all of the elements in the second row of

$$\begin{pmatrix} s_1 & s_2 & \cdots & s_n \\ s_1 s_j & s_2 s_j & \cdots & s_n s_j \end{pmatrix}$$

are distinct. It is easy to see that these permutations form a group that is a subgroup of the symmetric group on n symbols. For, by the corollary to Theorem 13, we have only to establish closure. Now

$$S_j S_k = \begin{pmatrix} s_1 & s_2 & \cdots & s_n \\ (s_1 s_j) s_k & (s_2 s_j) s_k & \cdots & (s_n s_j) s_k \end{pmatrix}$$

and $(s_i s_j) s_k = s_i(s_j s_k)$, where $s_j s_k = s_m$ is an element of G. Hence $S_j S_k$ is of the form

$$S_m = \begin{pmatrix} s_1 & s_2 & \cdots & s_n \\ s_1 s_m & s_2 s_m & \cdots & s_n s_m \end{pmatrix}$$

and the one-to-one correspondence $s_j \leftrightarrow S_j$ provides us with an isomorphism. For, if $s_j s_k = s_m$, then

$$s_m = s_j s_k \leftrightarrow S_m = S_j S_k = \begin{pmatrix} s_1 & s_2 & \cdots & s_n \\ s_1(s_j s_k) & s_2(s_j s_k) & \cdots & s_n(s_j s_k) \end{pmatrix}.$$

This permutation group is called a *regular permutation* group. Each of its elements except the identity displaces n symbols.

EXAMPLE. Find a regular permutation group isomorphic to the symmetric group on three symbols. Label the elements of the symmetric group on three symbols as follows: $s_1 = (1)(2)(3)$, $s_2 = (123)$, $s_3 = (132)$, $s_4 = (12)$, $s_5 = (13)$, $s_6 = (23)$. Then we can find the regular permutation representation from the following multiplication table. Note that we are multiplying each element of the group on the right by the element in the first column. We obtain another regular permutation group if we multiply on the left, but in that case we do not have the same isomorphism that was established in the theorem.

	s_1	s_2	s_3	s_4	s_5	s_6	Regular Permutation Group
s_1	s_1	s_2	s_3	s_4	s_5	s_6	$S_1 = (s_1)(s_2)(s_3)(s_4)(s_5)(s_6) = i \leftrightarrow s_1$
s_2	s_2	s_3	s_1	s_5	s_6	s_4	$S_2 = (s_1 s_2 s_3)(s_4 s_5 s_6) \leftrightarrow s_2$
s_3	s_3	s_1	s_2	s_6	s_4	s_5	$S_3 = (s_1 s_3 s_2)(s_4 s_6 s_5) \leftrightarrow s_3$
s_4	s_4	s_6	s_5	s_1	s_3	s_2	$S_4 = (s_1 s_4)(s_2 s_6)(s_3 s_5) \leftrightarrow s_4$
s_5	s_5	s_4	s_6	s_2	s_1	s_3	$S_5 = (s_1 s_5)(s_2 s_4)(s_3 s_6) \leftrightarrow s_5$
s_6	s_6	s_5	s_4	s_3	s_2	s_1	$S_6 = (s_1 s_6)(s_2 s_5)(s_3 s_4) \leftrightarrow s_6$

A permutation of the regular permutation group replaces each element of the first row in the table by the element below it in any given row. The isomorphism is given by assigning the regular permutation on the right to its corresponding element of the group in the first column.

Exercises

Find a regular permutation group isomorphic to each of the following groups:
1. The cyclic group of order 5.
2. The cyclic group of order 6.
3. The octic group.

4 Rings, Integral Domains, and Fields

1 · RINGS

We now turn to algebraic systems that deal with sets which are closed under two operations. The two operations will be called addition and multiplication, and we shall use the ordinary notation for these operations. However, it must be borne in mind that they may be not ordinary addition and multiplication but well-defined operations that satisfy the given postulates. The simplest of these systems is the ring.

DEFINITION. A set of elements $a, b, c, \cdots$ forms a *ring* R with respect to the two operations addition and multiplication if:

1. The set forms a commutative group with respect to addition.
2. The set is closed with respect to multiplication.
3. The associative law $a(bc) = (ab)c$ holds for multiplication.
4. The distributive laws $a(b + c) = ab + ac$ and $(b + c)a = ba + ca$ hold.

Since the ring is a group with respect to addition, all the group properties for addition hold. The unique identity of the additive group is called the zero element of the ring, and we shall denote it by the ordinary symbol for the number zero. Thus $a + 0 = 0 + a = a$ for every a in the ring. We shall denote the unique additive inverse of an element a by $-a$, and we shall write $a + (-a) = a - a = 0$ and $a + (-b) = a - b$. Note that the properties of the additive inverse and the zero element give us the cancellation law, if $a + b = a + c$, then $b = c$; a unique solution $x = b - a$ of the equation $a + x = b$; and the rule $-(-a) = a$.

We can also prove $a \cdot 0 = 0$, for $a \cdot 0 + a \cdot a = a(0 + a) = a \cdot a = 0 + a \cdot a$, and hence, by the above cancellation law for addition, $a \cdot 0 = 0$.

Similarly, by using the right distributive law, we can prove that $0 \cdot a = 0$. However, the converse that if a product $a \cdot b = 0$ one factor must be zero (the equivalent of the cancellation law for multiplication) need not necessarily hold, as we shall illustrate below.

A ring in which multiplication is commutative is called a *commutative* ring. We shall be interested primarily in commutative rings.

EXAMPLES.   The student can check that the integers, the even integers, and the residue classes modulo m all form commutative rings with respect to addition and multiplication. These rings differ in certain ways. The ring of integers and the ring of residue classes have identity elements for multiplication, but the ring of even integers does not. Again, the cancellation law for multiplication holds in the ring of integers and in the ring of even integers, but does not hold in the ring of residue classes modulo m unless m is a prime number. If $m = ab$ is composite, we see that $ab \equiv 0 \pmod{m}$, but neither $a \equiv 0$ nor $b \equiv 0 \pmod{m}$. On the other hand, if $ab \equiv 0 \pmod{p}$, where p is a prime, we have either $a \equiv 0 \pmod{p}$ or $b \equiv 0 \pmod{p}$.

Divisors of Zero

If $ab = 0$ and $a \neq 0$ and $b \neq 0$, then a and b are called proper divisors of zero. Thus we note that the ring of residue classes modulo m is a ring without proper divisors of zero if and only if m is a prime.

Unity Element

If a ring contains an element u such that $ua = au = a$ for every a in the ring, u is called the unity element. We shall denote it either by u or the number 1. It can be proved that the unity element is unique. For, if u' is a second unity element, we have $u \cdot u' = u' = u$.

The usual properties of additive inverses can be established for the elements of a ring. As an illustration, let us prove that $(-a)(-b) = ab$. Consider $s = (-a)(-b) + (-a)b + ab$. We will show that $s = (-a)(-b)$ and $s = ab$. First, $s = (-a)(-b) + (-a)b + ab = (-a)(-b) + [(-a) + a]b$ by applying the right-hand distributive law to the last two terms. Since $[(-a) + a]b = 0 \cdot b = 0$, $s = (-a)(-b) + 0 = (-a)(-b)$. On the other hand, if we apply the left-hand distributive law to the first two terms, we have $s = (-a)[(-b) + b] + ab = (-a) \cdot 0 + ab = 0 + ab = ab$.

Exercises

1. If the elements of the ring of residue classes modulo 10 are denoted by $0, 1, 2, \cdots, 9$, exhibit -2, -3, $-(3 \cdot 2)$, $3(-2)$, and $(-3)2$.
2. Prove that in a ring
   √a. $-(-a) = a$.
   √b. $-(ab) = (-a)b = a(-b)$;
   ＊c. $a(b - c) = ab - ac$.

★3. Check that the postulates for a ring are satisfied in the following definition of a number ring: A set of complex numbers forms a ring if the sum, difference, and product of any two numbers in the set are again in the set.

    Ans: $0, 1, -1, \ i, -i, \ \omega, -\omega, \ \omega^2, -\omega^2$

2 · INTEGRAL DOMAINS AND FIELDS

Rings may be specialized in many ways. We shall be interested particularly in the commutative rings that are integral domains or fields.

Integral Domain

A commutative ring of at least two elements is an integral domain if it contains a unity element u and no proper divisors of zero*.

Field

An integral domain is a field if every element $a \neq 0$ has a multiplicative inverse a^{-1} such that $a^{-1} \cdot a = u$.

In the above examples we note that the integers form an integral domain but not a field, that the even integers form a ring but not an integral domain, and that the residue classes modulo m form a field if and only if m is a prime. The rational numbers, the real numbers, and the complex numbers are examples of fields with respect to the operations of addition and multiplication. We define a *subfield* to be a subset of elements of a field that itself forms a field with respect to the given operations and note that the rational numbers and the real numbers are subfields of the field of complex numbers.

Of interest is a second definition of a field which is easily proved to be equivalent to the first definition.

Second Definition of a Field

A set of at least two elements forms a field with respect to two operations addition and multiplication, if:

1. It is closed with respect to addition and multiplication.

2. It forms a commutative group with respect to addition, whose identity is called the zero element.

3. Its nonzero elements form a commutative group with respect to multiplication, whose identity is called the unity element;

4. The distributive laws hold: $a(b + c) = ab + ac$ and $(b + c)a = ba + ca$.

---

* Some authors do not demand a unity element for an integral domain. See, for example, van der Waerden, *Modern Algebra*, Vol. 1, p. 34, Frederick Ungar Publishing Co., New York, 1949.

Exercises

Determine whether the following sets with respect to addition and multiplication are rings. If they are rings, are they fields or integral domains?

1. The positive integers.
2. Numbers of the form $b\sqrt{2}$, with b rational.
3. Numbers of the form $3m$, with m an integer.
4. The fourth roots of unity.
5. 0.
6. Numbers of the form $a + b\sqrt{2}$, with a and b integers.
7. Numbers of the form $a + b\sqrt{2}$, with a and b rational.
8. Numbers of the form $a + bi$, with a and b integers.
9. Numbers of the form $a + bi$, with a and b rational.
10. The residue classes modulo 15.
11. The residue classes modulo 11.
12. The set of numbers $a + b\sqrt[3]{9}$, with a and b rational.
13. The set of numbers $a + b\sqrt[4]{2}$, with a and b rational.
14. The pairs of rational numbers (a, b) with equality, addition, and multiplication defined as follows: $(a, b) = (c, d)$ if and only if $a = c$ and $b = d$; $(a, b) + (c, d) = (a + c, b + d)$; $(a, b) \cdot (c, d) = (ac, bd)$.
15. In an integral domain prove that $ax = ay$, $a \neq 0$, implies $x = y$.
16. Prove: The equation $ax = b$, where $a \neq 0$, has a unique solution x in a field. Thus division except by zero is always possible in a field.
17. Check that the postulates for a field are satisfied in the following definition of a number field: A set of at least two complex numbers forms a field if the sum, difference, product, and quotient of any two numbers are again numbers of the set. Division by zero is excluded.

3 · QUOTIENTS IN A FIELD

In a field the unique solution $a^{-1}b$ of the equation $ax = b$, where $a \neq 0$, is often denoted by the quotient b/a. For example, in the residue class ring modulo 5, $2/3$ means $2 \cdot 3^{-1} = 2 \cdot 2 = 4$. We may prove that the following rules govern quotients:

1. $a/b = c/d$ if and only if $ad = bc$;
2. $a/b + c/d = (ad + bc)/(bd)$;
3. $(a/b)(c/d) = (ac)/(bd)$.

Since these rules can easily be proved from the definition of a quotient, their proof is left to the student.

Exercises

1. Prove the statements (1), (2), and (3) given above.
2. In the ring of residue classes modulo 7 exhibit $1/3$, $-1/3$, $-3/5$.

3. Prove that in a field:

    a. $(a/b) - (c/d) = (ad - bc)/bd$;

    b. if $a/b \neq 0$, then $(a/b)(b/a) = u$;

    c. $(-a)^{-1} = -(a^{-1})$;

    d. $-(a/b) = (-a)/b = a/(-b)$;

    e. $(-a)/(-b) = a/b$.

4 · QUOTIENT FIELD

Just as the rational numbers were constructed from the integers so that the rational numbers contained a subset isomorphic to the integers, a field can be constructed from the elements of an integral domain such that a subset of the elements of the field is isomorphic to the integral domain. We say that the integral domain is *embedded* in the field. The construction of this field, called the *quotient field* of the integral domain, is very similar to the construction of the rational numbers as ordered pairs of integers. The student will find it helpful to compare each step in the construction given here with the corresponding step in the construction of the rational numbers.

Theorem 1. A field may be constructed from the elements of an integral domain.

Let $a, b, c, \cdots$ be the elements of the integral domain I. Consider the ordered pairs of elements (a, b), with $b \neq 0$. We define equality of two pairs as follows: $(a, b) = (c, d)$ if and only if $ad = bc$. This equality is an equivalence relation, for it is easily seen to be symmetric and reflexive, and it is easily proved to be transitive. If $(a, b) = (c, d)$ and if $(c, d) = (e, f)$, then $ad = bc$ and $cf = de$. Hence $adf = bcf = bde$. Since $d \neq 0$ we can apply the cancellation law for multiplication (see Exercise 15, p. 61) and obtain $af = be$, the required condition for the equality of (a, b) and (e, f). Thus we see that the pairs (a, b) are separated into classes of equal pairs. A given class can be represented by any pair in it.

Let (a, b) and (c, d) be representatives of any two classes. We define the sum and product of two classes represented by (a, b) and (c, d) as the classes whose representatives are obtained as follows:

$$(a, b) + (c, d) = (ad + bc, bd),$$
$$(a, b) \cdot (c, d) = (ac, bd).$$

The student can check that the same sum and product classes are obtained if (a, b) is replaced by a pair $(a', b') = (a, b)$ and (c, d) is replaced by a pair $(c', d') = (c, d)$.

It remains to be proved that these classes form a field with respect to addition and multiplication. The details of the proof are left to the student. He should check that the associative, commutative, and distributive laws hold; that the zero element is $(0, a)$, where 0 is the zero of the integral domain; that the additive inverse of (a, b) is $(-a, b)$; that the unity element is (u, u), where u is the unity element of the integral domain; and that the multiplicative inverse of (a, b), where $a \neq 0$, is (b, a).

Theorem 2. The quotient field of an integral domain contains a subset of elements isomorphic to the integral domain.

We set up the following one-to-one correspondence between the elements $a, b, c, \cdots$ of the integral domain and the classes with representatives $(a, u), (b, u), (c, u), \cdots$ of the quotient field. Thus, if

$$(a, u) \leftrightarrow a \quad \text{and} \quad (b, u) \leftrightarrow b,$$

then

$$(a, u) + (b, u) = (au + bu, u^2) = (a + b, u) \leftrightarrow a + b$$

and

$$(a, u) \cdot (b, u) = (ab, u^2) = (ab, u) \leftrightarrow ab,$$

and the isomorphism is established.

If the integral domain I is already a subset of a field F, then the quotient field of I is isomorphic to a subfield of the field F. For we may set up the one-to-one correspondence $(a, b) \leftrightarrow a/b = ab^{-1}$, where a and $b \neq 0$ are elements of the integral domain. Note that in general b^{-1} is not an element of the integral domain. Hence it is seen why the quotient field was given its name. Moreover, it can be proved that the quotient field is a minimum extension of the integral domain I to a field in the sense that any field containing I contains a subfield isomorphic to the quotient field of the integral domain.

EXAMPLES. Let F be the field of real numbers and I the integral domain of integers. The quotient field of I is then the field of rational numbers, a subfield of F.

Determine the quotient field of the integral domain of residue classes modulo 3. Here the classes of the quotient field are:

$$0: (0, 1), (0, 2);$$
$$1: (1, 1), (2, 2);$$
$$2: (2, 1), (1, 2);$$

We see that the quotient field is isomorphic to the integral domain of residue classes modulo 3 itself.

Exercises

1. Prove that the sum and product classes of the quotient field are independent of the particular pairs (a, b) and (c, d) used in the definition.
2. Prove that the classes of the quotient field of an integral domain obey the associative and commutative laws for addition and multiplication, and the distributive law.

3. Prove that the multiplicative inverse of the class represented by (a, b), where $a \neq 0$, is the class represented by (b, a).
4. What is the quotient field of the integral domain of residue classes modulo 5 ?
5. What is the quotient field of the integral domain of complex numbers $a + bi$, where a and b are integers ?

5 · POLYNOMIALS OVER AN INTEGRAL DOMAIN

Let x be an arbitrary symbol which is commutative with the elements of an integral domain I. For n a positive integer let $x^n = x \cdot x \cdots x$ to n factors. Further, we define $u \cdot x = x$, where u is the unity element of I. A *polynomial* over the integral domain I is a finite expression of the form

(1) $$f(x) = a_0 + a_1 x + a_2 x^2 + \cdots + a_n x^n,$$

where the coefficients a_i are elements of I. The power of x multiplying a_0 is x^0, which is defined to equal u. If a power of x does not appear in $f(x)$, its coefficient is considered to be zero.

Two polynomials are equal if and only if the coefficients of like powers of x are equal; i.e., if and only if they are identical. In this definition of equality the polynomials are regarded as forms; we are not discussing their functional values. Keep in mind that x is an arbitrary symbol to which we at present are assigning no meaning. It is called an *indeterminate*.

We now define the sum and product of two polynomials. Let $f(x)$ be the polynomial (1), and let $g(x)$ be the polynomial

(2) $$g(x) = b_0 + b_1 x + b_2 x^2 + \cdots + b_m x^m,$$

the b_i being elements in I. Then

(3) $$f(x) \pm g(x) = (a_0 \pm b_0) + (a_1 \pm b_1)x + \cdots$$
$$+ (a_m \pm b_m)x^m + a_{m+1} x^{m+1} + \cdots + a_n x^n, \quad m < n,$$

and

(4) $$f(x) \cdot g(x) = a_0 b_0 + (a_0 b_1 + a_1 b_0)x$$
$$+ (a_0 b_2 + a_1 b_1 + a_2 b_0)x^2 + \cdots + a_n b_m x^{n+m},$$

the coefficient of x^k being

$$a_0 b_k + a_1 b_{k-1} + a_2 b_{k-2} + \cdots + a_k b_0.$$

If $a_n \neq 0$, then n is called the *degree* of the polynomial $f(x)$. Note that the polynomials of zero degree are the nonzero elements of the integral domain I. The polynomial zero has no degree. Also note that the degree of the product of two polynomials is the sum $m + n$ of the degrees of the factors.

Theorem 3. *The polynomials* (1) *over an integral domain* I *with sum and product defined by* (3) *and* (4) *form an integral domain.*

This integral domain is denoted by $I[x]$. The proof in detail is left to the student. The commutative, associative, and distributive laws can be verified. The zero element and the unity element are obviously the zero element and the unity element of the integral domain of coefficients. There are no proper zero divisors, for if $f(x)$ and $g(x)$ are given by (1) and (2) with $a_n \neq 0$ and $b_m \neq 0$, the product (4) is not zero, since $a_n b_m = 0$ if and only if $a_n = 0$ or if $b_m = 0$.

Exercises

In $I(x)$ establish the following properties:

1. The commutative law for addition.
2. The commutative law for multiplication.
3. The associative law for addition.
4. The associative law for multiplication.
5. The left-hand and the right-hand distributive laws.

6 · CHARACTERISTIC OF AN INTEGRAL DOMAIN

Let u be the unity element of the integral domain I. The unity element generates an additive cyclic group. If k is a positive integer, $ku = u + u + \cdots + u$ with k terms. Interpreting additively the definitions and exponent laws derived for the powers of an element of a group, we have $0 \cdot u = 0$, $(-k)u = k(-u)$, $ru + su = (r + s)u$, and $s(ru) = (sr)u = r(su)$. Now, as we have seen, a cyclic group is isomorphic either to the additive group of integers or to the additive group of residue classes modulo m. In the latter case we shall prove that m is a prime.

Theorem 4. *If the additive cyclic group generated by* u, *the unity element of an integral domain, is of order* m > 0, m *is a prime* p.

Let $m = rs$. Then $(ru)(su) = (\underbrace{u + u + \cdots + u}_{r \text{ terms}})(\underbrace{u + u + \cdots + u}_{s \text{ terms}}) = \underbrace{u^2 + u^2 + \cdots + u^2}_{rs \text{ terms}} = (rs)u^2 = (rs)u = 0$. But ru and su are elements of the integral domain, which has no proper zero divisors. Hence $ru = 0$ or $su = 0$, contradicting the assumption that the cyclic group generated by u has order m. Thus m is a prime p.

DEFINITION. The order of the additive cyclic group generated by the unity element u of an integral domain is called the *characteristic* of the integral domain. Thus the characteristic is either a positive prime p or zero.

Theorem 5. *An integral domain whose characteristic is zero contains a subset of elements which is isomorphic to the integral domain of integers, and an integral domain whose characteristic is a prime* p *contains a subset of elements which is isomorphic to the field of residue classes modulo* p.

If the cyclic group generated by u is of order zero, then the elements ku are distinct and the one-to-one correspondence $ku \leftrightarrow k$ is an isomorphism, for, if $ru \leftrightarrow r$ and $su \leftrightarrow s$, then $ru + su = (r + s)u \leftrightarrow r + s$, and $(ru)(su) = (rs)u \leftrightarrow rs$. If the cyclic group generated by u is of prime order p, the elements ku for which k belongs to the same residue class modulo p are equal, and the correspondence $ku \leftrightarrow C_k$, where C_k denotes the residue class containing the integer k, gives us an isomorphism between the elements ku and the residue classes modulo p.

Theorem 6. In an integral domain all nonzero elements generate additive cyclic groups of the same order.

Let u be the unity element, and let a be any nonzero element of the integral domain. For an integral domain of characteristic p, it is easily checked that $pa = p(au) = p(ua) = (pu)a = 0$. Moreover, if $ma = 0$, where $a \neq 0$ and $m \neq 0$, then $ma = m(ua) = (mu)a = 0$, and, hence, $mu = 0$, giving us $m = kp$; i.e., p is the least integer m such that $ma = 0$. For an integral domain of characteristic zero, $ma \neq 0$ if $a \neq 0$ and $m \neq 0$, for again $ma = (mu)a$ and $mu \neq 0$ if $m \neq 0$. (Note here that we are using the symbol 0 in two quite different ways. When we write $a \neq 0$, we mean that a is not the additive identity of the integral domain under discussion. But when we write $m \neq 0$, we mean that m is not the additive identity for the integers.)

Since fields are integral domains, they may also be separated into two essentially different types, fields of characteristic a prime p and fields of characteristic zero. The quotient field of the integral domain of integral multiples of the unity element u is, in the case of characteristic p, isomorphic to the field of residue classes modulo p, and in the case of characteristic zero isomorphic to the field of rational numbers. Thus a field contains a subfield that is isomorphic either to the field of residue classes modulo p or to the field of rational numbers.

7 · DIVISION IN AN INTEGRAL DOMAIN

We shall now list some definitions that are used in any integral domain, and we shall see that they are similar to the corresponding definitions given when the divisibility properties of integers were studied.

Divisor

An element b in an integral domain I is a divisor of an element a in I, if there exists in I an element c such that $a = bc$.

Associates and Units

Two nonzero elements a and b in an integral domain I are associates if a divides b and b divides a. A unit is an associate of the unity element of I.

Theorem 7. *An element* a *in an integral domain* I *is a unit in* I *if and only if it has a multiplicative inverse in* I; *i.e., those and only those elements in* I *are units which have multiplicative inverses in* I.

Now, if a is a unit, it divides u the unity element of I, and we have $ab = u$. Thus b is a multiplicative inverse of a. On the other hand, if a has a multiplicative inverse b, $ab = u$ and a divides u. The unity element u divides any element a in I, for $au = a$. Hence a is a unit.

Theorem 8. *Two elements in* I *are associates if and only if one is a unit times the other.*

Let a and b be associates in I. Then $a = bc$ and $b = ad$. Thus $a = adc$. But also, $a = au$, and hence $au = adc$. Applying the cancellation law for multiplication, we have $u = dc$, which says that c and d are units. Thus, if two elements are associates, one is a unit times the other. On the other hand, if $b = au'$, where u' is a unit such that $u'u'' = u$, then b divides a, for $a = au = a(u'u'') = (au')u'' = bu''$. Since $b = au'$, a divides b and hence, a and b are associates if one is a unit times the other.

Corollary. *Any element* a *in* I *is divisible by the units of* I.

For if u' is a unit such that $u'u'' = u$, we have $a = au = a(u'u'') = (au'')u'$ and, hence, u' divides a.

Proper and Improper Divisors

Any nonzero element a of an integral domain is divisible by its associates (by definition) and by the units of the integral domain (by the corollary to Theorem 8). These divisors of a are called improper divisors of a. All other divisors are called proper divisors.

Prime or Irreducible Element

A nonzero element a of an integral domain which is not a unit and which has no proper divisors is called a prime or irreducible element. If an element has proper divisors, it is called *reducible*.

EXAMPLES. Since in a field every nonzero element has a multiplicative inverse, the units of a field are its nonzero elements.

In the polynomial domain $I[x]$ the units are the units of the integral domain I of coefficients. To prove this fact let $f(x) \cdot g(x) = u$, the unity element of I. Since the degree of the product of two polynomials is the sum of the degrees of the factors, both $f(x)$ and $g(x)$ must be polynomials of degree zero.

In the polynomial domain $F[x]$, where F is a field, the associates of the polynomial $f(x)$ are $cf(x)$, where c is any nonzero element of the field.

In the integral domain of integers the prime integers are the irreducible elements.

The polynomial $x^2 - 2$ is irreducible over the field of rational numbers, but since $(x - \sqrt{2})(x + \sqrt{2}) = x^2 - 2$, the polynomial $x^2 - 2$ is reducible over the field of real numbers. Note that irreducibility is thus a property dependent upon the particular integral domain considered.

To illustrate somewhat further the above definitions, consider the integral domain I whose elements are of the form $a + b\sqrt{13}$, where a and b are integers. It is left to the student to fill in the proofs that are omitted in the following statements. Let $\alpha = a + b\sqrt{13}$. We define $N(\alpha) = (a + b\sqrt{13})(a - b\sqrt{13}) = a^2 - 13b^2$, which we note is an integer. $N(\alpha)$ is called the *norm* of α.

1. Prove that $N(\alpha\beta) = N(\alpha)N(\beta)$.
2. The element α is a unit if and only if $N(\alpha) = \pm 1$.

If $N(\alpha) = \pm 1$, then α is a unit, for $(a + b\sqrt{13})(a - b\sqrt{13}) = \pm 1$, and $a + b\sqrt{13}$ divides the unity element 1. If α is a unit, we have $\alpha\beta = 1$, and hence $N(\alpha\beta) = N(\alpha)N(\beta) = 1$. As $N(\alpha)$ and $N(\beta)$ are integers, $N(\alpha) = \pm 1$ and $N(\beta) = \pm 1$.

3. $18 - 5\sqrt{13}$ and $-18 - 5\sqrt{13}$ are units.
4. $1 + \sqrt{13} = (-18 - 5\sqrt{13})(-47 + 13\sqrt{13})$ and $-47 + 13\sqrt{13} = (18 - 5\sqrt{13})(1 + \sqrt{13})$ are associates, but not units.
5. $2, -3 - \sqrt{13}$, and $3 - \sqrt{13}$ are primes of I. For suppose $\alpha\beta = 2$; then $N(\alpha\beta) = N(\alpha) N(\beta) = 4$ so that $N(\alpha) = \pm 2$ or ± 4, or $N(\beta) = \pm 2$ or ± 4. Suppose $N(\alpha) = \pm 4$; then $N(\beta) = \pm 1$ and β is a unit. Similarly, if $N(\beta) = \pm 4$, α is a unit, and we now suppose that $N(\alpha) = \pm 2 = a^2 - 13b^2$ where $\alpha = a + b\sqrt{13}$. Then $a^2 \equiv \pm 2 \pmod{13}$. It is easily seen by testing the possibilities $0, \pm 1, \pm 2, \pm 3, \pm 4, \pm 5$, and ± 6 for a that this congruence has no solution. Hence, if $\alpha\beta = 2$, α or β is a unit so that 2 is a prime in I. Similarly, if $\alpha\beta = -3 - \sqrt{13}$ or $3 - \sqrt{13}$, we have $N(\alpha) N(\beta) = -4$, and we can show in the same fashion that either α or β is a unit.
6. Note that $4 = 2 \cdot 2 = (-3 - \sqrt{13})(3 - \sqrt{13})$, and hence the unique factorization into prime or irreducible elements does not hold in I.

The divisiblity concepts discussed in this section will be applied in the next chapter to the particular integral domain of polynomials over a field.

Exercises

1. In the integral domain $F[x]$, where F is the field of rational numbers, is the polynomial $2x^2 - 2$ a divisor of $x^2 - 1$; is $2x^2 - 2$ divisible by the polynomial 3? Show the factorization if the answer is yes.
2. What are the units of the integral domain of residue classes modulo 5?
3. What are the units of the integral domain of complex numbers of the form $a + bi$, where a and b are rational?
4. Are $1, -1, i, -i$, units in the integral domain of complex numbers of the form $a + bi$, where a and b are integers?

8 · ORDERED INTEGRAL DOMAINS

The integers are divided into three classes: the positive integers, the negative integers, and zero. We now generalize this concept for an arbitrary integral domain.

DEFINITION.   An integral domain I is said to be *ordered* if there is a subset P of elements of I such that for every element a of I one and only one of the following alternatives hold; (1) a is in P; (2) $-a$ is in I; or (3) $a = 0$, and, if x is in P and y is in P, so are $x + y$ and xy. The set P is called the set of *positive elements* of I.

EXAMPLES.   The integers, the rational numbers, and the real numbers are all ordered integral domains under the usual definition of a positive number.

The complex numbers do not form an ordered integral domain. To show this we first prove a theorem.

Theorem 9.   If 1 *is the multiplicative identity of an ordered integral domain* I, *then* 1 *is a positive element of* I.

Now $1 \neq 0$ and, if 1 is not in P, -1 is in P. But then $(-1)(-1) = 1$ is in P, a contradiction.

Now consider the complex number i. Since $i \neq 0$, i is in P or $-i$ is in P. But if i is in P, $i \cdot i = -1$ is in P which contradicts Theorem 9. Hence $-i$ is in P. But, again, we then have $(-i)(-i) = -1$ in P and, hence, the complex numbers cannot be ordered.

Inequalities may be defined in any ordered integral domain: $a > b$ if and only if $a - b$ is in P. In particular, $a > 0$ if and only if $a - 0 = a$ is in P. Similarly we say that $a < b$ if and only if $b - a$ is in P. From these definitions the results of Sec. 9, Chap. 1 may be extended to any ordered integral domain.

Any field is also an integral domain and it is natural to define an *ordered field* as a field which, when considered as an integral domain, is an ordered integral domain. On the other hand, suppose that we have an ordered integral domain I that is not a field and we form the quotient field F, of I. We recall that the quotient field consists of classes of pairs (a, b) with a and b elements of I. Furthermore, we have shown that the additive identity of F is the class of pairs of the form $(0, a)$ and that I is isomorphic to the set of classes with representatives $(a, 1)$. Because of this isomorphism and the fact that a given class may be represented by any pair in it, we may consider any element of I to be an element of F. Now we will say that an ordering of I is *extended* to an ordering of F if an element a of I is a positive element of I if and only if it is a positive element of F.

Theorem 10.   Let I *be an ordered integral domain and* F *the quotient field of* I. *Then the ordering of* I *can be extended to an ordering of* F *in one and only one way. Specifically if* (a, b) *is a representative of one of the elements of* F *then* (a, b) *is a positive element of* F *if and only if ab is a positive element of* I.

In any ordered integral domain the square of any nonzero element is positive since $a^2 = (-a)^2$ and either a is positive or $-a$ is positive. Hence if (a, b) $(b \neq 0)$ is a positive element of F, so is $(a b,)(b, 1)^2 = (ab, 1)$. Thus if (a, b) is a positive element of F, ab is a positive element of I.

On the other hand, suppose we define (a, b) to be a positive element of F if and only if ab is a positive element of I. Now if $(a, b) \neq (0, 1)$, $ab \neq 0$ and, hence, $ab > 0$ or $ab < 0$. If $ab < 0$, $-(ab) = (-a)b > 0$. Hence either (a, b) is zero, (a, b) is positive, or $-(a, b) = (-a, b)$ is positive, and only one of these alternatives holds. If (a, b) and (c, d) are positive elements of F, then $(a, b)(c, d) = (ac, bd)$, is a positive element of F since $(ac)(bd) = (ab)(cd)$ is a positive element of I. Finally, if (a, b) and (c, d) are positive elements of F, then $(a, b) + (c, d) = (ad + bc, bd)$ is a positive element of F since $(ad + bc)(bd) = (ab)d^2 + (cd)b^2$ is a positive element of I. Hence F is an ordered field.

Exercises

1. In any ordered field, prove that:

   a. $0 < 1/a$ if and only if $a > 0$.
   b. $0 < a < b$ implies that $0 < 1/b < 1/a$.
   c. $a < b < 0$ implies that $0 > 1/a > 1/b$.
   d. $a_1^2 + a_2^2 + \cdots + a_n^2 \geq 0$

2. Show that:

   a. In any field, $a/b + a/c = a/(b + c)$ implies $a = 0$ or $a^2 + bc + c^2 = 0$.
   b. In an ordered field, it implies $a = 0$.

5 Polynomials over a Field

1 · DIVISION ALGORITHM

We now establish divisibility properties of polynomials over a field which are analogous to the divisibility properties of the integers.

Theorem 1.   Division algorithm.   If $g(x) \neq 0$ *and* $f(x)$ *are any two polynomials over a field* F, *there exist unique polynomials* $q(x)$ *and* $r(x)$ *over* F *such that*

$$f(x) = g(x) \cdot q(x) + r(x),$$

where $r(x)$ *either is zero or of degree less than the degree of* $g(x)$.

Let

$$f(x) = a_0 + a_1 x + \cdots + a_n x^n$$

and

$$g(x) = b_0 + b_1 x + \cdots + b_m x^m, \quad b_m \neq 0.$$

If $f(x)$ is zero or if the degree of $f(x)$ is less than the degree m of $g(x)$, we have the representation

$$f(x) = 0 \cdot g(x) + f(x).$$

Thus let $n \geq m$. Then form the difference

(1)
$$f(x) - \frac{a_n}{b_m} x^{n-m} g(x) = f_1(x).$$

Now $f_1(x)$ is a polynomial over F of degree less than n. We make the proof by induction. Assume the algorithm true for all polynomials over F of degree less than n. Since $f_1(x)$ is such a polynomial, we may write

(2)
$$f_1(x) = q_1(x) \cdot g(x) + r(x),$$

71

where $r(x)$ is either zero or of degree less than the degree of $g(x)$. We may then write (1) with the aid of (2) as

$$f(x) - \frac{a_n}{b_m} x^{n-m} g(x) = q_1(x) \cdot g(x) + r(x),$$

and hence

$$f(x) = \left[\frac{a_n}{b_m} x^{n-m} + q_1(x)\right] \cdot g(x) + r(x)$$

$$= q(x) \cdot g(x) + r(x),$$

and we have the desired representation of $f(x)$.

It remains to be proved that the polynomials $q(x)$ and $r(x)$ are unique. Suppose that there is a second pair of polynomials $q'(x)$ and $r'(x)$ such that

$$f(x) = q'(x) \cdot g(x) + r'(x),$$

where $r'(x)$ is either zero or of degree less than the degree of $g(x)$. Hence

$$q'(x) \cdot g(x) + r'(x) = q(x) \cdot g(x) + r(x)$$

and

$$g(x)[q'(x) - q(x)] = r(x) - r'(x).$$

Now the right-hand side of this equation is either zero or of degree less than the degree of $g(x)$. Thus, unless $q'(x) - q(x) = 0$, we have a contradiction. Consequently, $q'(x) = q(x)$ and $r(x) = r'(x)$.

The polynomial $q(x)$ is called the *quotient*, and the polynomial $r(x)$ is called the *remainder* in the division algorithm.

Corollary 1. Remainder theorem. The remainder when a polynomial f(x) *is divided by* x − a *is* f(a).

This is immediate from the division algorithm, for when we replace $g(x)$ by $x - a$ the remainder becomes r, an element in the field, and we have $f(a) = (a - a) \cdot q(a) + r = r$. Thus $f(x) = (x - a) \cdot q(x) + f(a)$. From this last formula we see immediately that $f(x)$ has the factor $x - a$ if and only if $f(a) = 0$. Hence we have the following corollary.

Corollary 2. Factor theorem. A polynomial f(x) *is divisible by* x − a *if and only if* f(a) = 0.

DEFINITION. An element a is called a *zero* of a polynomial $f(x)$ if $f(a) = 0$.

2 · SYNTHETIC DIVISION

To facilitate finding the quotient $q(x)$ and the remainder r when a polynomial $f(x)$ over a field F is divided by the polynomial $x - c$ over F, we introduce the method of synthetic division. Let

$$f(x) = a_0 + a_1x + \cdots + a_{n-1}x^{n-1} + a_nx^n$$

and

$$q(x) = b_0 + b_1x + \cdots + b_{n-1}x^{n-1}.$$

Then

$$f(x) = (x - c)q(x) + r$$
$$= (r - cb_0) + (b_0 - cb_1)x + (b_1 - cb_2)x^2 + \cdots$$
$$+ (b_{n-2} - cb_{n-1})x^{n-1} + b_{n-1}x^n.$$

Equating coefficients of $f(x)$ when we express it in these two ways, we have

$$a_n = b_{n-1}, a_{n-1} = b_{n-2} - cb_{n-1}, \cdots, a_1 = b_0 - cb_1, a_0 = r - cb_0.$$

For computation purposes the work may be arranged as follows:

a_n	a_{n-1}	$\cdots$	a_1	a_0	$\lfloor c$
	cb_{n-1}	$\cdots$	cb_1	cb_0	
$b_{n-1} = a_n$	$b_{n-2} = a_{n-1} + cb_{n-1}$	$\cdots$	$b_0 = a_1 + cb_1$	$r = a_0 + cb_0$	

Thus by merely listing the coefficients and performing simple multiplications and additions, we can read off the quotient and the remainder from the last line.

EXAMPLE. Find the quotient and the remainder when the polynomial $3x^3 - 4x + 2$ is divided by $x + 3$. Using synthetic division, we have

3	0	-4	2	$\lfloor -3$
	-9	27	-69	
3	-9	23	-67,	

which gives $3x^2 - 9x + 23$ as the quotient and -67 as the remainder.

Exercises

1. Find the quotient and the remainder when:

    a. $-x^4 + 7x^3 + 10x^2 - 5$ is divided by $x - 2$;

    b. $3x^5 + 6x^3 - 3x$ is divided by $x + 1$;

    c. $x^3 + i$ is divided by $x - i$.

2. If $f(x) = 2x^3 + 3x^2 - 1$, find $f(2), f(-3), f(i)$.

3. In the field of residue classes modulo 5, exhibit the quotient and the remainder when the polynomial $3x^3 - 4x^2 + 2x - 2$ is divided by $2x^2 + 1$.

4. Are the following polynomials reducible or irreducible over the field of residue classes modulo 5? over the field of residue classes modulo 7?

    a. $x^2 - x + 3$.

    b. $x^3 + 3x^2 + x - 4$.

3 · GREATEST COMMON DIVISOR

Monic Polynomial

A polynomial is called monic if the coefficient of the highest power of x is the unity element of the field.

Greatest Common Divisor

A polynomial $d(x)$ is a greatest common divisor of two polynomials $f(x)$ and $g(x)$ if $d(x)$ divides $f(x)$ and $g(x)$, and, if $a(x)$ is a common divisor of $f(x)$ and $g(x)$, then $a(x)$ divides $d(x)$. We note that, if a greatest common divisor $d(x)$ exists, then any associate of $d(x)$ is also a greatest common divisor of $f(x)$ and $g(x)$. We often speak of that associate of $d(x)$ which is monic as *the* greatest common divisor of $f(x)$ and $g(x)$.

Theorem 2.   Euclidean algorithm.   Two nonzero polynomials f(x) *and* g(x) *over a field* F *have a greatest common divisor* d(x) *over* F.

The proof is the same as the proof for the construction of the greatest common divisor of two nonzero integers. We apply the division algorithm to $f(x)$ and $g(x)$, obtaining

$$(3) \qquad\qquad f(x) = g(x) \cdot q(x) + r(x),$$

where $r(x)$ is either zero or of degree less than the degree of $g(x)$. If $r(x)$ is zero, then a greatest common divisor of $f(x)$ and $g(x)$ is $g(x)$ itself. If $r(x) \neq 0$, we prove that a greatest common divisor of $f(x)$ and $g(x)$ is a greatest common divisor of $g(x)$ and $r(x)$, thus reducing the problem of finding a g.c.d. of $f(x)$ and $g(x)$ to that of finding a g.c.d. of $g(x)$ and $r(x)$. Let $d(x)$ be a greatest common divisor of $f(x)$ and $g(x)$, and let $d'(x)$ be a greatest common divisor of $g(x)$ and $r(x)$. Since $d'(x)$ divides $g(x)$ and $r(x)$, we see by (3) that it divides $f(x)$, and hence it is a common divisor of $f(x)$ and $g(x)$. Therefore $d'(x)$ divides $d(x)$. Similarly (3) shows that $d(x)$ divides $r(x)$, and thus $d'(x)$ is divisible by $d(x)$. Hence $d(x)$ and $d'(x)$ are associates and differ only by a factor that is an element of F.

Now apply the division algorithm to $g(x)$ and $r(x)$, obtaining

$$g(x) = r(x) \cdot q_1(x) + r_1(x),$$

where $r_1(x)$ is either zero or of degree less than the degree of $r(x)$. If $r_1(x) = 0$, then $r(x)$ is a greatest common divisor of $f(x)$ and $g(x)$. If $r_1(x) \neq 0$, then we have, as before, that a g.c.d. of $g(x)$ and $r(x)$ is a g.c.d. of $r(x)$ and $r_1(x)$, thus reducing the problem of finding a g.c.d. of $f(x)$ and $g(x)$ to the problem of finding a g.c.d. of $r(x)$ and $r_1(x)$. We can continue in this manner, obtaining the sequence of equations

$$f(x) = g(x) \cdot q(x) + r(x),$$
$$g(x) = r(x) \cdot q_1(x) + r_1(x),$$
$$r(x) = r_1(x) \cdot q_2(x) + r_2(x),$$
$$r_1(x) = r_2(x) \cdot q_3(x) + r_3(x),$$

$$\cdot$$
$$\cdot$$
$$\cdot$$

(4) $$r_j(x) = r_{j+1}(x) \cdot q_{j+2}(x) + r_{j+2}(x),$$

$$\cdot$$
$$\cdot$$
$$\cdot$$

$$r_{n-2}(x) = r_{n-1}(x) \cdot q_n(x) + r_n(x),$$
$$r_{n-1}(x) = r_n(x) \cdot q_{n+1}(x).$$

This process shows that we must finally obtain a zero remainder, for a given remainder $r_j(x)$ is either zero or of degree less than the degree of the preceding remainder $r_{j-1}(x)$. We note that a polynomial of degree zero, i.e., an element of the field, divides every polynomial over the field. Hence, if the process does not end before we obtain a polynomial of degree zero, the next step assures us of a zero remainder. The last nonzero remainder, $r_n(x)$, is a g.c.d. of $f(x)$ and $g(x)$, for, denoting a g.c.d. of $f(x)$ and $g(x)$ by (f, g), we have $(f, g) = (g, r) = (r, r_1) = \cdots = (r_{n-2}, r_{n-1}) = (r_{n-1}, r_n) = r_n$.

In the actual computation of a g.c.d. of two polynomials the work may be simplified by multiplying one or more of the remainders or the given polynomials by a nonzero element of the field. Since all g.c.d.'s are associates, this multiplication does not change *the* g.c.d. The last remainder is merely multiplied by an element of the field. Further, it should be noted that the process of finding a g.c.d. involves only rational operations on the coefficients of the given polynomials. Thus the coefficients of a g.c.d. are always elements in the least field containing the coefficients of the given polynomial.

Theorem 3. Let d(x) *be a g.c.d. of the two polynomials* f(x) *and* g(x) *over the field* F. *Then there exist polynomials* m(x) *and* n(x) *over* F *such that*

$$d(x) = m(x) \cdot g(x) + n(x) \cdot f(x).$$

This can be proved by expressing the successive remainders in equations (4) in terms of $f(x)$ and $g(x)$ thus:

$$r(x) = f(x) - g(x) \cdot q(x),$$
$$r_1(x) = g(x) - r(x) \cdot q_1(x) = g(x) - q_1(x)[f(x) - g(x) \cdot q(x)]$$
$$= -q_1(x) \cdot f(x) + [1 + q(x) \cdot q_1(x)]g(x), \text{ etc.}$$

A general proof can be given by induction. Let

$$r_j(x) = m_j(x) \cdot g(x) + n_j(x) \cdot f(x)$$

for all $j < k$. Denoting $r(x)$ by $r_0(x)$, we see that $r_j(x)$ has been expressed in the desired form for $j = 0, 1$. From equations (4) we have

$$r_{k-2}(x) = r_{k-1}(x) \cdot q_k(x) + r_k(x).$$

Solving this equation for $r_k(x)$ and substituting the values for $r_{k-1}(x)$ and $r_{k-2}(x)$ as given by our induction hypothesis, we have

$$
\begin{aligned}
r_k(x) &= -q_k(x)[m_{k-1}(x) \cdot g(x) + n_{k-1}(x) \cdot f(x)] \\
&\qquad + [m_{k-2}(x) \cdot g(x) + n_{k-2}(x) \cdot f(x)] \\
&= [-q_k(x) \cdot m_{k-1}(x) + m_{k-2}(v)]g(x) + [-q_k(x) \cdot n_{k-1}(x) \\
&\qquad\qquad\qquad\qquad\qquad\qquad\qquad + n_{k-2}(x)]f(x),
\end{aligned}
$$

and the induction is complete.

DEFINITION. Two polynomials $f(x)$ and $g(x)$ over a field F are said to be *relatively prime* if their greatest common divisor is the unity element of F.

EXAMPLE. Find the g.c.d. of the two polynomials $f(x) = x^5 + 2x^3 + x^2 + 2x + 3$ and $g(x) = x^4 + x^3 + 4x^2 + 3x + 3$ over the field of residue classes modulo 5 and express it in the form $m(x) \cdot g(x) + n(x) \cdot f(x)$. We find that

$$
\begin{aligned}
f(x) &= g(x)(x + 4) + 4x^3 + 2x^2 + 2x + 1, \\
g(x) &= (4x^3 + 2x^2 + 2x + 1)(4x + 2) + 2x^2 + 1, \\
4x^3 &+ 2x^2 + 2x + 1 = (2x^2 + 1)(2x + 1).
\end{aligned}
$$

Therefore $2x^2 + 1$ is a g.c.d., and its monic associate, $x^2 + 3$, is the g.c.d. To express the g.c.d. in the desired form, we use the above equations, obtaining

$$
\begin{aligned}
2x^2 + 1 &= g(x) - (4x^3 + 2x^2 + 2x + 1)(4x + 2) \\
&= g(x) - [f(x) - g(x)(x + 4)](4x + 2) \\
&= (4x^2 + 3x + 4)g(x) - (4x + 2)f(x),
\end{aligned}
$$

and

$$x^2 + 3 = (2x^2 + 4x + 2)g(x) + (3x + 4)f(x).$$

Exercises

1. Find the greatest common divisor of the two polynomials $f(x)$ and $g(x)$ over the indicated field of coefficients and express it in the form $m(x) \cdot g(x) + n(x) \cdot f(x)$.

    a. $f(x) = x^5 - x^4 - 6x^3 - 2x^2 + 5x + 3$, $g(x) = x^3 - 3x - 2$ over the field of rational numbers.

    b. $f(x) = x^4 - 5x^3 + 6x^2 + 4x - 8$, $g(x) = x^3 - x^2 - 4x + 4$ over the field of rational numbers.

    c. $f(x) = x^4 - 4ix + 3$, $g(x) = x^3 - i$ over the field of complex numbers.

2. Find the g.c.d. of the following pairs of polynomials over the field of rational numbers.

   a. $f(x) = 4x^4 - 4x^3 + 5x^2 - 4x + 1,$ $g(x) = 8x^3 - 6x^2 + 5x - 2.$
   b. $f(x) = x^4 + x^3 + 2x^2 + x + 1,$ $g(x) = x^3 - 1.$

3. Find the g.c.d. of the following pairs of polynomials over the field of residue classes modulo 3:

   a. $f(x) = x^5 + 2x^3 + x^2 + 2x,$ $g(x) = x^4 + x^3 + x^2.$
   b. $f(x) = x^3 + 2x^2 + 2x + 1,$ $g(x) = x^2 + 2.$

4. Determine the constant c if the greatest common divisor of $f(x)$ and $g(x)$ over the field of rational numbers is linear. For each value of c obtained, what is the greatest common divisor?

   a. $f(x) = x^3 + cx^2 - x + 2c,$ $g(x) = x^2 + cx - 2.$
   b. $f(x) = x^2 + (c - 6)x + 2c - 1,$ $g(x) = x^2 + (c + 2)x + 2c.$

4 · FACTORIZATION THEOREMS

We continue with our list of theorems for polynomials over a field which are analogous to the theorems proved for integers.

Theorem 4. If p(x) *is an irreducible polynomial over a field* F *and if* p(x) *divides the product* f(x) · g(x) *of two polynomials over* F, *then* p(x) *divides* f(x) *or* p(x) *divides* g(x).

Suppose that $p(x)$ does not divide $f(x)$. Since $p(x)$ is irreducible over F, its only divisors are its associates and the units of the field. Hence $p(x)$ and $f(x)$ are relatively prime and their g.c.d. is the unity element u of the field. Thus there exist polynomials $m(x)$ and $n(x)$ over F such that

$$u = m(x) \cdot p(x) + n(x) \cdot f(x).$$

Multiply this equation by $g(x)$ to obtain

$$g(x) = m(x) \cdot p(x) \cdot g(x) + n(x) \cdot f(x) \cdot g(x).$$

Using the hypothesis that $p(x)$ divides $f(x) \cdot g(x)$, we see that $p(x)$ is a factor of the right-hand side of the above equation. Hence it is also a factor of the left-hand side of the equation, and the theorem is established.

The proofs of the next two theorems are left to the student.

Theorem 5. If an irreducible polynomial p(x) *over a field* F *divides the product of* n *polynomials* $q_1(x) \cdot q_2(x) \cdots q_n(x)$ *over* F, *it divides some factor* $q_i(x)$.

Theorem 6. If f(x) *and* g(x) *are relatively prime polynomials over a field* F, *and if* f(x) *divides the product* g(x) · h(x) *over* F, *then* f(x) *divides* h(x).

Theorem 7.   Unique factorization theorem. A polynomial f(x) *of positive degree over a field* F *can be expressed as an element of* F *times a product of monic irreducible polynomials over* F. *This decomposition is unique except for the order in which the factors occur.*

We first prove that such a decomposition is possible. If $f(x)$ is irreducible, the decomposition is accomplished. (Note that if $f(x)$ is of degree 1 it is irreducible.) Now suppose $f(x)$ is reducible so that $f(x) = g(x) \cdot h(x)$, where $g(x)$ and $h(x)$ are polynomials of degree less than the degree of $f(x)$. We make the induction hypothesis that the decomposition is possible for all polynomials of degree less than the degree of $f(x)$. Thus

$$g(x) = cp_1(x) \cdot p_2(x) \cdots p_r(x)$$

and

$$h(x) = c'p_1'(x) \cdot p_2'(x) \cdots p_s'(x),$$

where c and c' are elements of the field, and where the $p_i(x)$ and $p_i'(x)$ are monic irreducible polynomials over F. We have then

$$f(x) = g(x) \cdot h(x) = cc'p_1(x) \cdots p_r(x) \cdot p_1'(x) \cdots p_s'(x).$$

Thus the induction is completed and the decomposition is accomplished.

It remains to be proved that the decomposition is unique. Assume the existence of two decompositions

$$f(x) = cp_1(x) \cdot p_2(x) \cdots p_n(x)$$
$$= dq_1(x) \cdot q_2(x) \cdots q_m(x).$$

Since these irreducible polynomials are monic, $c = d$. Since $p_1(x)$ is irreducible, it divides some $q_i(x)$. As both $p_1(x)$ and $q_i(x)$ are monic and irreducible, their quotient is the unity element of the field, and hence $p_1(x) = q_i(x)$. Dividing by this common factor and c, we obtain

$$f_1(x) = p_2(x) \cdots p_n(x) = q_1(x) \cdots q_{i-1}(x) \cdot q_{i+1}(x) \cdots q_m(x).$$

Now $f_1(x)$ is a polynomial of degree less than the degree of $f(x)$. Consequently, we can make an induction hypothesis to the effect that the decomposition is unique for all polynomials of degree less than the degree of $f(x)$. Thus the decomposition of $f_1(x)$ is unique, $n = m$, and the two sets of polynomials are identical. Hence we have the unique decomposition of $f(x)$.

Exercises

1. Prove Theorems 5 and 6.
2. List the monic polynomials of the second degree over the field of residue classes modulo 3. Which are irreducible? Find the decomposition of the reducible polynomials.

3. Find the decomposition of the following polynomials over the field of rational numbers and over the field of complex numbers: (a) $x^3 - 1$, (b) $x^4 - 1$, (c) $x^6 - 1$. (*Hint:* Recall that the zeros of these polynomials are roots of unity.)

4. Find the decomposition of the following polynomials over the field of residue classes modulo 3: (a) $x^4 + x + 2$; (b) $2x^3 + x^2 + 1$.

5. Show that $x^3 + x + 1$ is an irreducible polynomial over the field of residue classes modulo 5.

6. If $h(x)$ is relatively prime to both $f(x)$ and $g(x)$ over a field F, prove that $h(x)$ is relatively prime to the product $f(x) \cdot g(x)$.

5 · ZEROS OF A POLYNOMIAL

Theorem 8.   A polynomial f(x) *of positive degree* n *over a field* F *has at most* n *zeros in* F.

Let $f(x) = a_0 + a_1 x + \cdots + a_n x^n$, with $a_n \neq 0$. If $f(x)$ has a zero r_1, the factor theorem gives us $f(x) = (x - r_1)q(x)$. It is seen by substitution that a zero of $q(x)$ is a zero of $f(x)$. Thus $f(x)$ has r_1 and the zeros of $q(x)$ as zeros. On the other hand, $f(x)$ has no zeros other than r_1 and the zeros of $q(x)$, for, if a were a zero of $f(x)$ that is neither r_1 nor a zero of $q(x)$, we would have $f(a) = 0 = (a - r_1)q(a)$. Since neither $q(a)$ nor $a - r_1$ is zero and since there are no proper divisors of zero in a field, this equality is impossible. The proof can now be made by induction. The polynomial $q(x)$ is of degree $n - 1$, and hence we make the induction hypothesis that $q(x)$ has at most $n - 1$ zeros. Thus $f(x)$ has at most n zeros, and the proof is completed by observing that a polynomial of degree 1, $a_0 + a_1 x$ ($a_1 \neq 0$), has the one zero, $-a_0/a_1$.

Theorem 9.   If the polynomial f(x) = a₀ + a₁x + · · · + aₙxⁿ *over a field* F *has the* n *zeros* r₁, r₂, · · · , rₙ *in* F, *then* f(x) *can be written uniquely as* aₙ(x − r₁)(x − r₂) · · · (x − rₙ).

Since r_1 is a zero, $f(x) = (x - r_1)q(x)$. As in Theorem 8, the zeros of $f(x)$ are r_1 and the zeros of $q(x)$. If $f(x)$ is of degree 1, $q(x)$ is an element of F, and the theorem certainly holds. Hence we suppose that $f(x)$ is of degree greater than 1 and that the zeros of $q(x)$ are $r_2, r_3, \cdots, r_n$. Now we make the induction hypothesis that if a polynomial of degree $m < n$ has m zeros it can be written in factored form. Note that $q(x)$ is of degree $n - 1$ and that the coefficient of its highest power of x is a_n. Thus $q(x) = a_n(x - r_2)$ $(x - r_3) \cdots (x - r_n)$, and $f(x) = (x - r_1)q(x)$ has the required factored form. The unique factorization theorem tells us that this decomposition is unique, for the $x - r_i$ are monic irreducible polynomials over F.

We give without proof* the so-called fundamental theorem of algebra.

Theorem 10.   A polynomial of positive degree over the field of complex numbers has a zero that is a complex number.

Theorem 11.   A polynomial $f(x) = a_0 + a_1 x + \cdots + a_n x^n$, *with* $a_n \neq 0$, *over the field of complex numbers has exactly* n *zeros that are complex numbers.*

If $n = 1$, $f(x) = a_0 + a_1 x$, and the theorem certainly holds. If $n > 1$, we observe that by the fundamental theorem of algebra, $f(x)$ has a zero r_1 that is a complex number. Hence $f(x) = (x - r_1)q(x)$. Moreover, $q(x)$ is of degree $n - 1$, and, if $n - 1 > 0$, $q(x)$ has a root r_2 that is a complex number. We make the induction hypothesis that a polynomial of degree $m < n$ over the field of complex numbers has exactly m zeros. Hence $q(x)$ has exactly $n - 1$ zeros, and $f(x)$ has exactly n zeros, as was to be proved.

Hence by Theorem 9, $f(x)$ can be written uniquely in the form $f(x) = a_n(x - r_1)(x - r_2) \cdots (x - r_n)$. Thus the only irreducible monic polynomials over the field of complex numbers are linear.

We now specialize our field of coefficients to the field of real numbers and see what decomposition is given by the unique factorization theorem.

Theorem 12.   If a polynomial $f(x)$ *over the field of real numbers has the zero* a + bi, *where* b $\neq$ 0, *it has the conjugate zero* a − bi.

Form the product $[x - (a + bi)][x - (a - bi)] = (x - a)^2 + b^2$, which we observe is a polynomial with real coefficients. Hence when we divide $f(x)$ by this polynomial we obtain a quotient and a remainder over the field of real numbers. Thus $f(x) = [(x - a)^2 + b^2]q(x) + r(x)$, where $r(x)$ is either zero or of degree 1 at most. We, of course, wish to prove that $r(x) = 0$. Let $r(x) = mx + n$. Now $f(a + bi) = 0 = m(a + bi) + n$. Therefore, $ma + n = 0$ and $mb = 0$. Since $b \neq 0$, $m = 0$, and hence $n = 0$. Thus $r(x) = 0$, and $f(x)$ has the factor $x - (a - bi)$ if it has the factor $x - (a + bi)$. (Another proof of this theorem will be given in Chap. 9.)

Recall that a quadratic polynomial $ax^2 + bx + c$ over the field of real numbers has no real zeros if its discriminant $b^2 - 4ac < 0$. Thus real quadratic polynomials with negative discriminants are irreducible over the field of real numbers. Now regard a polynomial with real coefficients as a polynomial over the field of complex numbers. It then has a factorization into linear factors. Theorem 12 tells us that every linear factor corresponding to a zero of the form $a + bi$ ($b \neq 0$) can be paired with a linear

---

* All proofs involve nonalgebraic concepts (e.g., continuity). See, for example, G. D. Birkhoff and S. MacLane, *A Survey of Modern Algebra* (revised edition), New York, The Macmillan Co., 1953, pp. 107–109.

factor corresponding to the conjugate zero $a - bi$, and that the product of two such linear factors is a real quadratic polynomial. Hence we have the following theorem.

Theorem 13.   A polynomial over the field of real numbers can be written uniquely as the product of a real number times a product of real monic irreducible quadratic factors and real monic linear factors.

For a polynomial over the field of rational numbers, the following theorem gives us a means of determining its rational zeros. This theorem and its corollary are sometimes helpful in determining whether a polynomial over the field of rational numbers is reducible. We first note that multiplication by the proper integer replaces a polynomial with rational coefficients by an associate that has integral coefficients. Thus we reduce our problem to that of finding the rational zeros of a polynomial with integral coefficients.

Theorem 14.   Let c/d, where $(c, d) = 1$, be a rational zero of the polynomial $a_0 + a_1x + \cdots + a_nx^n$ with integral coefficients. Then c divides a_0 and d divides a_n.

Now $a_0 + a_1(c/d) + \cdots + a_{n-1}(c/d)^{n-1} + a_n(c/d)^n = 0$, and hence the integer

$$(5) \qquad a_0d^n + a_1cd^{n-1} + \cdots + a_{n-1}c^{n-1}d + a_nc^n = 0.$$

Thus $d(a_0d^{n-1} + a_1cd^{n-2} + \cdots + a_{n-1}c^{n-1}) + a_nc^n = 0$, and d divides a_nc^n. However, $(c^n, d) = 1$ (see Exercise 7, p. 18), and hence d divides a_n. Similarly the integer (5) may be written $a_0d^n + c(a_1d^{n-1} + \cdots + a_nc^{n-1}) = 0$, and c divides a_0d^n, but again $(c, d^n) = 1$, and hence c divides a_0.

Corollary.   All rational zeros of the polynomial $a_0 + a_1x + \cdots + a_{n-1}x^{n-1} + x^n$ with integral coefficients are integers and divisors of a_0.

The corollary follows from the theorem when we note that d divides $a_n = 1$.

We note that the above corollary gives us a simple way of proving that certain real numbers such as $\sqrt{3}$ and $\sqrt[3]{5}$ are irrational, for they are zeros respectively of the polynomials $x^2 - 3$ and $x^3 - 5$. It is easily checked that these polynomials have no rational zeros.

EXAMPLE.   Find the rational zeros and the decomposition of the polynomial $f(x) = 6x^4 - 7x^3 + 6x^2 - 1$ over the field of rational numbers. By the above theorem the possible rational zeros are $\pm 1, \pm 1/2, \pm 1/3, \pm 1/6$. Using synthetic division, we find that neither ± 1 are zeros but that $1/2$ is a zero:

$$
\begin{array}{rrrrr|l}
6 & -7 & 6 & 0 & -1 & \tfrac{1}{2} \\
  & 3 & -2 & 2 & 1 & \\
\hline
6 & -4 & 4 & 2 & 0. &
\end{array}
$$

As we now know that $f(x) = (x - 1/2)(6x^3 - 4x^2 + 4x + 2)$, we use the quotient divided by 2, namely $3x^3 - 2x^2 + 2x + 1$, to discover the remaining rational zeros of $f(x)$. Now it is necessary only to try $\pm 1/3$. We find that $-1/3$ is a zero and that $3x^2 - 3x + 3$ is the second quotient. Since $x^2 - x + 1$ has no rational zeros, $6(x - 1/2)(x + 1/3)(x^2 - x + 1)$ is the decomposition of $f(x)$ over the field of rational numbers.

Exercises

1. Find the decomposition of the polynomial $x^4 + 9x^3 + 28x^2 + 36x + 16$ over the field of rational numbers.
2. Find the decomposition of the polynomial $4x^4 + 8x^3 + 7x^2 + 8x + 3$ over the field of rational numbers and over the field of complex numbers.
3. Find the decomposition of the polynomial $x^3 - 25x - 48$ over the field of rational numbers and over the field of real numbers.
4. Find the decomposition of $x^5 - 1$ over the field of complex numbers and over the field of real numbers.
5. Find the decompositions of $x^8 - 1$ and $x^{12} - 1$ over the field of complex numbers, over the field of real numbers, and over the field of rational numbers.
6. Find the decomposition over the field of residue classes modulo 5 of the polynomial $2x^3 + 3x^2 + 3x + 1$.
7. Find the greatest common divisor of $2x^4 + 9x^2 + 17x - 21$ and $x^3 + 2x^2 + 4x + 21$. Hence find the decomposition of the first polynomial over the field of real numbers and over the field of complex numbers.
8. Find the zeros of the following polynomials over the field of complex numbers and express each zero in the form $a + bi$, a and b being real numbers.

   a. $x^2 + ix + 1$.   c. $x^2 - ix + i$.

   b. $x^2 - x + i$.   d. $x^2 + \sqrt{2}\,x + 2i$.

6 · RELATION BETWEEN THE ZEROS AND COEFFICIENTS OF A POLYNOMIAL

In any field F in which the polynomial

$$f(x) = a_0 + a_1 x + \cdots + a_n x^n$$

over F has the decomposition

$$f(x) = a_n(x - r_1)(x - r_2) \cdots (x - r_n),$$

there are certain relations between the coefficients of the polynomial and its zeros which will be described below. The following combinations of the zeros $r_1, r_2, \cdots, r_n$ are called the *elementary symmetric functions* of $r_1, r_2, \cdots, r_n$:

$$S_1 = r_1 + r_2 + \cdots + r_n = \sum r_1,$$
$$S_2 = r_1 r_2 + r_1 r_3 + \cdots + r_{n-1} r_n = \sum r_1 r_2,$$
$$\cdot \ \cdot \ \cdot \ \cdot \ \cdot \ \cdot \ \cdot \ \cdot \ \cdot \ \cdot \ \cdot \ \cdot$$
$$S_n = r_1 r_2 r_3 \cdots r_n.$$

Thus the jth elementary symmetric function is the sum of the products, consisting of j distinct factors each, that can be formed from the zeros $r_1, r_2, \cdots, r_n$. Hence there are $C(n, j) = n!/[(n - j)!\,j!]$ terms in the jth elementary symmetric function. These functions are called symmetric functions because they remain unchanged or invariant when they are operated on by the elements of the symmetric group on n symbols.

In order to obtain the desired relations we now prove the following lemma.

Lemma

(6) $(x - r_1)(x - r_2) \cdots (x - r_n) = x^n - S_1 x^{n-1}$

$$+ S_2 x^{n-2} + \cdots + (-1)^j S_j x^{n-j} + \cdots + (-1)^n S_n.$$

Note that, when $n = 1$, $x - r_1 = x - S_1$, and when $n = 2$,

$$(x - r_1)(x - r_2) = x^2 - (r_1 + r_2)x + r_1 r_2 = x^2 - S_1 x + S_2,$$

where the S's are the elementary symmetric functions of one and two variables respectively. Thus the lemma is true for $n = 1$ and $n = 2$, and we complete our proof by induction.

Assume the lemma true for $n = k$:

(7) $(x - r_1)(x - r_2) \cdots (x - r_k) = x^k - S_1 x^{k-1}$

$$+ S_2 x^{k-2} + \cdots + (-1)^j S_j x^{k-j} + \cdots + (-1)^k S_k.$$

Here S_j is the jth elementary symmetric function of $r_1, r_2, \cdots, r_k$. Multiply both sides of equation (7) by $x - r_{k+1}$, obtaining

(8) $(x - r_1)(x - r_2) \cdots (x - r_k)(x - r_{k+1})$

$$= x^{k+1} - (S_1 + r_{k+1})x^k + (S_2 + r_{k+1}S_1)x^{k-1} + \cdots$$

$$+ (-1)^j(S_j + r_{k+1}S_{j-1})x^{k-j+1} + \cdots + (-1)^{k+1} r_{k+1} S_k.$$

Let $S_1', S_2', \cdots, S_{k+1}'$ be the elementary symmetric functions of $r_1, r_2, \cdots, r_k, r_{k+1}$. Then $S_1' = S_1 + r_{k+1}$, $S_2' = S_2 + r_{k+1}S_1$, $\cdots$, $S_j' = S_j + r_{k+1}S_{j-1}$. For we note that the sum of the products of j distinct factors each of $r_1, r_2, \cdots, r_k, r_{k+1}$ is the sum of the products of j distinct factors each of $r_1, r_2, \cdots, r_k$ plus r_{k+1} times the sum of the products of $j - 1$ factors each of these zeros. Thus (8) is of the form (6) with $n = k + 1$, and the induction is complete.

Now

$$f(x) = a_0 + a_1 x + \cdots + a_n x^n = a_n(x - r_1)(x - r_2) \cdots (x - r_n)$$

$$= a_n(x^n - S_1 x^{n-1} + \cdots + (-1)^n S_n),$$

and, equating the first and the last forms of the polynomial, we have the following theorem.

Theorem 15. *If* $f(x) = a_0 + a_1x + \cdots + a_nx^n$ *over a field F has the* n *zeros* $r_1, r_2, \cdots, r_n$ *in* F, *then* $S_j = (-1)^j a_{n-j}/a_n$, $j = 1, 2, \cdots, n$.

Exercises

1. Using the relation between the zeros and the coefficients of a polynomial, find a polynomial over the field of rational numbers whose zeros are: (a) $-1, 2, 3$; (b) $2, 2, 2$; (c) $0, 0, 1, 2$; (d) $-1, -1, 3, 4$.

2. Denote the zeros of the following polynomials by r_1, r_2, r_3, r_4. Find the values of their elementary symmetric functions for each of the polynomials:

   a. $x^4 + 4x^3 - 2x + 3$.
   b. $4x^4 + 4x^3 + x^2 - x + 2$.
   c. $3x^4 - 4x^2 + 2$.

3. If r_1, r_2, r_3 are the zeros of $x^3 - 3x^2 + 2x + 1$, find a polynomial whose zeros are $2r_1, 2r_2, 2r_3$.

4. Let r_1, r_2, r_3 be the zeros of the polynomial $2x^3 - 3x^2 + kx - 1$. Determine the constant k if the sum of two of them is 2. Find the zeros of the resulting polynomial.

5. Let r_1, r_2, r_3 be the zeros of the polynomial $\sqrt{2}x^3 + kx^2 - 2\sqrt{2}x + 2$. Determine the constant k if the product of two of the zeros is 1. Find the zeros of the resulting polynomial.

6. Determine k so that one zero of the polynomial $3x^3 - kx^2 - 7x + 3$ is the reciprocal of another. Hence determine the zeros of the polynomial.

7 · DERIVATIVE OF A POLYNOMIAL

We formally define the derivative of $f(x) = a_0 + a_1x + \cdots + a_nx^n$ to be $f'(x) = a_1 + 2a_2x + \cdots + na_nx^{n-1}$. (Here, of course, $2a_2$ means $a_2 + a_2$, $3a_3$ means $a_3 + a_3 + a_3$, etc.) This definition can be used to prove the usual formulas for the derivatives of sums, products, and powers of polynomials, and we shall use these formulas. We note, for example, that, if the polynomial is a polynomial over the field of complex numbers, the only polynomials whose derivatives are zero are the constants. However, if, for example, $f(x) = x^p$ is regarded as a polynomial over the field of residue classes modulo p, where p is a prime, $f(x)$ has the derivative px^{p-1}, which is zero. The results due to the use of derivatives depend upon whether the derivative of a polynomial is zero only when the polynomial is an element in a field or whether it may also be zero when the polynomial is of positive degree. To avoid this complication we shall *restrict our field of coefficients to the field of complex numbers or to one of its subfields.* The interested student may read in more advanced texts what can be proved when this restriction is not made.

Exercises

1. Find the derivative of the following polynomials:

    a. $3x^5 + 2x^2 + x + 5.$ c. $5x^3 - 3x^2 + 2.$

    b. $2x^4 - 3x^2 + x - 2.$ d. $7x^5 - 2x^3 - x^2 + 5.$

2. Prove that, if $f(x)$ and $g(x)$ are polynomials and $h(x) = f(x) + g(x)$, then $h'(x) = f'(x) + g'(x)$.

3. Prove that, if $f(x)$ and $g(x)$ are polynomials and $h(x) = f(x) g(x)$, then $h'(x) = f(x) g'(x) + g(x) f'(x)$.

4. Prove that, if $f(x)$ is a polynomial, n is a positive integer, and $g(x) = [f(x)]^n$, then $g'(x) = n[f'(x)]^{n-1}$.

8 · MULTIPLE FACTORS

DEFINITIONS. If the polynomial $[p(x)]^m$ divides the polynomial $f(x)$ and if no higher power of $p(x)$ divides $f(x)$, $p(x)$ is said to be a *factor of multiplicity m* of $f(x)$. If $(x - a)^m$ divides the polynomial $f(x)$ and if no higher power of $x - a$ divides $f(x)$, a is called a *zero of multiplicity m*.

In the following theorems we shall restrict the field of coefficients of the polynomial $f(x)$ to the field of complex numbers or one of its subfields.

Theorem 16. *Let* p(x) *be an irreducible factor of* f(x) *of multiplicity* $m > 1$. *Then* $[p(x)]^{m-1}$ *is the highest power of* p(x) *that occurs as a factor of the greatest common divisor of* f(x) *and its derivative* f'(x). *Conversely, if the greatest common divisor of* f(x) *and* f'(x) *has the irreducible factor* p(x) *as a factor of multiplicity* $m - 1$, p(x) *is an irreducible factor of* f(x) *of multiplicity* m.

First, let $p(x)$ be an irreducible factor of multiplicity m of $f(x)$. Then we may write $f(x) = [p(x)]^m q(x)$, where $p(x)$ and $q(x)$ are relatively prime, for $f(x)$ has a unique factorization into irreducible polynomials. Using the standard rules for differentiation we have

$$f'(x) = [p(x)]^{m-1}[mp'(x) \cdot q(x) + p(x) \cdot q'(x)].$$

It is obvious that $[p(x)]^{m-1}$ is a common factor of $f(x)$ and $f'(x)$ and hence that it divides their g.c.d. We show that no higher power of $p(x)$ occurs as a factor of the g.c.d. by proving that $m - 1$ is the highest power of $p(x)$ that divides $f'(x)$. Now $p(x)$ is relatively prime to its derivative $p'(x)$, because $p'(x)$ is of degree less than the degree of $p(x)$ and hence it can have no factor in common with the irreducible polynomial $p(x)$. Thus $p(x)$ does not divide the second factor of $f'(x)$, for it is relatively prime to $p'(x) \cdot q(x)$ and divides $p(x) \cdot q'(x)$. Hence $m - 1$ is the highest power of $p(x)$ that divides the g.c.d. of $f(x)$ and $f'(x)$.

It remains to prove the converse. Now let the g.c.d. of $f(x)$ and $f'(x)$ have the irreducible factor $p(x)$ of multiplicity $m - 1$. Let k be the highest power of $p(x)$ that divides $f(x)$. Using the unique factorization theorem, we again have $f(x) = [p(x)]^k q(x)$, where $p(x)$ and $q(x)$ are relatively prime polynomials. By the above proof the g.c.d. of $f(x)$ and $f'(x)$ has $p(x)$ as an irreducible factor of multiplicity $k - 1$. Hence $k - 1 = m - 1$ and $k = m$, as was to be proved.

Corollary 1. A polynomial f(x) *has no repeated factor of multiplicity greater than* 1 *if and only if it and its derivative are relatively prime.*

This corollary is easily seen to be true when we consider that any factor of $f(x)$ can be decomposed into its irreducible factors.

Corollary 2. If r *is a zero of multiplicity* m *of the g.c.d. of* f(x) *and its derivative, then* r *is a zero of multiplicity* m + 1 *of* f(x).

This corollary is immediate from the theorem, for a zero of a polynomial corresponds to an irreducible linear factor of the polynomial.

To show that this theorem cannot be applied to a polynomial over any field of coefficients, we consider the polynomial $f(x) = x^3 - 1$ over the field of residue classes modulo 3. We see that $x^3 - 1 = (x - 1)^3$ and hence $x^3 - 1$ has an irreducible factor of multiplicity 3. However, $f'(x) = 3x^2 = 0$.

EXAMPLE.   Determine whether the polynomial $f(x) = x^4 + 2x^3 - 2x - 1$ has any irreducible factors of multiplicity greater than 1. If it has, find them and hence find the decomposition of the polynomial over the field of rational numbers.

Now $f'(x) = 4x^3 + 6x^2 - 2$, and $4f(x) = f'(x) \cdot (x + 1/2) - 3(x^2 + 2x + 1)$. The g.c.d. of $f(x)$ and $f'(x)$ divides $(x + 1)^2$, the monic remainder when $4f(x)$ is divided by $f'(x)$. Hence, if an irreducible factor of multiplicity greater than 1 of $f(x)$ exists, it must be $x + 1$. By synthetic division we find that $f'(x) = 2(x + 1)^2(2x - 1)$. Thus $f(x)$ has the factor $x + 1$ as a factor of multiplicity 3, and by synthetic division we find that $f(x) = (x + 1)^3(x - 1)$. (At any stage in the greatest common divisor process the student should simplify his work by observing what possible factors the remainder has.)

Exercises

1. Determine whether the following polynomials have zeros of multiplicity greater than 1. If zeros of multiplicity greater than 1 exist, find all the zeros of the polynomial.

   a. $x^4 - 4x^3 + 5x^2 - 4x + 4$.   b. $x^4 + 2x^3 - x^2 - 4x - 2$.
   c. $x^3 - 7x^2 + 15x - 9$.   d. $8x^4 - 4x^3 - 6x^2 + 5x - 1$.

2. Find the decomposition of the following polynomials over the field of rational numbers, the field of real numbers, and the field of complex numbers:

   a. $x^5 - x^4 + 2x^3 - 2x^2 + x - 1$.   b. $x^6 - 2x^4 - 4x^2 + 8$.

3. Show that the following polynomials have no repeated factors:

   a. $x^n - a$, $a \neq 0$.   b. $x^6 - 6x + 1$.
   c. $x^5 + x^4 - 4x^3 + 4$.   d. $x^6 - 6x^3 + 1$.

4. Find the condition that the coefficients must satisfy if the following polynomials have no repeated factors:

   a. $ax^2 + bx + c$, $a \neq 0$.   b. $x^3 + 3ax + b$.

5. For what real values of a has the polynomial $x^n + nax + n - 1$, where $n > 1$, a repeated factor?

9 · TAYLOR'S THEOREM FOR POLYNOMIALS

Theorem 17.   Let f(x) *be a polynomial of degree* n. *Then* f(x + h) = f(h) + xf'(h) + x²f"(h)/2! + · · · + x^k f^{(k)}(h)/k! + · · · + x^n f^{(n)}(h)/n!.

The polynomial $f(x + h)$ may be expressed as a polynomial in x whose coefficients are functions of h and of the coefficients of $f(x)$. Thus let

$$f(x + h) = b_0 + b_1 x + b_2 x^2 + \cdots + b_k x^k + \cdots + b_n x^n.$$

Its successive derivatives are:

$$f'(x + h) = b_1 + 2b_2 x + 3b_3 x^2 + \cdots + kb_k x^{k-1} + \cdots + nb_n x^{n-1},$$

$$f''(x + h) = 2b_2 + 3 \cdot 2b_3 x + \cdots$$

$$+ k(k - 1)b_k x^{k-2} + \cdots + n(n - 1)b_n x^{n-2},$$

· ·

$$f^{(k)}(x + h) = k! b_k + \cdots + n(n - 1) \cdots (n - k + 1)b_n x^{n-k},$$

· ·

$$f^{(n)}(x + h) = n! b_n.$$

For $x = 0$, we have $f(h) = b_0$, $f'(h) = b_1$, $f''(h) = 2b_2, \cdots, f^{(k)}(h) = k! b_k, \cdots, f^{(n)}(h) = n! b_n$. Substituting these values of b_i in $f(x + h)$, we have the desired result

$$f(x + h) = f(h) + xf'(h) + x^2 \frac{f''(h)}{2!} + \cdots + x^n \frac{f^{(n)}(h)}{n!}.$$

This is one form of Taylor's theorem for polynomials. If in it we replace x by $x - h$, we have

$$f(x) = f(h) + (x - h)f'(h) + (x - h)^2 \frac{f''(h)}{2!} + \cdots$$

$$+ (x - h)^k \frac{f^{(k)}(h)}{k!} + \cdots + (x - h)^n \frac{f^{(n)}(h)}{n!}$$

This second form indicates how we can easily calculate the values of $f(h)$, $f'(h)$, $f''(h)/2!, \cdots, f^{(n)}(h)/n!$. Using this second form of Taylor's theorem, we see that when $f(x)$ is divided by $x - h$ the remainder is $f(h)$ and the quotient is

$$f'(h) + (x - h)\frac{f''(h)}{2!} + \cdots + (x - h)^{n-1}\frac{f^{(n)}(h)}{n!}.$$

If this quotient is divided by $x - h$, the remainder is $f'(h)$. We can continue in this fashion, dividing the successive quotients by $x - h$, and obtain the desired coefficients $f''(h)/2!, \cdots, f^{(n)}(h)/n!$. The student should recall that the simplest method of dividing a polynomial by $x - h$ is synthetic division.

Consider the relation between the zeros of $f(x)$ and those of $f(x + h)$. Let x_1 be a zero of $f(x)$. Thus $x_1 - h$ is a zero of $f(x + h)$, for $f(x_1 - h + h) = f(x_1) = 0$. Thus each zero of $f(x + h)$ is h less than the corresponding zero of $f(x)$.

EXAMPLE. We wish to find a polynomial each of whose zeros is 2 less than the zeros of $f(x) = 3x^3 - 2x^2 - 5x - 1$. By the foregoing remark, we know that this is equivalent to finding $f(x + 2)$, and that $f(x + 2)$ can be found by repeated synthetic division. Thus we have

$$\begin{array}{r|rrrr} 2 & 3 & -2 & -5 & -1 \\ & & +6 & +8 & +6 \\ \hline 2 & 3 & +4 & +3 & +5 \qquad f(2) = 5, \\ & & +6 & +20 \\ \hline 2 & 3 & +10 & +23 \qquad f'(2) = 23, \\ & & +6 \\ \hline 2 & 3 & +16 \qquad f''(2)/2! = 16, \quad f'''(2)/3! = 3. \end{array}$$

Hence $f(x) = 3x^3 + 16x^2 + 23x + 5$ is the desired polynomial.

Theorem 18. *A polynomial* f(x) *has the number* a *as a zero of multiplicity* m *if and only if* f(a) = 0, f'(a) = 0, $\cdots$, $f^{(m-1)}(a) = 0$, *and* $f^{(m)}(a) \neq 0$.

If a is a zero of multiplicity m of $f(x)$, then $f(x)$ is divisible by $(x - a)^m$ and no higher power of $x - a$. Write

$$f(x) = f(a) + (x - a)f'(a) + (x - a)^2\frac{f''(a)}{2!} + \cdots + (x - a)^n\frac{f^{(n)}(a)}{n!}.$$

Hence we see that if a is a zero of multiplicity m, it is necessary that $f(a) = 0, f'(a) = 0, \cdots, f^{(m-1)}(a) = 0$, but that $f^{(m)}(a) \neq 0$. Conversely, if $f(a) = 0, f'(a) = 0, \cdots, f^{(m-1)}(a) = 0$ but if $f^{(m)}(a) \neq 0$, $f(x)$ is exactly divisible by $(x - a)^m$ and by no higher power of $x - a$.

Exercises

1. Express the polynomial $x^3 + 2x - 5$ as a polynomial in $x - 3$ and as a polynomial in $x + 2$.
2. Find a polynomial each of whose zeros is 3 less than the zeros of $x^4 - x^2 + 2x - 1$.
3. Find a polynomial each of whose zeros is 2 greater than the zeros of the polynomial $3x^3 - 4x^2 + 2$.
4. Find a polynomial each of whose zeros is 4 less than the zeros of the polynomial $3x^5 - 14x^4 + 6x^2 - 9$.
5. Find a polynomial each of whose zeros is 5 greater than the zeros of the polynomial $2x^3 + 12x^2 + 3$.
6. Show that the polynomial $8x^4 + 84x^3 + 114x^2 + 55x + 9$ has a zero of multiplicity 3.

6 Vectors and Matrices

1 · VECTOR SPACES

In our study of complex numbers we considered ordered pairs of real numbers (a, b) and had $(a, b) + (c, d) = (a + c, b + d)$. Furthermore, in elementary algebra we have $c(a + bi) = ca + (cb)i$ for any real number c so that it is natural to define $c(a, b)$ as equal to (ca, cb). Now we will consider ordered n-tuples $(x_1, x_2, \cdots, x_n)$, with $x_1, x_2, \cdots, x_n$ elements of a field F, and will call such n-tuples *vectors of order n over F*. *Addition* of two vectors of the same order is defined by

$$(x_1, x_2, \cdots, x_n) + (y_1, y_2, \cdots, y_n) = (x_1 + y_1, x_2 + y_2, \cdots, x_n + y_n),$$

and *scalar multiplication* by

$$c(x_1, x_2, \cdots, x_n) = (cx_1, cx_2, \cdots, cx_n),$$

when c is any element of F. Finally, $(x_1, x_2, \cdots, x_n) = (y_1, y_2, \cdots, y_n)$ if and only if $x_1 = y_1, x_2 = y_2, \cdots, x_n = y_n$; i.e, two vectors of the same order are equal if and only if they are identical.

Addition and scalar multiplication of vectors of order 2 or 3 over the field of real numbers may be pictured geometrically, as shown in the figures on page 91 for vectors of order 2.

DEFINITION. Any set of vectors, over a field F, that is closed under addition and scalar multiplication is called a *vector space* over F.

Clearly, the set of *all* vectors of order n over a field F constitutes a vector space which we will designate by $V_n(F)$. In general, if $\xi_1, \xi_2, \cdots, \xi_m$ are any m vectors of $V_n(F)$, the set of all *linear combinations*, $c_1\xi_1 + c_2\xi_2 + \cdots + c_m\xi_m$ ($c_1, c_2, \cdots, c_m$ in F) of the vectors $\xi_1, \xi_2, \cdots, \xi_m$ forms a vector space over F. For, if $\alpha = a_1\xi_1 + a_2\xi_2 + \cdots + a_m\xi_m$ and $\beta = b_1\xi_1 + b_2\xi_2 + \cdots + b_m\xi_m$, then

$$\alpha + \beta = (a_1 + b_1)\xi_1 + (a_2 + b_2)\xi_2 + \cdots + (a_m + b_m)\xi_m$$

and

$$c\alpha = (ca_1)\xi_1 + (ca_2)\xi_2 + \cdots + (ca_m)\xi_m.$$

The vector space consisting of all linear combinations of a given set of vectors is called the vector space *generated* by (or *spanned* by) the given set of vectors.

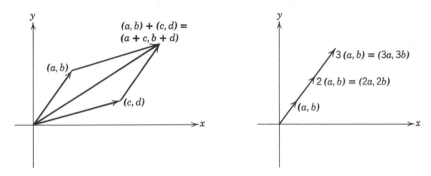

EXAMPLE. The vector space over the field of real numbers spanned by the vectors $(1, 0, 0)$ and $(0, 0, 1)$ is the set of all vectors of the form $(a, 0, b)$, where a and b are real numbers.

The identity for addition in any vector space consisting of vectors of order n is the vector $(0, 0, \cdots, 0)$ which we will designate by $\mathbf{0}_n$ or, unless confusion could arise, simply by $\mathbf{0}$. Then the additive inverse of $(x_1, x_2, \cdots, x_n)$ is clearly $(-x_1, -x_2, \cdots, -x_n)$, and we leave it to the student to prove that a vector space forms an abelian group under addition.

Frequently we omit the phrase "over a field" when discussing vectors or vector spaces. In such cases, of course, the student should realize that a fixed field is to be assumed throughout the discussion. Also, when we write a sum, $\xi + \eta$, it is to be assumed that ξ and η are both vectors of the same order.

Exercises

1. Prove that, for every vector ξ, $0\xi = \mathbf{0}$, $1\xi = \xi$, and $(-1)\xi = -\xi$, where $-\xi$ is the additive inverse of ξ.
2. Prove that $a(b\xi) = (ab)\xi$ for all scalars a and b and all vectors ξ.
3. Prove that $a(\xi_1 + \xi_2) = a\xi_1 + a\xi_2$ for all vectors ξ_1 and ξ_2 and scalars a.
4. Prove that $(a + b)\xi = a\xi + b\xi$ for all scalars a and b and vectors ξ.
5. Prove that a vector space forms an abelian group under addition.

2 · LINEAR DEPENDENCE AND INDEPENDENCE

DEFINITION.   Let $\xi_1, \xi_2, \cdots, \xi_m$ be vectors of $V_n(F)$. If there exist elements $c_1, c_2, \cdots, c_m$ of F not all equal to 0 such that $c_1\xi_1 + c_2\xi_2 + \cdots + c_m\xi_m = 0$, we will say that $\xi_1, \xi_2, \cdots, \xi_m$ are *linearly dependent*. If the vectors $\xi_1, \xi_2, \cdots, \xi_m$ are not linearly dependent, we will say that they are *linearly independent*.

EXAMPLE.   In $V_3(F)$ where F is the field of real numbers, the vectors $(1, -1, 1)$, $(2, 1, -2)$, and $(8, 1, -4)$ are linearly dependent since $2(1, -1, 1) + 3(2, 1, -2) + (-1)(8, 1, -4) = (0, 0, 0)$.   On the other hand, $(1, 0, 0)$, $(0, 1, 0)$, and $(0, 0, 1)$ are linearly independent since, if $a(1, 0, 0) + b(0, 1, 0) + c(0, 0, 1) = (a, b, c), = (0, 0, 0)$ then $a = b = c = 0$.

Subspace

If W is a subset of a vector space V over a field F such that W itself is a vector space over F, we will call W a subspace of V.

EXAMPLE.   The set of vectors spanned by $(1, 0, 0)$ and $(0, 1, 0)$ is a subspace of $V_3(F)$.

Theorem 1.   The vectors $\xi_1, \xi_2, \cdots, \xi_m$ over a field F *are linearly dependent if and only if one of these vectors belongs to the subspace generated by the remaining* m − 1.

For if $\xi_1, \xi_2, \cdots, \xi_m$ are linearly dependent, there exist elements $c_1, c_2, \cdots, c_m$ of F, not all zero, such that

$$c_1\xi_1 + c_2\xi_2 + \cdots + c_m\xi_m = 0.$$

Suppose $c_i \neq 0$.   Then

$$\xi_i = -\frac{c_1}{c_i}\xi_1 - \frac{c_2}{c_i}\xi_2 - \cdots - \frac{c_{i-1}}{c_i}\xi_{i-1} - \frac{c_{i+1}}{c_i}\xi_{i+1} - \cdots - \frac{c_m}{c_i}\xi_m.$$

On the other hand, if

$$\xi_i = a_1\xi_1 + a_2\xi_2 + \cdots + a_{i-1}\xi_{i-1} + a_{i+1}\xi_{i+1} + \cdots + a_m\xi_m,$$

then

$$a_1\xi_1 + a_2\xi_2 + \cdots + a_{i-1}\xi_{i-1} - \xi_i + a_{i+1}\xi_{i+1} + \cdots + a_m\xi_m = 0.$$

Corollary 1.   If the vectors $\xi_1, \xi_2, \cdots, \xi_m$ are linearly independent, then any subset of r < m *of these vectors is linearly independent.*

Corollary 2.   A set of vectors which contains the zero vector is always a linearly dependent set.

The proofs of these corollaries are left to the student.

Detailed questions about linear dependence of vectors are best handled with the use of matrices. Hence we will postpone further discussion of this topic and turn now to a study of matrices.

Exercises

1. Prove that the vectors (a_1, a_2) and (b_1, b_2) in $V_2(F)$ are linearly dependent if and only if $a_1 b_2 - a_2 b_1 = 0$.
2. In $V_3(R)$, where R is the field of rational numbers, examine each of the following sets of vectors for linear dependence.

   a. $(1, 2, 3)$ and $(3, 2, 1)$.   d. $(1, 2, 3)$, $(1, 0, 1)$, and $(0, 1, 0)$.
   b. $(8, 4, 8)$ and $(2, 1, 2)$.   e. $(1, 2, 0)$, $(0, 3, 1)$, and $(-1, 0, 1)$.
   c. $(2, 3, 5)$ and $(4, 9, 25)$.   f. $(-1, 2, 1)$, $(3, 0, -1)$, and $(-5, 4, 3)$.

3. Prove Corollary 1.
4. Prove Corollary 2.

3 · MATRIX NOTATION

In solving systems of simultaneous linear equations, the student soon realizes that the coefficients play the important role in finding solutions. The "unknowns" merely act as marks of position. For this reason new notations were introduced to simplify the writing of a system of equations. For example, the system

$$a_{11}x_1 + a_{12}x_2 + \cdots + a_{1n}x_n = c_1,$$
$$a_{21}x_1 + a_{22}x_2 + \cdots + a_{2n}x_n = c_2,$$
$$\cdots\cdots\cdots\cdots\cdots\cdots\cdots\cdots\cdots$$
$$a_{m1}x_1 + a_{m2}x_2 + \cdots + a_{mn}x_n = c_m$$

might be denoted as follows:

$$\begin{bmatrix} a_{11} & a_{12} & \cdots & a_{1n} \\ a_{21} & a_{22} & \cdots & a_{2n} \\ \cdots & \cdots & & \cdots \\ a_{m1} & a_{m2} & \cdots & a_{mn} \end{bmatrix} \begin{bmatrix} x_1 \\ x_2 \\ \cdot \\ x_n \end{bmatrix} = \begin{bmatrix} c_1 \\ c_2 \\ \cdot \\ c_m \end{bmatrix}.$$

Here we have a rectangular array of the a_{ij} arranged in m rows and n columns, a column of n unknowns x_j, and a column of m constants c_i. Such a notation leads us to the study of rectangular arrays of elements called matrices. We shall restrict our study to matrices with elements in a field.

Definition of a Matrix

An m by n matrix A over a field F is a rectangular array of mn elements a_{ij} in F arranged in m rows and n columns, thus:

$$A = \begin{bmatrix} a_{11} & a_{12} & \cdots & a_{1n} \\ a_{21} & a_{22} & \cdots & a_{2n} \\ \cdots\cdots\cdots\cdots\cdots\cdots \\ a_{m1} & a_{m2} & \cdots & a_{mn} \end{bmatrix}.$$

It is customary to enclose the array with brackets, parentheses, or double straight lines on each side of the array. We shall use the above notation. The elements $a_{i1}, a_{i2}, \cdots, a_{in}$ are the elements of the ith row, whereas the elements $a_{1k}, a_{2k}, \cdots, a_{mk}$ are the elements of the kth column. Thus the first subscript indicates the row in which the element lies, while the second subscript indicates the column in which it lies. A single row $[a_{i1} \, a_{i2} \cdots a_{in}]$ is itself a 1 by n (or, as we shall write it, $1 \times n$) matrix. It is, of course, also an nth order vector and we will call such vectors *row vectors*. On the other hand, a single column

$$\begin{bmatrix} a_{1k} \\ a_{2k} \\ \vdots \\ a_{mk} \end{bmatrix}$$

is an $m \times 1$ matrix which we will call a *column vector*. To save space, the matrix A is often simply written

$$[a_{ij}], \qquad i = 1, 2, \cdots, m \quad j = 1, 2, \cdots, n.$$

If $m = n$, the matrix is called a *square matrix*.

If we define the *transpose*, A^t, of the matrix A as

$$A^t = \begin{bmatrix} a_{11} & a_{21} & \cdots & a_{m1} \\ a_{12} & a_{22} & \cdots & a_{m2} \\ \cdots\cdots\cdots\cdots\cdots\cdots \\ a_{1n} & a_{2n} & \cdots & a_{mn} \end{bmatrix}.$$

we have an $n \times m$ matrix the rows of which are the columns of A and the columns of which are the rows of A. Then if ξ is a column vector (an $m \times 1$ matrix), ξ^t is a $1 \times m$ matrix or a row vector. (A^t is frequently written as A'. But we often want to use A' to refer simply to another matrix and the notation A^t is less ambiguous than A'.)

4 · ADDITION AND SCALAR MULTIPLICATION

Before we define operations on matrices we must define equality of two matrices. Two $m \times n$ matrices $A = [a_{ij}]$ and $B = [b_{ij}]$ are equal if and only if $a_{ij} = b_{ij}$ for all i and j. In other words, two matrices are equal if and only if they are identical.

Sum

The sum $A + B$ of the two $m \times n$ matrices A and B is the $m \times n$ matrix $C = [c_{ij}]$, where $c_{ij} = a_{ij} + b_{ij}$. Thus to add two matrices of the same dimensions we merely add elements in corresponding positions. Note that the sum of matrices of different dimensions is not defined and that, when the matrices are vectors, the definition coincides with the previous definition of the addition of vectors. Moreover, as addition in a field is commutative and associative, we see that the addition of matrices also obeys these laws, and that the $m \times n$ matrix with every element equal to 0 is the additive identity for the set of all $m \times n$ matrices.

Scalar Multiplication

We define $c[a_{ij}]$ for c in the field F to be $[ca_{ij}]$ and note that this reduces to the scalar multiplication of vectors previously defined in the case when $[a_{ij}]$ is a vector.

We leave the proof of the following result to the student.

Theorem 2.   If A *and* B *are* m $\times$ n *matrices, then* $(A + B)^t = A^t + B^t$ *and if* c *is a scalar,* $(cA)^t = cA^t$.

Exercises

1. If $A = \begin{bmatrix} 2 & -1 & 0 \\ 1 & 3 & -2 \end{bmatrix}$ and $B = \begin{bmatrix} 3 & -1 & 2 \\ -1 & 0 & 1 \end{bmatrix}$, calculate:

   a. $A + 2B$.   c. $A^t + B^t$.

   b. $3A - B$.   d. $(A + B)^t$.

2. Prove Theorem 2.

5 · MATRIX MULTIPLICATION

Before we define multiplication of matrices, it is convenient to introduce a multiplication of vectors.

DEFINITION.   The *inner product** of two vectors $\xi = (x_1, x_2, \cdots, x_n)$ and $\eta = (y_1, y_2, \cdots, y_n)$ is $\xi \cdot \eta = x_1 y_1 + x_2 y_2 + \cdots + x_n y_n$.

* Also called *dot product* or *scalar product*.

Note that the inner product of two vectors is not a vector but a scalar. For example, $(2, -1) \cdot (3, 4) = 2 \cdot 3 + (-1)4 = 2$.

Now consider an $m \times n$ matrix A and an $n \times p$ matrix B so that the number of columns of A is equal to the number of rows of B. We may write A as

$$(1) \qquad A = \begin{bmatrix} A_1 \\ A_2 \\ \cdot \\ \cdot \\ \cdot \\ A_m \end{bmatrix},$$

where A_i is the vector $(a_{i1}, a_{i2}, \cdots, a_{in})$. Similarly, we may write B as

$$(2) \qquad B = [B_1, B_2, \cdots, B_p],$$

where $B_k{}^t = (b_{1k}, b_{2k}, \cdots, b_{nk})$.

DEFINITION.   If A is given by equation (1) and B by equation (2), then AB is the matrix $[c_{ik}]$, where $c_{ik} = A_i \cdot B_k{}^t$ for $i = 1, 2, \cdots, n$ and $k = 1, 2, \cdots, p$.

Thus AB is an $n \times p$ matrix whose element in the ith row and kth column is the inner product of the ith row of A by the transpose of the kth column of B.

EXAMPLES

1. Let $A = \begin{bmatrix} a_{11} & a_{12} \\ a_{21} & a_{22} \end{bmatrix}$ and $B = \begin{bmatrix} b_{11} & b_{12} & b_{13} \\ b_{21} & b_{22} & b_{23} \end{bmatrix}$. Then

$$AB = \begin{bmatrix} (a_{11}, a_{12}) \cdot (b_{11}, b_{21}) & (a_{11}, a_{12}) \cdot (b_{12}, b_{22}) & (a_{11}, a_{12}) \cdot (b_{13}, b_{23}) \\ (a_{21}, a_{22}) \cdot (b_{11}, b_{21}) & (a_{21}, a_{22}) \cdot (b_{12}, b_{22}) & (a_{21}, a_{22}) \cdot (b_{13}, b_{23}) \end{bmatrix}$$

$$= \begin{bmatrix} a_{11}b_{11} + a_{12}b_{21} & a_{11}b_{12} + a_{12}b_{22} & a_{11}b_{13} + a_{12}b_{23} \\ a_{21}b_{11} + a_{22}b_{21} & a_{21}b_{12} + a_{22}b_{22} & a_{21}b_{13} + a_{22}b_{23} \end{bmatrix}.$$

2. Let $A = \begin{bmatrix} 1 & 2 \\ 3 & 1 \\ -1 & 2 \end{bmatrix}$ and $B = \begin{bmatrix} 1 & 2 & 3 \\ 4 & 0 & 1 \end{bmatrix}$. Then

$$AB = \begin{bmatrix} 1(1) + 2(4) & 1(2) + 2(0) & 1(3) + 2(1) \\ 3(1) + 1(4) & 3(2) + 1(0) & 3(3) + 1(1) \\ (-1)(1) + 2(4) & (-1)(2) + 2(0) & (-1)(3) + 2(1) \end{bmatrix}$$

$$= \begin{bmatrix} 9 & 2 & 5 \\ 7 & 6 & 10 \\ 7 & -2 & -1 \end{bmatrix}.$$

We shall now prove that the associative and distributive laws hold if the matrices involved are of the proper dimension. To do this we note that

$$A_i \cdot B_k{}^t = a_{i1}b_{1k} + a_{i2}b_{2k} + \cdots + a_{in}b_{nk} = \sum_{j=1}^{n} a_{ij}b_{jk}.$$

Thus $AB = [c_{ik}]$, where

$$c_{ik} = \sum_{j=1}^{n} a_{ij}b_{jk}.$$

Associative Law for Multiplication

Let $A = [a_{ij}]$, with $i = 1, 2, \cdots, m$, and with $j = 1, 2, \cdots, n$; let $B = [b_{jk}]$, with $k = 1, 2, \cdots, p$; and let $C = [c_{kr}]$, with $r = 1, 2, \cdots, q$. Then $AB = [d_{ik}]$, where $d_{ik} = \sum_{j=1}^{n} a_{ij}b_{jk}$; and $(AB)C = [e_{ir}]$, where $e_{ir} = \sum_{k=1}^{p} d_{ik}c_{kr} = \sum_{k=1}^{p} \sum_{j=1}^{n} a_{ij}b_{jk}c_{kr}$.

Now $BC = [f_{ir}]$, where $f_{jr} = \sum_{k=1}^{p} b_{jk}c_{kr}$; and $A(BC) = [g_{ir}]$, where $g_{ir} = \sum_{j=1}^{n} a_{ij}f_{jr} = \sum_{j=1}^{n} a_{ij} \sum_{k=1}^{p} b_{jk}c_{kr} = \sum_{j=1}^{n} \sum_{k=1}^{p} a_{ij}b_{jk}c_{kr} = e_{ir}$. The summations may be interchanged, for these are sums in a field.

Distributive Laws

Let A and B be the above matrices, and $C = [c_{jk}]$, with $j = 1, 2, \cdots, n$, and with $k = 1, 2, \cdots, p$. We prove that $A(B + C) = AB + AC$. Note that, if B is an $n \times p$ matrix, C must also be an $n \times p$ matrix in order that the addition may be performed. Now $B + C = [b_{jk} + c_{jk}] = [g_{jk}]$, and $A(B + C) = [h_{ik}]$, where $h_{ik} = \sum_{j=1}^{n} a_{ij}g_{jk} = \sum_{j=1}^{n} a_{ij}(b_{jk} + c_{jk}) = \sum_{j=1}^{n} a_{ij}b_{jk} + \sum_{j=1}^{n} a_{ij}c_{jk} = d_{ik} + s_{ik}$. But $[d_{ik}] = AB$, and $[s_{ik}] = AC$. Thus $A(B + C) = AB + AC$. It is left to the student to prove the second distributive law $(B + C)A = BA + CA$, where, of course, the matrices must be chosen with the proper dimensions.

In general, if A and B are both $m \times m$ matrices, we do not have $AB = BA$. Thus,

$$\begin{bmatrix} 1 & -1 \\ 2 & 0 \end{bmatrix}\begin{bmatrix} -1 & -1 \\ 0 & 1 \end{bmatrix} = \begin{bmatrix} -1 & -2 \\ -2 & -2 \end{bmatrix},$$

but

$$\begin{bmatrix} -1 & -1 \\ 0 & 1 \end{bmatrix}\begin{bmatrix} 1 & -1 \\ 2 & 0 \end{bmatrix} = \begin{bmatrix} -3 & 1 \\ 2 & 0 \end{bmatrix}.$$

However, if $A = [a_{ij}]$ is an $m \times m$ matrix with $a_{ij} = 0$ for $i \neq j$, $a_{ii} = a$ for $i = 1, 2, \cdots, m$, and B is any other $m \times m$ matrix, it is easy to see that $AB = BA = aB$. Such a matrix A is called a *scalar* matrix. If $a = 1$, we have the $m \times m$ *identity* matrix I_m with the property that $I_m B = BI_m = B$.

Theorem 3. If A is an m × n *matrix and* B *is an* n × r *matrix, then* $(AB)^t = B^t A^t$.

Let $A = [a_{ij}]$ and $B = [b_{jk}]$, where $i = 1, 2, \cdots, m$, $j = 1, 2, \cdots, n$, and $k = 1, 2, \cdots, r$.

Then $AB = [c_{ij}]$, where

$$c_{ij} = \sum_{k=1}^{n} a_{ik} b_{kj}.$$

Now

$$B^t = \begin{bmatrix} b_{11} & b_{21} & \cdots & b_{n1} \\ b_{12} & b_{22} & \cdots & b_{n2} \\ \cdots\cdots\cdots\cdots\cdots \\ b_{1r} & b_{2r} & \cdots & b_{nr} \end{bmatrix}, \quad A^t = \begin{bmatrix} a_{11} & a_{21} & \cdots & a_{m1} \\ a_{12} & a_{22} & \cdots & a_{m2} \\ \cdots\cdots\cdots\cdots\cdots \\ a_{1n} & a_{2n} & \cdots & a_{mn} \end{bmatrix}.$$

Hence if $B^t A^t = [d_{ij}]$, we have

$$d_{ij} = (b_{1i}, b_{2i}, \cdots, b_{ni}) \cdot (a_{j1}, a_{j2}, \cdots, a_{jn}) = \sum_{k=1}^{n} b_{ki} a_{jk}.$$

Since

$$(a_{j1}, a_{j2}, \cdots, a_{jn}) \cdot (b_{1i}, b_{2i}, \cdots, b_{ni}) = \sum_{k=1}^{n} a_{jk} b_{ki}$$

is the element in the jth row and ith column of AB, it follows that $B^t A^t = (AB)^t$ since

$$d_{ij} = \sum_{k=1}^{n} b_{ki} a_{jk} = \sum_{k=1}^{n} a_{jk} b_{ki}.$$

Exercises

1. Perform the following matrix multiplications:

a. $\begin{bmatrix} 1 & 2 & -1 \\ 3 & 2 & 4 \\ 2 & 1 & 3 \end{bmatrix} \begin{bmatrix} 1 & 0 \\ 3 & -1 \\ 0 & 0 \end{bmatrix}$;   b. $\begin{bmatrix} 1 & 2 & 3 \end{bmatrix} \begin{bmatrix} 2 & -1 & 4 \\ 0 & 1 & 5 \\ 2 & 3 & 0 \end{bmatrix}$.

2. If $A = \begin{bmatrix} 1 & -1 \\ 0 & 2 \end{bmatrix}$ $B = \begin{bmatrix} 1 & 3 & 0 \\ 2 & 0 & 1 \end{bmatrix}$, and $C = \begin{bmatrix} 2 \\ 3 \\ -1 \end{bmatrix}$ show by computation that $(AB)C = A(BC)$.

3. If $A = \begin{bmatrix} 2 & -1 \\ 0 & 1 \end{bmatrix}$ and $B = \begin{bmatrix} 1 & 0 \\ -1 & -1 \end{bmatrix}$, show that $(A + B)(A + B) = A^2 + AB + BA + B^2 \neq A^2 + 2AB + B^2$.

4. If $A = \begin{bmatrix} 0 & i \\ -i & 0 \end{bmatrix}$, find A^2, A^3, A^4.

5. If $A = \begin{bmatrix} 0 & 1 \\ 1 & 0 \end{bmatrix}$ and $B = \begin{bmatrix} 0 & 0 \\ 1 & 0 \end{bmatrix}$, find AB, A^2, B^2, B^2A, and $2A + 3B$.

6. If $A = [a_{ij}]$ is a 4×3 matrix, and if $B = [b_{jk}]$ is a 3×4 matrix, find the element in the third row and second column of AB.

7. If the dimensions of the matrices A, B, C are properly chosen, prove that $(A + B) + C = A + (B + C)$.

8. If the dimensions of the matrices A, B, C are properly chosen, prove that $(B + C)A = BA + CA$.

9. Let $B = [b_{ij}]$ be an $m \times n$ matrix and let A be the $n \times n$ matrix $[a_{jk}]$, with $a_{jj} = a$, and with $a_{jk} = 0$ when $j \neq k$. Prove that $BA = Ba$.

10. Let ξ and η be vectors of order n. Prove that $a(\xi \cdot \eta) = (a\xi) \cdot \eta = \xi \cdot (a\eta)$ for all scalars a.

6 · MATRIX MULTIPLICATION AND LINEAR TRANSFORMATIONS

We return to the system of equations given on p. 93. Now that matrix multiplication has been defined, we see that the system of equations can be written $AX^t = C^t$ if we denote the $m \times n$ matrix by A, the matrix $[x_1, x_2, \cdots, x_n]$ by X, and the matrix $[c_1, c_2, \cdots, c_m]$ by C.

Consider the set of equations

$$
\begin{aligned}
x' &= x \cos \theta_1 - y \sin \theta_1, \\
y' &= x \sin \theta_1 + y \cos \theta_1.
\end{aligned}
$$
(3)

These equations may be regarded as transforming the point (x, y) in the plane into the point (x', y') in the plane. The point (x', y') is obtained from the point (x, y) by rotating the plane about the origin of the coordinate system through an angle θ_1, the rotation being a counterclockwise rotation when $\theta_1 > 0$ and a clockwise rotation when $\theta_1 < 0$. This set of equations is also given by the matrix equation

$$
\begin{bmatrix} x' \\ y' \end{bmatrix} = \begin{bmatrix} \cos \theta_1 & -\sin \theta_1 \\ \sin \theta_1 & \cos \theta_1 \end{bmatrix} \begin{bmatrix} x \\ y \end{bmatrix},
$$

which we shall abbreviate as $X' = AX$. Suppose now that it is desired to make a second counterclockwise rotation of the plane through an angle θ_2. This rotation will carry the point (x', y') into a third point (x'', y''), and the relation between the coordinates is given by

$$
\begin{aligned}
x'' &= x' \cos \theta_2 - y' \sin \theta_2, \\
y'' &= x' \sin \theta_2 + y' \cos \theta_2.
\end{aligned}
$$
(4)

It is geometrically obvious that these two rotations carried out successively carry the point (x, y) into the point (x'', y''). The relations between the coordinates x, y and the coordinates x'', y'' are

$$
\begin{aligned}
x'' &= x \cos (\theta_1 + \theta_2) - y \sin (\theta_1 + \theta_2), \\
y'' &= x \sin (\theta_1 + \theta_2) + y \cos (\theta_1 + \theta_2).
\end{aligned}
$$
(5)

We see that we can obtain equations (5) by eliminating x' and y' from equations (3) and (4). This elimination is most easily accomplished by writing equations (3) and (4) in matrix form thus: $X' = AX$, $X'' = BX'$. Then it is easily seen that $X'' = BX' = B(AX) = (BA)X$. The student should check that, if equations (5) are written in the matrix form $X'' = CX$, the matrix $C = BA$.

In general, if the set of m linear equations

$$x_1' = a_{11}x_1 + a_{12}x_2 + \cdots + a_{1n}x_n,$$
$$x_2' = a_{21}x_1 + a_{22}x_2 + \cdots + a_{2n}x_n,$$
$$\cdots\cdots\cdots\cdots\cdots\cdots\cdots\cdots\cdots$$
$$x_m' = a_{m1}x_1 + a_{m2}x_2 + \cdots + a_{mn}x_n$$

expresses the m variables x_i' as linear functions of the n variables x_j, and if a second set of p linear equations

$$x_1'' = b_{11}x_1' + b_{12}x_2' + \cdots + b_{1m}x_m',$$
$$x_2'' = b_{21}x_1' + b_{22}x_2' + \cdots + b_{2m}x_m',$$
$$\cdots\cdots\cdots\cdots\cdots\cdots\cdots\cdots\cdots$$
$$x_p'' = b_{p1}x_1' + b_{p2}x_2' + \cdots + b_{pm}x_m'$$

expresses the p variables x_k'' as linear functions of the m variables x_i', then the variables x_k'' may be expressed as linear functions of the variables x_i. This computation can be done most easily by means of matrices. Let $A = [a_{ij}]$, with $i = 1, 2, \cdots, m$, and $j = 1, 2, \cdots, n$; $B = [b_{ki}]$, with $k = 1, 2, \cdots, p$, and $i = 1, 2, \cdots, m$; $X^t = [x_1, x_2, \cdots, x_n]$; $(X')^t = [x_1', x_2', \cdots, x_m']$; $(X'')^t = [x_1'', x_2'', \cdots, x_p'']$. We can then write the above two systems of equations as $X' = AX$ and $X'' = BX'$. Thus $X'' = BX' = B(AX) = (BA)X$, and we have the desired result. The student thus sees a reason for defining matrix multiplication in the particular way it was done.

Exercises

1. Given $x_1' = 2x_1 - 3x_2, x_2' = x_1 + x_2, x_1'' = 3x_1' - 4x_2'$, and $x_2'' = x_1' - x_2'$, express the variables x_1'' and x_2'' as linear functions of x_1 and x_2. Make the computation by means of matrices and write the final result as a system of equations.

2. Given $x_1' = x_1 - x_2 + x_3, x_2' = x_1 + x_2, x_1'' = 2x_1' + x_2'$, and $x_2'' = 3x_1' - x_2'$, express the variables x_1'' and x_2'' as linear functions of x_1, x_2, and x_3. Make the computation by means of matrices and write the final result as a system of equations.

7 · PARTITIONING OF MATRICES

Let $A = [a_{ij}]$ be an $m \times n$ matrix. The $r \times s$ array of elements obtained from A be deleting any $m - r$ rows and any $n - s$ columns of A is called a *submatrix* of A. The matrix A may be partitioned into submatrices in many ways. For example, the matrix A may be partitioned as follows:

$$A = \begin{bmatrix} A_1 & A_2 \\ A_3 & A_4 \end{bmatrix},$$

where

$$A_1 = \begin{bmatrix} a_{11} & \cdots & a_{1s} \\ \cdots & \cdots & \cdots \\ a_{r1} & \cdots & a_{rs} \end{bmatrix}, \qquad A_2 = \begin{bmatrix} a_{1,\,s+1} & \cdots & a_{1n} \\ \cdots & \cdots & \cdots \\ a_{r,\,s+1} & \cdots & a_{rn} \end{bmatrix},$$

$$A_3 = \begin{bmatrix} a_{r+1,\,1} & \cdots & a_{r+1,\,s} \\ \cdots & \cdots & \cdots \\ a_{m1} & \cdots & a_{ms} \end{bmatrix}, \qquad A_4 = \begin{bmatrix} a_{r+1,\,s+1} & \cdots & a_{r+1,\,n} \\ \cdots & \cdots & \cdots \\ a_{m,\,s+1} & \cdots & a_{mn} \end{bmatrix}.$$

Here A_1 is an $r \times s$ matrix, A_2 an $r \times (n-s)$ matrix, A_3 an $(m-r) \times s$ matrix, and A_4 an $(m-r) \times (n-s)$ matrix. Sometimes, in order to facilitate the multiplication of two matrices, it is useful to partition both matrices so that the multiplication can be carried out by using submatrices. Thus, if we wish to obtain the matrix AB, where $B = [b_{jk}]$ is an $n \times p$ matrix, it might be useful to partition A as indicated above. Then, B must be partitioned so that it is possible to carry out the submatrix multiplication. For example, B may be partitioned to become a 2×1 matrix whose elements are the submatrices B_1 and B_2, thus: $B = \begin{bmatrix} B_1 \\ B_2 \end{bmatrix}$, where B_1 is an $s \times p$ matrix and B_2 an $(n-s) \times p$ matrix. With this partitioning perform the multiplication AB by using the submatrices A_i and B_j as elements. Thus, $AB = \begin{bmatrix} A_1B_1 + A_2B_2 \\ A_3B_1 + A_4B_2 \end{bmatrix}$, a 2×1 matrix with matrices as elements. It is necessary, of course, to prove that this product actually equals the usual product AB, when the multiplication rule by elements is used. We shall illustrate the proof. For example, the element in the rth row and the tth column of AB is $\sum_{j=1}^{n} a_{rj}b_{jt}$ by definition. Moreover, it is the element in the rth row and the tth column of $A_1B_1 + A_2B_2$, for we may write this element as $\sum_{j=1}^{s} a_{rj}b_{jt} + \sum_{j=s+1}^{n} a_{rj}b_{jt}$. Similarly any other element of AB may be written so that it is seen to belong to either one of the two submatrices of AB.

EXAMPLE

Let

$$A = \begin{bmatrix} 0 & 0 & \vdots & 1 & 2 \\ 0 & 0 & \vdots & 1 & -1 \end{bmatrix} = [A_1 \quad A_2]$$

and

$$B = \begin{bmatrix} 1 & 2 \\ 3 & 4 \\ \cdots \\ 1 & 0 \\ 0 & 1 \end{bmatrix} = \begin{bmatrix} B_1 \\ B_2 \end{bmatrix},$$

the partitioning being denoted by the dotted lines. Then $AB = [A_1B_1 + A_2B_2] = [0 + A_2B_2] = [A_2B_2] = \begin{bmatrix} 1 & 2 \\ 1 & -1 \end{bmatrix}$.

8 · ROW EQUIVALENCE

The student will recall that the first method he encountered in solving systems of simultaneous linear equations was the method of elimination. Thus to solve the system of equations

(6)
$$3x - y = 6,$$
$$x + 2y = 2$$

the student might multiply the first equation by 2, add the second equation to the first, obtaining $7x = 14$, and then divide by 7, finally obtaining the equation $x = 2$ in place of the first equation. He might now replace the second equation with one found by subtracting $x = 2$ from the second equation, obtaining $2y = 0$ and finally $y = 0$. Thus the process of solving (6) was to find the simpler pair of equations $x = 2, y = 0$. It is necessary to prove, of course, that the values of x and y given by the final set satisfy the original equations and that no other values of x and y satisfy the original pair. This question of the equivalence of the two sets of equations will be discussed later.

The student's attention now will be directed to the essential manipulation involved in the method. Note that, if the equations (6) are written in matrix form

(7)
$$\begin{bmatrix} 3 & -1 \\ 1 & 2 \end{bmatrix}\begin{bmatrix} x \\ y \end{bmatrix} = \begin{bmatrix} 6 \\ 2 \end{bmatrix},$$

the operations performed on equations (6) are essentially operations performed on the rows of the matrices $\begin{bmatrix} 3 & -1 \\ 1 & 2 \end{bmatrix}$ and $\begin{bmatrix} 6 \\ 2 \end{bmatrix}$. The first operation, namely the multiplication of the first equation by 2, replaces equation (7) by

(8)
$$\begin{bmatrix} 6 & -2 \\ 1 & 2 \end{bmatrix}\begin{bmatrix} x \\ y \end{bmatrix} = \begin{bmatrix} 12 \\ 2 \end{bmatrix}.$$

The second operation, namely the addition of the second equation of (6) to the first equation of (6), replaces the matrix equation (8) by

$$(9) \qquad \begin{bmatrix} 7 & 0 \\ 1 & 2 \end{bmatrix}\begin{bmatrix} x \\ y \end{bmatrix} = \begin{bmatrix} 14 \\ 2 \end{bmatrix}.$$

Continuing in this fashion, we successively obtain

$$\begin{bmatrix} 1 & 0 \\ 1 & 2 \end{bmatrix}\begin{bmatrix} x \\ y \end{bmatrix} = \begin{bmatrix} 2 \\ 2 \end{bmatrix}, \qquad \begin{bmatrix} 1 & 0 \\ 0 & 2 \end{bmatrix}\begin{bmatrix} x \\ y \end{bmatrix} = \begin{bmatrix} 2 \\ 0 \end{bmatrix},$$

and

$$\begin{bmatrix} 1 & 0 \\ 0 & 1 \end{bmatrix}\begin{bmatrix} x \\ y \end{bmatrix} = \begin{bmatrix} 2 \\ 0 \end{bmatrix}.$$

Performing the matrix multiplication in the last matrix equation, we have $\begin{bmatrix} x \\ y \end{bmatrix} = \begin{bmatrix} 2 \\ 0 \end{bmatrix}$, which gives us the final two linear equations.

Such operations on the rows of a matrix lead us to ask the question: exactly what is the form that a matrix will finally assume if we perform such operations on its rows? This question brings us to a more precise definition of these row operations.

Elementary Row Operations

Let $A = [a_{ij}]$ be an $m \times n$ matrix. Denote the ith row of A by A_i. The elementary row operations on the matrix A are:

1. The interchange of any two rows; i.e., the row A_k of A may be replaced by the row A_j of A and the row A_j by A_k.
2. The multiplication of a row by an element $c \neq 0$ of the field; i.e., the row A_k may be replaced by the row cA_k, if $c \neq 0$.
3. The addition of one row to another; i.e., the row A_k may be replaced by the row $A_j + A_k$.

DEFINITION. An $m \times n$ matrix B is said to be *row equivalent* to an $m \times n$ matrix A if B can be obtained from A by a finite number of elementary row operations. We write $B \cong A$.

It is easily seen that row equivalence is a true equivalence relation. It is obvious that A is row equivalent to A, for we may regard having obtained A from A by using row operation (2) with $c = 1$, the unity element of the field. Moreover, if B is row equivalent to A, A is row equivalent to B. For, if B had been obtained from A by elementary row operation (1), the same elementary row operation performed on B would give A; if B had been obtained from A by row operation (2), A could be obtained from B by using a similar row operation with c replaced by $1/c$; finally, if B had been obtained from A by row operation (3), A could be obtained from B by adding -1 times the jth row to the kth row. Thus each elementary row operation has an inverse that is either an elementary row operation or a combination of elementary row operations. Finally, the transitive property is obvious, for if B can be obtained from A and if C can be obtained from B, then C can be obtained from A by elementary row operations.

Echelon Form of a Matrix

A matrix is said to be in echelon form* if : (a) all the nonzero rows (if any) precede the zero rows; (b) if in each successive nonzero row the number of zeros preceding the first nonzero entry is greater than the number of such zeros in the preceding row; and (c) the first nonzero element (if any) in a row is 1.

EXAMPLES.   The matrices

$$\begin{bmatrix} 0 & 1 & 2 & 3 \\ 0 & 0 & 1 & -1 \\ 0 & 0 & 0 & 0 \end{bmatrix} \quad \text{and} \quad \begin{bmatrix} 1 & 3 & 0 & 0 \\ 0 & 0 & 1 & 0 \\ 0 & 0 & 0 & 1 \end{bmatrix}$$

are in echelon form. The matrices

$$\begin{bmatrix} 0 & 0 & 2 & 1 \\ 0 & 3 & 1 & 4 \\ 0 & 0 & 0 & 0 \end{bmatrix} \quad \text{and} \quad \begin{bmatrix} 0 & 1 & 2 \\ 0 & 0 & -1 \\ 0 & 0 & 3 \end{bmatrix}$$

are not in echelon form.

A matrix is said to be in *reduced* echelon form if it is in echelon form and, when the first nonzero element in the ith row lies in the jth column, all other elements in the jth column are zero. Thus the first matrix in echelon form above is not in reduced echelon form whereas the second one is.

Theorem 4.   An m × n *matrix is row equivalent to an* m × n *matrix in reduced echelon form.*

Either every element in the first column of the given matrix A is zero, or there exists an element x that is not zero in the kth row, say, of this column. In the latter case, interchange the first and kth rows of A. Then x appears in the first row and first column of the resulting matrix, and it can be replaced by 1 by multiplying the first row of the matrix by x^{-1}. The remaining elements of the first column can then be made zero by adding proper multiples of the first row to the other rows. Thus A is row equivalent

---

* Various definitions of echelon form are found in different texts. In particular, some authors do not require condition (c).

to a matrix in either of the forms $[0 \quad C]$ or $\begin{bmatrix} 1 & D \\ 0 & E \end{bmatrix}$, where in the first case 0 represents the $m \times 1$ zero matrix and C an $m \times (n-1)$ matrix, whereas in the second case 0 represents the $(m-1) \times 1$ zero matrix, D a $1 \times (n-1)$ matrix, and E an $(m-1) \times (n-1)$ matrix. In the first case repeat the above process with the matrix C, whereas in the second case repeat the process with the matrix E. If in the latter case E has been replaced by a matrix with 1 in the first row and column, a proper multiple of this row in the whole matrix can be added to the first row to make the first element of D zero without changing the first column of the whole matrix. Thus in all cases a continuation of the process leads to the desired form.

Elementary Matrices

An $m \times m$ matrix obtained from the $m \times m$ identity matrix I by means of one elementary row operation on I is called an elementary matrix. Thus there are three types of elementary matrices corresponding to the three elementary row operations. These types will now be described. Denote the ith row of a matrix A by A_i. Let P, Q, and R be the matrices obtained from I by performing elementary row operations (1), (2), and (3) respectively on I. Then these elementary matrices may be described as follows:

$$P \text{ with } P_i = I_i, \quad i \neq j, k, \quad P_j = I_k, \quad P_k = I_j;$$
$$Q \text{ with } Q_i = I_i, \quad i \neq k, \quad Q_k = cI_k, \quad c \neq 0;$$
$$R \text{ with } R_i = I_i, \quad i \neq k, \quad R_k = I_j + I_k.$$

EXAMPLES

$$P = \begin{bmatrix} 1 & 0 & 0 \\ 0 & 0 & 1 \\ 0 & 1 & 0 \end{bmatrix}; \quad Q = \begin{bmatrix} 1 & 0 & 0 \\ 0 & c & 0 \\ 0 & 0 & 1 \end{bmatrix}; \quad R = \begin{bmatrix} 1 & 0 & 0 \\ 0 & 1 & 1 \\ 0 & 0 & 1 \end{bmatrix}.$$
$$j = 2, k = 3. \qquad\qquad k = 2. \qquad\qquad j = 3, k = 2.$$

Theorem 5.   Each elementary row operation on an m $\times$ n *matrix* A *can be effected by premultiplication of* A *by an elementary matrix.*

To interchange the jth and kth rows of A, we form the product PA. Let $[PA]_i$ denote the ith row of PA. Recall that the ith row of PA is obtained by taking the inner product of the ith row of P with the transpose of each column of A in turn. Thus $[PA]_i = P_iA = I_iA = A_i$ when $i \neq j, k$; $[PA]_j = P_jA = I_kA = A_k$; and $[PA]_k = P_kA = I_jA = A_j$. The student can easily check that the matrix QA is the matrix obtained from A by means of row operation (2). Similarly RA is the matrix obtained from A by performing row operation (3) on A, for we have $[RA]_i = R_iA = I_iA = A_i$ when $i \neq k$, and $[RA]_k = R_kA = (I_j + I_k)A = I_jA + I_kA = A_j + A_k$.

Corollary. *If an* m × n *matrix* B *is row equivalent to an* m × n *matrix* A, *then* B = SA, *where* S *is a product of elementary matrices.*

Exercises

1. Find matrices in reduced echelon form row equivalent to:

a.
$$\begin{bmatrix} 1 & 2 & -1 & 4 \\ 3 & 2 & 0 & 2 \\ 0 & 1 & 3 & 2 \\ 3 & 3 & 3 & 4 \end{bmatrix};$$
b.
$$\begin{bmatrix} 1 & 2 \\ 3 & 4 \\ -1 & 2 \\ 1 & 1 \end{bmatrix};$$
c.
$$\begin{bmatrix} 0 & -1 & 3 \\ 2 & -4 & 1 \\ 0 & 3 & 2 \end{bmatrix}.$$

2. Let I be the $m \times m$ identity matrix and let A be an $m \times n$ matrix. Prove that (a) $I_i A = A_i$ and (b) $(I_j + I_k)A = A_j + A_k$.

3. We are given the matrix $A = \begin{bmatrix} 2 & -1 & 4 \\ 3 & 3 & 6 \end{bmatrix}$. In each of the following cases exhibit the matrix E such that EA is (a) the matrix obtained from A by interchanging the two rows; (b) the matrix obtained from A by dividing the second row by 2; (c) the matrix obtained from A by adding the first row to the second.

4. If $A = \begin{bmatrix} 1 & 2 \\ 0 & 1 \\ 2 & 1 \end{bmatrix}$, exhibit the elementary matrix E such that $EA = \begin{bmatrix} 2 & 1 \\ 0 & 1 \\ 1 & 2 \end{bmatrix}$

and the elementary matrix F such that $FA = \begin{bmatrix} 1 & 2 \\ 0 & 1 \\ 2 & 2 \end{bmatrix}$.

5. If $A = \begin{bmatrix} 1 & 3 & -1 \\ 2 & 2 & 0 \end{bmatrix}$, exhibit the product of the elementary matrices that reduce it to a row equivalent matrix in reduced echelon form.

6. Show that $\begin{bmatrix} 1 & 2 & 1 \\ 3 & 1 & 2 \\ 0 & 1 & 2 \end{bmatrix}$ is row equivalent to the 3×3 identity matrix.

9 · NONSINGULAR MATRICES

DEFINITION. A square matrix A is said to be *nonsingular* if a matrix B exists such that $BA = AB = I$. If B exists, it will be denoted by A^{-1} and it is called the *inverse* of A. If A^{-1} does not exist, the matrix A is said to be *singular*.

Theorem 6. The inverse of a nonsingular matrix is unique.

Let $BA = AB = I$, and let $CA = AC = I$. Then $BA = CA$, $(BA)B = (CA)B$, $B(AB) = C(AB)$, $BI = CI$, and $B = C$.

Theorem 7. *If* A *and* B *are nonsingular matrices, then the product* AB *is a nonsingular matrix. Moreover,* $(AB)^{-1} = B^{-1}A^{-1}$.

Now B^{-1} and A^{-1} exist. Hence $(B^{-1}A^{-1})(AB) = B^{-1}[A^{-1}(AB)] = B^{-1}[(A^{-1}A)B] = B^{-1}(IB) = B^{-1}B = I$. Similarly $(AB)(B^{-1}A^{-1}) = I$. Thus AB is nonsingular, and $B^{-1}A^{-1}$ is its inverse.

Theorem 8. *The elementary matrices* P, Q, *and* R *are nonsingular.*

Since $PP = I$, P is its own inverse. The matrices Q^{-1} and R^{-1} are described by exhibiting their rows: $Q_i^{-1} = I_i$ when $i \neq k$, and $Q_k^{-1} = c^{-1}I_k$; $R_i^{-1} = I_i$ when $i \neq k$, and $R_k^{-1} = I_k - I_j$.

Since the product of nonsingular matrices is nonsingular, a product of elementary matrices is nonsingular. Hence the corollary to Theorem 5 becomes

Theorem 9. *If a matrix* B *is row equivalent to a matrix* A, *then* B $=$ SA, *where* S *is nonsingular.*

Theorem 10. *An* n × n *matrix* A *is row equivalent to the identity matrix if and only if it is nonsingular.*

First, let A be nonsingular. Find a matrix B in reduced echelon form row equivalent to A. Then $B = SA$, where S is a nonsingular matrix. Hence B is nonsingular, for the product of nonsingular matrices is nonsingular, and B^{-1} exists. We shall show that B cannot have a zero in its principal diagonal; i.e., if the element in the ith row and jth column of B is denoted by b_{ij}, then $b_{kk} \neq 0$ for all k. Recall that at least $j - 1$ zeros precede the first nonzero element in the jth row of B. Hence if $b_{kk} = 0$, the $(k + 1)$st row of B has at least $k + 1$ zeros preceding its first nonzero element. If $k = n$, the nth row of B consists of zeros, and, if $k < n$, at least one row of B after the kth consists of zeros. Consequently, if $b_{kk} = 0$, B has a row of zeros. Then $BB^{-1} = I$ has a row of zeros, contrary to the definition of I. Thus $b_{ii} = 1$ and $b_{ij} = 0$ when $i \neq j$. Thus B is the identity matrix, and hence A is row equivalent to the identity matrix.

Second, let A be row equivalent to the identity matrix I. Then $I = SA$, where S is nonsingular, and hence $A = S^{-1}I$ is nonsingular.

Theorem 11. *If a square matrix is reduced to the identity matrix by a sequence of row operations, the same sequence of row operations performed on the identity produces the inverse of the given matrix.*

Let A be the given matrix and let E_i denote elementary matrices. (Note that we are not using the notation for a row of a matrix here.) Now we are given $(E_s \cdots E_2E_1)A = I$. Hence $(E_s \cdots E_2E_1)(AA^{-1}) = IA^{-1}$, giving $(E_s \cdots E_2E_1)I = A^{-1}$, the desired result.

EXAMPLE.   Find the inverse of the matrix $A = \begin{bmatrix} 1 & -2 \\ 1 & 1 \end{bmatrix}$.

Now, performing a single row operation at a time, we exhibit the successive matrices row equivalent to A in the left-hand column and the successive matrices row equivalent to I in the right-hand column:

$$\begin{bmatrix} 0 & -3 \\ 1 & 1 \end{bmatrix} \begin{bmatrix} 1 & -1 \\ 0 & 1 \end{bmatrix}$$

$$\begin{bmatrix} 0 & 1 \\ 1 & 1 \end{bmatrix} \begin{bmatrix} -\frac{1}{3} & \frac{1}{3} \\ 0 & 1 \end{bmatrix}$$

$$\begin{bmatrix} 0 & 1 \\ 1 & 0 \end{bmatrix} \begin{bmatrix} -\frac{1}{3} & \frac{1}{3} \\ \frac{1}{3} & \frac{2}{3} \end{bmatrix}$$

$$\begin{bmatrix} 1 & 0 \\ 0 & 1 \end{bmatrix} \begin{bmatrix} \frac{1}{3} & \frac{2}{3} \\ -\frac{1}{3} & \frac{1}{3} \end{bmatrix} = A^{-1}.$$

Combining the results of the preceding three theorems, we now have the following two corollaries.

Corollary 1.   A matrix is nonsingular if and only if it can be written as a product of elementary matrices.

Corollary 2.   A matrix B *is row equivalent to a matrix* A *if and only if* B = SA, *where* S *is a nonsingular matrix.*

Exercises

1. Prove: If A is a nonsingular matrix, then its transpose, A^t, is a nonsingular matrix.
2. Find the inverses of the following matrices over the field of rational numbers and over the field of residue classes modulo 5:

a. $\begin{bmatrix} 1 & -3 & 2 \\ 2 & 0 & 0 \\ 1 & 4 & 1 \end{bmatrix}$; b. $\begin{bmatrix} 2 & 4 & 3 \\ 0 & 1 & 1 \\ 2 & 2 & -1 \end{bmatrix}$; c. $\begin{bmatrix} 1 & 2 & -2 \\ -1 & 3 & 0 \\ 0 & -2 & 1 \end{bmatrix}$.

3. Find the inverse of the matrix over the field of complex numbers:

$$\begin{bmatrix} i & -1 & 2i \\ 2 & 0 & 2 \\ -1 & 0 & 1 \end{bmatrix}.$$

4. Has the following matrix an inverse over the field of rational numbers?

$$\begin{bmatrix} 2 & 1 & 3 & 1 \\ 1 & 2 & -1 & 4 \\ 3 & 3 & 2 & 5 \\ 1 & -1 & 4 & -3 \end{bmatrix}.$$

5. Prove Corollary 1 and Corollary 2.

6. Prove that the matrix $\begin{bmatrix} a & b \\ c & d \end{bmatrix}$ is nonsingular if and only if $ad - bc \neq 0$.

7. If A is an $n \times n$ matrix such that $A^2 - A + I$ is the zero matrix, prove that A is nonsingular and that $A^{-1} = I - A$.

8. Prove that the set of all $n \times n$ nonsingular matrices forms a group with respect to matrix multiplication.

10 · COLUMN EQUIVALENCE

If in the definition of an elementary row operation on a matrix, the word row is replaced by the word column, we have the definition of an elementary column operation on a matrix. Similarly, the definition of column equivalence of two matrices can be read from the definition of row equivalence of two matrices by replacing the word row by the word column. An elementary column operation on a matrix A becomes an elementary row operation on the transpose, A^t, of A. Let B be obtained from A by an elementary column operation. Then B^t can be obtained from A^t by an elementary row operation. Thus $B^t = EA^t$, where E is an elementary matrix, and consequently $B = AE^t$. Hence we have the following theorem.

Theorem 12. An elementary column operation on an m $\times$ n *matrix* A *can be effected by multiplying* A *on the right by an* n $\times$ n *matrix obtained from the* n $\times$ n *identity matrix by the same elementary column operation.*

Similarly, if B is column equivalent to a matrix A, B^t is row equivalent to A^t, $B^t = SA^t$, and $B = AS^t$, where S^t is nonsingular. Conversely, if $B = AT$, where T is nonsingular, $B^t = T^tA^t$, so that B^t is row equivalent to A^t, and consequently B is column equivalent to A. Hence we have the following theorem.

Theorem 13. An m $\times$ n *matrix* B *is column equivalent to an* m $\times$ n *matrix* A *if and only if* B = AT, *where* T *is an* n $\times$ n *nonsingular matrix.*

11 · EQUIVALENCE OF MATRICES

Now both row and column operations may be applied to a matrix. If an $m \times n$ matrix B can be obtained from an $m \times n$ matrix A by a finite number of elementary row and column operations, the matrix B is said to be *equivalent* to the matrix A. Thus row and column equivalence are special cases of the general concept of equivalence of matrices. Combining our previous results, we have the following theorem, which is often used as a definition of the equivalence of two matrices.

Theorem 14.   An m × n *matrix* B *is equivalent to an* m × n *matrix* A *if and only if* B = SAT, *where* S *and* T *are* m × m *and* n × n *nonsingular matrices respectively.*

Theorem 15.   Canonical form.   Every nonzero m × n *matrix* A *is equivalent to an* m × n *matrix of the form* $\begin{bmatrix} I & 0 \\ 0 & 0 \end{bmatrix}$, *where* I *is the* r × r *identity matrix, and where the remaining submatrices are zero matrices.*

Let some element a of A be different from zero. By performing elementary row and column operations on A, we obtain an equivalent matrix with the element a in the first row and the first column. Multiply the first row of this matrix by a^{-1}. Then by subtracting suitable multiples of the first row from the remaining rows and suitable multiples of the first column from the remaining columns, we obtain an equivalent matrix of the form $B = \begin{bmatrix} 1 & 0 \\ 0 & C \end{bmatrix}$, where C is an $(m-1) \times (n-1)$ submatrix and where the other submatrices are the 1×1 identity matrix and the $1 \times (n-1)$ and the $(m-1) \times 1$ zero matrices. The canonical form can now be established by an induction on m. If $m = 1$, then B is in canonical form. Assume the theorem true for all $(m-1) \times (n-1)$ matrices. Hence the submatrix C of B is equivalent to a matrix D in canonical form. Consequently B is equivalent to a matrix in canonical form, for the row and column operations performed on C to obtain D may be performed on the last $m-1$ rows and the last $n-1$ columns of B.

In Theorem 5 of the next chapter we prove that the canonical form of a matrix is unique.

Exercises

1. Given the matrix $A = \begin{bmatrix} 1 & 2 & 3 \\ 0 & 1 & 2 \end{bmatrix}$, find nonsingular matrices T and U such that $AT = \begin{bmatrix} 2 & 1 & 3 \\ 1 & 0 & 2 \end{bmatrix}$ and $AU = \begin{bmatrix} 1 & 2 & 5 \\ 0 & 1 & 3 \end{bmatrix}$.

2. Find the canonical forms of the matrices in Exercise 1, p. 106 and in Exercise 4, p. 108.

3. Using Theorem 14 as the definition of equivalence of two matrices, prove that the equivalence of matrices is a true equivalence relation; i.e., show that it is symmetric, reflexive, and transitive.

12 · TESTS FOR LINEAR DEPENDENCE OF VECTORS

We return to the problem of determining whether or not a given set of vectors $\xi_1, \xi_2, \cdots, \xi_m$ of $V_n(F)$ is a set of linearly dependent vectors. We will call a linear combination $c_1\xi_1 + c_2\xi_2 + \cdots + c_m\xi_m$ a *nontrivial* linear combination if at least one of the $c_1, c_2, \cdots, c_m$ is nonzero. If $c_1 = c_2 = \cdots = c_m = 0$, we will call the linear combination a *trivial* combination.

Theorem 16. Let $\xi_1, \xi_2, \cdots, \xi_m$ be vectors of $V_n(F)$ and let a and b be scalars with $b \neq 0$. Then each nontrivial linear combination of $\xi_1, \xi_2, \cdots, \xi_m$ is a nontrivial combination of $\xi_1, \xi_2, \cdots, \xi_{j-1}, a\xi_i + b\xi_j, \xi_{j+1}, \cdots, \xi_m$ and, conversely, each nontrivial linear combination of $\xi_1, \xi_2, \cdots, \xi_{j-1}, a\xi_i + b\xi_j, \xi_{j+1}, \cdots, \xi_m$ is a nontrivial combination of $\xi_1, \xi_2, \cdots, \xi_m$.

We have

$$c_1\xi_1 + c_2\xi_2 + \cdots + c_m\xi_m = c_1\xi_1 + c_2\xi_2 + \cdots + c_{i-1}\xi_{i-1}$$

$$+ \left(c_i - \frac{c_j a}{b} \right) \xi_i + c_{i+1}\xi_{i+1} + \cdots + c_{j-1}\xi_j$$

$$+ \frac{c_j}{b}(a\xi_i + b\xi_j) + c_{j+1}\xi_{j+1} + \cdots + c_m\xi_m.$$

If

$$c_1 = c_2 = \cdots = c_{i-1} = c_i - \frac{c_j a}{b} = c_{i+1} = \cdots = c_{j-1} = \frac{c_j}{b}$$

$$= c_{j+1} = \cdots = c_m = 0,$$

then $c_j = 0$ so that $c_i = 0$. Hence $c_1 = c_2 = \cdots = c_m = 0$.

Conversely, we have

$$c_1\xi_1 + c_2\xi_2 + \cdots + c_{j-1}\xi_j + c_j(a\xi_i + b\xi_j) + c_{j+1}\xi_{j+1}$$

$$+ \cdots + c_m\xi_m = c_1\xi_1 + c_2\xi_2 + \cdots + c_{i-1}\xi_{i-1}$$

$$+ (c_i + ac_j)\xi_i + c_{i+1}\xi_{i+1} + \cdots + (bc_j)\xi_j$$

$$+ c_{j+1}\xi_{j+1} + \cdots + c_m\xi_m.$$

If

$$c_1 = c_2 = \cdots = c_{i-1} = c_i + ac_j = c_{i+1} = \cdots = bc_j$$

$$= c_{j+1} = \cdots = c_m = 0,$$

then $bc_j = 0$, $c_j = 0$ and $c_i = 0$. Hence $c_1 = c_2 = \cdots = c_m = 0$.

Theorem 17. If a set of nonzero vectors $\xi_1, \xi_2, \cdots, \xi_m$ over $V_n(F)$ is linearly dependent over F, then there exists a maximum subset of $r < m$ vectors which is linearly independent over F. The remaining $m - r$ vectors are linear combinations of the r linearly independent ones.

We choose some vector $\xi_j \neq 0$. Then ξ_j is linearly independent over F since $c\xi_j = 0$ implies $c = 0$. Now if $\xi_1, \xi_2, \cdots, \xi_{j-1}, \xi_{j+1}, \cdots, \xi_m$ are all scalar multiples of ξ_j, we are done. If not, there is a vector ξ_k $(k \neq j)$ which is not a scalar multiple of ξ_j. Now we have two linearly independent vectors ξ_j and ξ_k. If the remaining $m - 2$ vectors are all linear combinations of ξ_j and ξ_k, we are finished. If not, we have a vector ξ_i $(i \neq j, i \neq k)$ which is not a linear combination of ξ_j and ξ_k. We continue in this fashion until we have a set of $r (< m)$ linearly independent vectors such that the remaining $m - r$ vectors are linear combinations of these r vectors.

At each stage of this process we must choose a vector ξ_j, ξ_k, ξ_i, etc., and we must now ask whether or not different choices of vectors at various stages would result in a greater maximum number of linearly independent vectors. Suppose, then, that we have first chosen a set of linearly independent vectors $\eta_1, \eta_2, \cdots, \eta_r$, where each η_i $(i = 1, 2, \cdots, r)$ is one of the ξ_j $(j = 1, 2, \cdots, m)$, and each of the remaining $m - r$ vectors among the $\xi_1, \xi_2, \cdots, \xi_m$ is a linear combination of $\eta_1, \eta_2, \cdots, \eta_r$. Next suppose that we have also selected a set of linearly independent vectors $\zeta_1, \zeta_2, \cdots, \zeta_s$, where each ζ_i $(i = 1, 2, \cdots, s)$ is one of the ξ_j $(j = 1, 2, \cdots, m)$ and each of the remaining $m - s$ vectors among the $\xi_1, \xi_2, \cdots, \xi_m$ is a linear combination of $\zeta_1, \zeta_2, \cdots, \zeta_s$.

Suppose $s \geq r$. We now assert that at least one of the vectors η_i $(i = 1, 2, \cdots, r)$ is a linear combination, $b_1\zeta_1 + b_2\zeta_2 + \cdots + b_s\zeta_s$, of the ζ_i with $b_1 \neq 0$. For, every vector ξ_j is a linear combination of the η_i and, if each η_i could be expressed as a linear combination of $\zeta_2, \zeta_3, \cdots, \zeta_s$, every vector ξ_j could be expressed as a linear combination of $\zeta_2, \zeta_3, \cdots, \zeta_s$. In particular, ζ_1 (being one of the ξ_j) could be so expressed, contrary to the linear independence of $\zeta_1, \zeta_2, \cdots, \zeta_s$.

By renumbering our vectors, if necessary, we may now suppose that $\eta_1 = b_1\zeta_1 + b_2\zeta_2 + \cdots + b_s\zeta_s$ with $b_1 \neq 0$. We now claim that $\eta_1, \zeta_2, \zeta_3, \cdots, \zeta_s$ form a linearly independent set of vectors such that the remaining $m - s$ vectors of the set $\xi_1, \xi_2, \cdots, \xi_m$ are linear combinations of $\eta_1, \zeta_2, \zeta_3, \cdots, \zeta_s$. For if $\xi_j = a_1\zeta_1 + a_2\zeta_2 + \cdots + a_s\zeta_s$, we have $\zeta_1 = (1/b_1)(\eta_1 - b_2\zeta_2 - \cdots - b_s\zeta_s)$ and, hence, $\xi_j = (a_1/b_1)\eta_1 + (a_2 - b_2/b_1)\zeta_2 + \cdots + (a_s - b_s/b_1)\zeta_s$. Furthermore, if $c_1\eta_1 + c_2\zeta_2 + c_3\zeta_3 + \cdots + c_s\zeta_s = \mathbf{0}$, we have $c_1b_1\zeta_1 + (c_1b_2 + c_2)\zeta_2 + (c_1b_3 + c_3)\zeta_3 + \cdots + (c_1b_s + c_s)\zeta_s = \mathbf{0}$. Since $\zeta_1, \zeta_2, \cdots, \zeta_s$ are linearly independent, $c_1b_1 = 0$. But $b_1 \neq 0$, so $c_1 = 0$ and, hence, $c_2 = c_3 = \cdots c_s = 0$ and $\eta_1, \zeta_2, \zeta_3, \cdots, \zeta_s$ are linearly independent.

Now at least one of the vectors $\eta_2, \eta_3, \cdots, \eta_r$ is a linear combination, $b_1\eta_1 + b_2\zeta_2 + b_3\zeta_3 + \cdots + b_s\zeta_s$, with $b_2 \neq 0$. For we have just shown that every one of the vectors $\xi_1, \xi_2, \cdots, \xi_m$ is such a linear combination.

Hence, if every one of the η_i $(i = 2, 3, \cdots, r)$ can be expressed as a linear combination of $\eta_1, \zeta_3, \zeta_4, \cdots, \zeta_s$, every vector ξ_j can be expressed as a linear combination of $\eta_1, \zeta_3, \zeta_4, \cdots, \zeta_s$. In particular, then, ζ_2 can be so expressed contrary to the linear independence of $\eta_1, \zeta_2, \zeta_3, \cdots, \zeta_s$.

We renumber our vectors if necessary so that $\eta_2 = b_1\eta_1 + b_2\zeta_2 + b_3\zeta_3 + \cdots + b_s\zeta_s$ with $b_2 \neq 0$, and we may prove as before that now $\eta_1, \eta_2, \zeta_3, \zeta_4, \cdots, \zeta_s$ form a set of linearly independent vectors such that the remaining $m - s$ vectors of the set $\xi_1, \xi_2, \cdots, \xi_m$ are linear combinations of $\eta_1, \eta_2, \zeta_3, \zeta_4, \cdots, \zeta_s$.

Continuing, we obtain the linearly independent set $\eta_1, \eta_2, \cdots, \eta_r, \zeta_{r+1}, \cdots, \zeta_s$, so that, by the maximum property of $\eta_1, \eta_2, \cdots, \eta_r$, we have $s = r$.

From Theorems 16 and 17 and the definition of equivalent matrices it is clear that, if B is a matrix equivalent to A, the row vectors of A are linearly dependent if and only if the row vectors of B are linearly dependent. Furthermore, it is obvious that the nonzero row vectors of a matrix in echelon form are linearly independent. For example, if we have the matrix

$$\begin{bmatrix} 1 & 2 & -1 & 2 \\ 0 & 0 & 1 & 1 \\ 0 & 0 & 0 & 1 \\ 0 & 0 & 0 & 0 \end{bmatrix}$$

in echelon form and have $c_1(1, 2, -1, 2) + c_2(0, 0, 1, 1) + c_3(0, 0, 0, 1) = (0, 0, 0, 0)$, we must have $c_1 = c_2 = c_3 = 0$. Note that, in applying this test, the same results are obtained if the leading nonzero entries of each row are simply any nonzero numbers and not necessarily all 1's. Thus we see that the vectors $(2, 0, -1)$ and $(0, 3, 1)$ are linearly independent by an examination of the matrix

$$\begin{bmatrix} 2 & 0 & -1 \\ 0 & 3 & 1 \end{bmatrix}.$$

Hence, to determine whether or not a given set of m vectors is linearly dependent, we arrange the vectors as the rows of a matrix and put this matrix in echelon form (with the leading nonzero entry, however, not necessarily 1). Then the given set of vectors is linearly dependent if and only if at least one of the rows in this echelon form is a zero row. Furthermore, if there are r nonzero rows, then r is the maximum number of the m vectors that are linearly independent over F.

Exercises

1. Test the following sets of vectors for linear dependence over the field of rational numbers. If the vectors are linearly dependent, find the maximum number of the vectors of the set that are linearly independent.

   a. $(1, 3, -2), (2, 2, 6), (3, -2, 5)$.
   b. $(1, 0, 1), (0, 2, 2), (3, 7, 1)$.
   c. $(-2, 4 \; 6), (5, 7, -3), (1, 15, 9)$.
   d. $(1, -1, 1, 3), (2, -5, 3, 10), (3, 3, 1, 2)$.
   e. $(1, 6, -2, 5), (4, 0, 4, -2), (7, 2, 0, 2), (-6, 3, -3, 3)$.
   f. $(2, 4, 3, -1, -2, 1), (2, 2, 4, 2, 6, 2), (0, -1, 0, 3, 6, 1)$.

2. Are the vectors $(1, 1, 0), (1, 0, 1), (0, 1, 1)$ linearly independent over the field of integers modulo 2? Over the field of integers modulo 3?

3. A set of vectors $\xi_1, \xi_2, \cdots, \xi_m$ is called a *mutually orthogonal* set if $\xi_i \cdot \xi_j = 0$ for $i, j = 1, \cdots, m$ and $i \neq j$. Prove that any set of mutually orthogonal nonzero vectors is linearly independent.

4. Prove that a set of vectors ξ_1 and ξ_2 is a linearly dependent set if and only if one of these vectors is a scalar times the other.

7 Systems of Linear Equations

1 · RANK OF A MATRIX

Row Rank of a Matrix

The maximum number r of linearly independent rows over a field F of an $m \times n$ matrix over F is called the row rank of the matrix.

Theorem 1. Row equivalent matrices have the same row rank.

Let A and B be row equivalent $m \times n$ matrices. We consider the row vectors $\xi_1, \xi_2, \cdots, \xi_m$ of A and $\eta_1, \eta_2, \cdots, \eta_m$ of B. Now A and B have the same row rank if and only if the maximum number of the vectors ξ_1, $\xi_2, \cdots, \xi_m$ that are linearly independent is equal to the maximum number of the vectors $\eta_1, \eta_2, \cdots, \eta_m$ that are linearly independent. Now since A and B are row equivalent matrices, $\eta_1, \eta_2, \cdots, \eta_m$ may be obtained from $\xi_1, \xi_2, \cdots, \xi_m$ by a sequence of the following operations: (a) the interchange of ξ_i and ξ_k; (b) the multiplication of some ξ_j by an element $b \neq 0$ of the field; and (c) the replacement of ξ_i by $\xi_i + \xi_j$.

Obviously, the set obtained from $\xi_1, \xi_2, \cdots, \xi_m$ by application of (a) has the same maximum number of linearly independent vectors. By Theorem 16 of Chap. 6 we see that the maximum number of linearly independent vectors does not change by application of (b) (take $a = 0$ in Theorem 16) or by application of (c) (take $a = b = 1$ in Theorem 16).

Corollary 1. If a matrix A has the row rank r, then SA, where S is a nonsingular matrix, has row rank r.

This is obvious when we recall that SA is a matrix row equivalent to A.

Corollary 2.   The row rank of an n × n *nonsingular matrix is* n.

We need merely recall that a nonsingular matrix is row equivalent to the identity matrix, and the rows of the identity matrix are obviously linearly independent.

Column Rank of a Matrix

The column rank of a matrix is the maximum number of linearly independent columns of the matrix. Obviously the preceding theorems on the row rank of a matrix can be translated into corresponding theorems on the column rank of a matrix. Thus we have the following two theorems.

Theorem 2.   Column equivalent matrices have the same column rank.

Theorem 3.   If T *is a nonsingular matrix, the matrix* A *and the matrix* AT *have the same column rank.*

Theorem 4.   The row rank of a matrix equals its column rank.

Let A be any nonzero matrix. There exist nonsingular matrices S and T such that $SAT = C$ is a matrix in canonical form. The row rank and the column rank of C are equal to r, the dimension of the identity submatrix of C. The row rank of A and SA is the same, say r_1. Thus the row rank of $CT^{-1} = SA$ is r_1. But CT^{-1} has at most r nonzero rows since if $T^{-1} = \begin{bmatrix} T_1 \\ T_2 \end{bmatrix}$, $CT^{-1} = \begin{bmatrix} I & 0 \\ 0 & 0 \end{bmatrix}\begin{bmatrix} T_1 \\ T_2 \end{bmatrix} = \begin{bmatrix} IT_1 \\ 0 \end{bmatrix} = \begin{bmatrix} T_1 \\ 0 \end{bmatrix}$, where T_1 is an r-rowed matrix. Since T^{-1} is nonsingular, its rows are linearly independent, and thus the rows of T_1 are linearly independent. Hence CT^{-1} is of row rank r, and $r_1 = r$. Now consider the transpose $T^t A^t S^t = C^t$. The row ranks of $T^t A^t$ and A^t are the same. Thus, as above, the row rank of $T^t A^t = C^t(S^t)^{-1}$ is r, and hence the column rank of AT and hence of A is r.

Thus the term the rank of a matrix can mean either the row or the column rank.

Theorem 5.   The canonical form of a matrix is unique.

In the preceding theorem we proved that the rank of A equals the rank of C. If, now, there exist nonsingular matrices S_1 and T_1 such that $S_1 A T_1 = C_1$, a canonical form different from C, the rank of A equals the rank of C_1. Hence the ranks of C and C_1 are equal, and hence the matrices C and C_1 are identical.

We may rephrase our previous work on linear dependence and independence of sets of vectors in the following two theorems.

Theorem 6. Two m × n *matrices are equivalent if and only if they have the same rank.*

Theorem 7. The rank of a matrix in echelon form is equal to the number of its nonzero rows.

Exercises

1. Are the following pairs of matrices equivalent? Why?

a. $\begin{bmatrix} 2 & -1 & 3 & 4 \\ 0 & 3 & 4 & 1 \\ 2 & 3 & 7 & 5 \\ 2 & 5 & 11 & 6 \end{bmatrix}$, $\begin{bmatrix} 1 & 0 & -5 & 6 \\ 3 & -2 & 1 & 2 \\ 5 & -2 & -9 & 14 \\ 4 & -2 & -4 & 8 \end{bmatrix}$.

b. $\begin{bmatrix} 4 & -1 & 2 \\ 3 & 4 & 0 \\ 1 & 0 & 0 \end{bmatrix}$, $\begin{bmatrix} 2 & 1 & 4 & 7 \\ 3 & 6 & 2 & 1 \\ 0 & 0 & 1 & 5 \end{bmatrix}$.

2. Determine the rank of each of the following matrices for rational values of the parameter k:

a. $\begin{bmatrix} 2 & 1 & -1 & 2 \\ 1 & 1 & 0 & 1 \\ k & 3 & -2 & 0 \\ 0 & 1 & -4 & 4 \end{bmatrix}$. b. $\begin{bmatrix} k & 1 & 1 \\ 1 & k & 1 \\ 1 & 1 & k \end{bmatrix}$.

c. $\begin{bmatrix} 1 & 1 & -1 & 2 \\ k & 1 & 1 & 1 \\ 1 & -1 & 3 & -3 \\ 4 & 2 & 0 & k \end{bmatrix}$.

3. Are the m rows of an $m \times n$ matrix over a field F linearly dependent or linearly independent over F when $m > n$? Why?

2 · SIMULTANEOUS LINEAR EQUATIONS OVER A FIELD

We now apply the preceding matrix theory to the solution of m simultaneous linear equations in n unknowns $x_1, x_2, \cdots, x_n$ with coefficients and constant terms in a field F. Write the system of equations

(1)
$$a_{11}x_1 + a_{12}x_2 + \cdots + a_{1n}x_n = c_1,$$
$$a_{21}x_1 + a_{22}x_2 + \cdots + a_{2n}x_n = c_2,$$
$$\cdots\cdots\cdots\cdots\cdots\cdots\cdots\cdots\cdots$$
$$a_{m1}x_1 + a_{m2}x_2 + \cdots + a_{mn}x_n = c_m$$

in matrix form $AX = C$, where A is the $m \times n$ matrix $[a_{ij}]$, $X^t = [x_1, x_2, \cdots, x_n]$, and $C^t = [c_1, c_2, \cdots, c_m]$. The matrix A is called the *matrix of coefficients* of the system of equations. The simplest case to solve is that in which the number of equations equals the number of unknowns and the matrix of coefficients is nonsingular.

Theorem 8. The equation $AX = C$, *with* $m = n$ *and* A *nonsingular, has the unique solution* $X = A^{-1}C$.

Since A is nonsingular, multiplication of $AX = C$ by A^{-1} gives $X = A^{-1}C$. Substituting this result in $AX = C$, we have $A(A^{-1}C) = IC = C$.

We turn now to the case in which the relation between the number of unknowns and the number of equations is not restricted. Here we need to consider the ranks of the matrix of coefficients and of the *augmented* matrix $A^* = [AC]$, which is an $m \times (n + 1)$ matrix obtained by augmenting A with the column of constants c_i, $i = 1, 2, \cdots, m$. We note that the rank of A^* is always greater than or equal to the rank of A, for A^* has at least as many linearly independent columns as A.

In the following lemma we show the relation between the solutions of the equation $AX = C$ and those of the equation $SAX = SC$, where S is a nonsingular matrix. Note that premultiplication by the nonsingular matrix S is equivalent to performing row operations on A and C or to performing these operations on the linear equations (1).

Lemma. If a solution $x_1', x_2', \cdots, x_n'$ *of the equation* $AX = C$ *exists, then it is also a solution of the equation* $SAX = SC$, *where* S *is a nonsingular matrix. Conversely, if* $x_1', x_2', \cdots, x_n'$ *is a solution of the equation* $SAX = SC$, *where* S *is nonsingular, it is a solution of the equation* $AX = C$.

Let X', where $(X')^t = [x_1', x_2', \cdots, x_n']$, be a solution of $AX = C$; i.e., $AX' = C$ is an identity. Then obviously $SAX' = SC$ is an identity. Conversely, if X' is a solution of $SAX = SC$, i.e., if $SAX' = SC$ is an identity, then $S^{-1}(SAX') = S^{-1}(SC)$ gives the identity $AX' = C$. Thus we have shown that all solutions of $AX = C$ are solutions of $SAX = SC$ and that no new solutions to the original equation $AX = C$ are introduced by multiplication by a nonsingular matrix.

DEFINITION.   If the system of equations (1) has a solution, the equations are said to be *consistent*. If the system has no solution, the equations are said to be *inconsistent*.

Theorem 9.   The equation $AX = C$ *has a solution if and only if the rank of* A, *the matrix of coefficients, equals the rank of the augmented matrix* A^*. *If* A *and* A^* *have the same rank, let* r *be their common rank. Then* r *of the unknowns may be expressed as linear functions of the constants* c_i *and the remaining* $n - r$ *unknowns, to which may be assigned arbitrary values.*

Let A be of rank r. Transform A to a row equivalent reduced echelon matrix. Only the first r rows contain nonzero elements. Let the first nonzero elements in these r rows lie in the $k_1, k_2, \cdots, k_r$th columns respectively. These row operations on A may be effected by premultiplication by a nonsingular matrix S. Multiply each side of the equation $AX = C$ by S, obtaining $SAX = SC$. Now the last $m - r$ rows of SA are composed of zeros, and hence the last $m - r$ rows of SAX are composed of zeros. Thus, if the equation $AX = C$ is consistent, the last $m - r$ rows of SC are necessarily composed of zeros. Now let the last $m - r$ rows of SC be composed of zeros, and let $b_1, b_2, \cdots, b_r$ be the nonzero elements of SC. Further, let p_{ij} denote the element in the ith row and the jth column of SA. Then the matrix equation $SAX = SC$ yields the following set of r equations:

$$x_{k_1} + p_{1,k_1+1}x_{k_1+1} + \cdots + p_{1n}x_n = b_1,$$
$$x_{k_2} + p_{2,k_2+1}x_{k_2+1} + \cdots + p_{2n}x_n = b_2,$$
$$\cdots\cdots\cdots\cdots\cdots\cdots\cdots\cdots$$
$$x_{k_r} + p_{r,k_r+1}x_{k_r+1} + \cdots + p_{rn}x_n = b_r.$$

where $p_{1,k_j} = 0$ for $j = 2, 3, \cdots, r$; $p_{2,k_j} = 0$ for $j = 3, 4, \cdots, r; \cdots$, $p_{r-1,k_j} = 0$ for $j = r$. Thus we can express the $x_{k_1}, x_{k_2}, \cdots, x_{k_r}$ as linear functions of the remaining x_j's and the constants b_i. The lemma tells us that this is a solution of the equation $AX = C$.

We have that the last $m - r$ rows of SA are composed of zeros and that the equation $AX = C$ has a solution if and only if the last $m - r$ rows of SC are composed of zeros. Hence, if $AX = C$ has a solution, SA and SA^* have the same rank since SA^* is the matrix SA augmented by the column of b_i. Thus, if $AX = C$ has a solution, A and A^* have the same rank. Conversely, if A and A^* have the same rank, so do SA and SA^* and, hence, SA^* has $m - r$ zero rows, and the equation $AX = C$ has a solution. Thus the equation $AX = C$ has a solution if and only if A and A^* have the same rank.

EXAMPLE.   Solve the following system of equations:

$$x - y + 2z + w = 2,$$
$$3x + 2y + w = 1,$$
$$4x + y + 2z + 2w = 3.$$

Write the system in matrix form

$$\begin{bmatrix} 1 & -1 & 2 & 1 \\ 3 & 2 & 0 & 1 \\ 4 & 1 & 2 & 2 \end{bmatrix} \begin{bmatrix} x \\ y \\ z \\ w \end{bmatrix} = \begin{bmatrix} 2 \\ 1 \\ 3 \end{bmatrix}.$$

We transform A^* to a reduced echelon matrix, thus simultaneously transforming A to a reduced echelon matrix.

$$A^* = \begin{bmatrix} 1 & -1 & 2 & 1 & 2 \\ 3 & 2 & 0 & 1 & 1 \\ 4 & 1 & 2 & 2 & 3 \end{bmatrix} \simeq \begin{bmatrix} 1 & 0 & \frac{4}{5} & \frac{3}{5} & 1 \\ 0 & 1 & -\frac{6}{5} & -\frac{2}{5} & -1 \\ 0 & 0 & 0 & 0 & 0 \end{bmatrix}.$$

Thus the rank of both A and A^* is 2 and, hence, the equations are consistent. The matrix equation becomes

$$\begin{bmatrix} 1 & 0 & \frac{4}{5} & \frac{3}{5} \\ 0 & 1 & -\frac{6}{5} & -\frac{2}{5} \\ 0 & 0 & 0 & 0 \end{bmatrix} \begin{bmatrix} x \\ y \\ z \\ w \end{bmatrix} = \begin{bmatrix} 1 \\ -1 \\ 0 \end{bmatrix},$$

giving

$$x = -\tfrac{4}{5}z - \tfrac{3}{5}w + 1,$$

$$y = \tfrac{6}{5}z + \tfrac{2}{5}w - 1.$$

When these values for x and y are substituted in the equations of the original system, the equations reduce to identities. Arbitrary values may be given to z and w, and thus this system of equations has an infinite number of solutions.

Exercises

Solve the following systems of equations. If a parameter k is involved, consider solutions for rational values of k.

1. $3x - 2y + z + 6 = 0,$
   $2x + 5y - 3z - 2 = 0,$
   $4x - 9y + 5z + 14 = 0.$

2. $4x + 7y - 14z = 10,$
   $2x + 3y - 4z = -4,$
   $x + y + z = 6.$

3. $4x - y + z = 5,$
   $2x - 3y + 5z = 1,$
   $x + y - 2z = 2,$
   $5x - z = 2.$

4. $2x - y - 2z = 0,$
   $x - 2y + z = 0,$
   $2x - 3y - z = 0.$

5. $kx - 3y - 5 = 0,$
   $8x + y - 17 = 0,$
   $kx + 2y - 10 = 0.$

6. $6x + 4y + 3z - 84w = 0,$
   $x + 2y + 3z - 48w = 0,$
   $x - 2y + z - 12w = 0,$
   $4x - 4y - z - 24w = 0.$

7. $x + y - z = 2,$
   $kx + y + z = 1,$
   $x - y + 3z = -3,$
   $4x + 2y = k.$

8. $x + y + 2z = 9,$
   $x + y - z = 0,$
   $2x - y + z = 3,$
   $x + 3y + 2z = 1.$

9. $x + y + 2w = 0$,
   $y + z = 0$,
   $x + z = 0$,
   $x + y + z + w = 0$,
   $x + y + 2z = 0$.

10. $x + ky + 3 = 0$,
    $kx + 3y + 1 = 0$,
    $kx + 4y - 6 = 0$.

11. $2x + y + 3z = 1$,
    $4x + 2y - z = -3$,
    $2kx + y - 4z = -4$,
    $10x + y - 6z = -10$.

12. $2x + y + 3z = 1$,
    $4x + 2y - z = -3$,
    $2kx + y - 4z = -4$.

13. $3x + y - z = 4$,
    $kx + y + z = 2$,
    $x + y - z = 1$,
    $x - z = k$.

14. $2x - y - 3z + 4w = 0$,
    $x + 3y + z - w = 0$,
    $4x + 5y - 2z + 6w = 0$,
    $3x - y - z - 7w = 0$.

3 · HOMOGENEOUS LINEAR EQUATIONS

If, in the matrix equation $AX = C$, the matrix C is a zero matrix, the system of equations (1) is a set of homogeneous linear equations. We note that in this case the ranks of the augmented matrix and the matrix of coefficients are the same, so that there are always solutions of a set of homogeneous linear equations. Moreover, it is obvious that $(0, 0, \cdots, 0)$ is always a solution. The question of interest, then, is when do homogeneous linear equations have solutions other than $(0, 0, \cdots, 0)$, the trivial solution.

Theorem 10.   A system of m *homogeneous linear equations in* n *unknowns has a solution other than* $(0, 0, \cdots, 0)$ *if and only if the rank of the matrix of coefficients is less than* n.

This is an obvious corollary of Theorem 9. If the rank of the matrix of coefficients is $r < n$, then $n - r > 0$, and r of the unknowns may be expressed as linear functions of the $n - r > 0$ unknowns. If $r = n$, the equation $SAX = 0$ shows that the n unknowns must all be equal to zero. Thus only if $r < n$ are there an infinite number of solutions other than $(0, 0, \cdots, 0)$.

The special case $m = n$ warrants attention.

Corollary.   A system of n *homogeneous linear equations in* n *unknowns has a solution other than* $(0, 0, \cdots, 0)$ *if and only if the matrix of coefficients is singular.*

If the matrix of coefficients is singular its rank is less than n.

It may be of interest to note that the general solution of the equation $AX = C$ can be expressed as the sum of the general solution of the equation $AX = 0$ plus a particular solution of the equation $AX = C$, a particular solution of $AX = C$ being one in which the arbitrary parameters in the general solution are given particular values. In the illustrative example on p. 120, the general solution of the homogeneous system of equations

$$x - y + 2z + w = 0,$$
$$3x + 2y + w = 0,$$
$$4x + y + 2z + 2w = 0$$

is $x = -(4/5)z - (3/5)w, y = (6/5)z + (2/5)w$. A particular solution of the nonhomogeneous system is $z = 0, w = 0, x = 1, y = -1$.

4 · LINEARLY INDEPENDENT SOLUTIONS OF SYSTEMS OF LINEAR EQUATIONS

It is of interest to determine the number of linearly independent solutions of a consistent system $AX = C$ of m linear equations in n unknowns. We prove the following theorem.

Theorem 11. If a system of m *nonhomogeneous linear equations in* n *unknowns has a solution, it has exactly* n − r + 1 *linearly independent solutions, where* r *is the rank of the matrix of coefficients. A system of* m *homogeneous linear equations in* n *unknowns has exactly* n − r *linearly independent solutions,* r *being the rank of the matrix of coefficients.*

Let r be the rank of the matrix of coefficients and the augmented matrix of the system $AX = C$ of m linear equations in n unknowns. Then the solutions may be expressed as follows:

$$x_1 = \sum_{j=r+1}^{n} d_{1j}x_j + b_1,$$

(2)
$$x_2 = \sum_{j=r+1}^{n} d_{2j}x_j + b_2,$$

$$\cdots\cdots\cdots\cdots\cdots\cdots$$

$$x_r = \sum_{j=r+1}^{n} d_{rj}x_j + b_r.$$

Note that, if $r = n$, there is only the one solution $b_1, b_2, \cdots, b_n$. If the equations are homogeneous, all the b's are zero. Thus the theorem holds for $r = n$. Now assume $r < n$. We form a matrix whose rows represent particular solutions of the equation $AX = C$. First let $x_j = 0, j = r + 1,$ $\cdots, n$. Then one solution is $x_1 = b_1, x_2 = b_2, \cdots, x_r = b_r, x_j = 0,$ $j = r + 1, \cdots, n$. In turn let $x_k = 1$, with $k \geq r + 1$, and let $x_j = 0,$

with $k \neq j$ and $j \geq r + 1$. Thus we obtain $n - r + 1$ solutions. Let x_1', $x_2', \cdots, x_n'$ be any other solution. The matrix of these solutions is an $(n - r + 2) \times n$ matrix:

$$
\begin{bmatrix}
x_1' & x_2' & \cdots & x_r' & x_{r+1}' & x_{r+2}' & \cdots & x_n' \\
b_1 & b_2 & \cdots & b_r & 0 & 0 & \cdots & 0 \\
d_{1,r+1} + b_1 & d_{2,r+1} + b_2 & \cdots & d_{r,r+1} + b_r & 1 & 0 & \cdots & 0 \\
d_{1,r+2} + b_1 & d_{2,r+2} + b_2 & \cdots & d_{r,r+2} + b_r & 0 & 1 & \cdots & 0 \\
\cdot\cdot\cdot & \cdot\cdot\cdot & & \cdot\cdot\cdot & \cdot & \cdot & & \cdot \\
d_{1n} + b_1 & d_{2n} + b_2 & \cdots & d_{rn} + b_r & 0 & 0 & \cdots & 1
\end{bmatrix}
$$

Note that the last $n - r$ rows of this matrix are linearly independent, for their last $n - r$ columns form the $(n - r) \times (n - r)$ identity matrix. Thus the column rank of this $(n - r) \times n$ submatrix is $\geq n - r$, but its row rank is $\leq n - r$. Hence its rank is $n - r$ as stated. Furthermore, if the b_i are not all zero, the last $n - r + 1$ rows are linearly independent, for these rows contain the $(n - r + 1) \times (n - r + 1)$ submatrix, consisting of the last $n - r$ columns and the column containing $b_k \neq 0$, whose columns are linearly independent. Thus, if the b_i are not all zero, we have exhibited a set of $n - r + 1$ linearly independent solutions. If the b_i are all zero, the equations are homogeneous, for, from (2), $(0, 0, \cdots, 0)$ is a solution. In this case we have exhibited a set of $n - r$ linearly independent solutions. It remains to prove that any other solution $x_1', x_2', \cdots, x_n'$ is a linear combination of the given set. To do this let R_i denote the ith row of the given matrix of solutions. Then

$$
R_1 - \sum_{j=r+1}^{n} x_j'(R_{j-r+2} - R_2) - R_2 = 0,
$$

for we need observe only that $x_1', x_2', \cdots, x_n'$ satisfy equations (2) by hypothesis. Thus any solution $x_1', x_2', \cdots, x_n'$ is a linear combination of the given set of linearly independent solutions.

EXAMPLE. In the example on p. 122 $n = 4$ and $r \doteq 2$, so there exist 3 linearly independent solutions. These may be taken to be $x = 1, \ y = -1, \ z = 0$, $w = 0$; $x = 1/5, \ y = 1/5, \ z = 1, \ w = 0$; and $x = 2/5, \ y = -3/5, \ z = 0, \ w = 1$.

Exercises

1. Do m homogeneous linear equations in n unknowns have solutions other than $(0, 0, \cdots, 0)$ when $m < n$? Why?

2. Exhibit a maximum set of linearly independent solutions for each of the following systems of equations:

a. $2x - 3y + 4z + w = 0$,
   $x + z - w = 0$,
   $3x - 3y + 5z = 0$,
   $4x - 3y + 6z - w = 0$.

b. $2x - 2y + 5z + 3w = 0$,
   $4x - y + z + w = 0$,
   $3x - 2y + 3z + 4w = 0$,
   $x - 3y + 7z + 6w = 0$.

c. $x + y - z = 2$,
   $3x + y + z = 1$,
   $x - y + 3z = -3$,
   $4x + 2y = 3$.

d. $2x + 3y - 4z + 5w = 2$,
   $3x + 5y - z + 2w = 1$,
   $7x + 11y - 9z + 12w = 5$,
   $3x + 4y - 11z + 13w = 5$.

3. Let $\xi_1 = (1, 2, 3)$, $\xi_2 = (2, -1, 1)$, and $\xi_3 = (1, 7, 8)$. Find numbers c_1, c_2, c_3 not all zero such that $c_1\xi_1 + c_2\xi_2 + c_3\xi_3 = \mathbf{0}$.

4. Let $\xi_1 = (1, -1, 3)$, $\xi_2 = (2, 3, 5)$, $\xi_3 = (-1, 4, -2)$, and $\xi_4 = (4, 1, -2)$. Find numbers c_1, c_2, c_3, and c_4 not all zero such that $c_1\xi_1 + c_2\xi_2 + c_3\xi_3 + c_4\xi_4 = \mathbf{0}$.

5 · DIMENSION AND BASIS OF A VECTOR SPACE

DEFINITION. The *dimension* of a vector space V over F is equal to the maximum number of linearly independent vectors in V.

We might expect the dimension of $V_n(F)$ to be n. To establish this result we first prove a lemma.

Lemma. *Any set of* r *vectors of* $V_n(F)$ *is linearly dependent if* r $>$ n.

Suppose that our vectors are $\xi_1 = (a_{11}, a_{21}, \cdots, a_{n1})$, $\xi_2 = (a_{12}, a_{22}, \cdots, a_{n2})$, $\cdots$, $\xi_r = (a_{1r}, a_{2r}, \cdots, a_{nr})$. Then $\xi_1, \xi_2, \cdots, \xi_r$ are linearly dependent if and only if there exist scalars $x_1, x_2, \cdots, x_r$ not all zero such that $x_1\xi_1 + x_2\xi_2 + \cdots + x_r\xi_r = (0, 0, \cdots, 0)$. Thus $\xi_1, \xi_2, \cdots, \xi_r$ are linearly dependent if and only if there is a nontrivial solution to the system of n homogeneous linear equations in the r unknowns:

$$x_1 a_{11} + x_2 a_{12} + \cdots + x_r a_{1r} = 0$$

$$x_1 a_{21} + x_2 a_{22} + \cdots + x_r a_{2r} = 0$$

$$\cdots\cdots\cdots\cdots\cdots\cdots\cdots\cdots$$

$$x_1 a_{n1} + x_2 a_{n2} + \cdots + x_r a_{nr} = 0.$$

Since the rank of the matrix of coefficients of this system is $\leq n < r$, it follows by Theorem 10 that there is a nontrivial solution.

Theorem 12. *The vector space* $V_n(F)$ *has dimension* n.

By the lemma, the dimension of $V_n(F)$ is not greater than n. Now we observe that the n vectors $\xi_1 = (1, 0, 0, \cdots, 0)$, $\xi_2 = (0, 1, 0, \cdots, 0)$, $\cdots$,

$\xi_n = (0, 0, 0, \cdots, 1)$ are linearly independent over F since $c_1\xi_1 + c_2\xi_2 + \cdots + c_n\xi_n = (c_1, c_2, \cdots, c_n) = (0, 0, \cdots, 0)$ implies $c_1 = c_2 = \cdots = c_n = 0$. Thus the dimension of $V_n(F)$ is greater than or equal to n and, hence, the dimension is n.

Theorem 13. *If the vector space* V *over* F *is spanned by the* m *vectors* $\xi_1, \xi_2, \cdots, \xi_m$ *and* r $>$ m, *then any set of* r *vectors of* V *is linearly dependent.*

Let $\eta_1, \eta_2, \cdots, \eta_r$ be any set of r vectors of V. Since $\xi_1, \xi_2, \cdots, \xi_m$ span V, we know that there exist scalars a_{ij} in F $(i = 1, 2, \cdots, m; j = 1, 2, \cdots, r)$ such that

$$\eta_1 = a_{11}\xi_1 + a_{21}\xi_2 + \cdots + a_{m1}\xi_m$$
$$\eta_2 = a_{12}\xi_1 + a_{22}\xi_2 + \cdots + a_{m2}\xi_m$$
$$\cdots\cdots\cdots\cdots\cdots\cdots\cdots\cdots\cdots$$
$$\eta_r = a_{1r}\xi_1 + a_{2r}\xi_r + \cdots + a_{mr}\xi_m.$$

Now we must show that there exist scalars $x_1, x_2, \cdots, x_r$ of F such that $x_1\eta_1 + x_2\eta_2 + \cdots + x_r\eta_r = 0$. But

$$x_1\eta_1 + x_2\eta_2 + \cdots + x_r\eta_r$$
$$= (x_1a_{11} + x_2a_{12} + \cdots + x_ra_{1r})\xi_1 + (x_1a_{21} + x_2a_{22} + \cdots + x_ra_{2r})\xi_2$$
$$+ \cdots + (x_1a_{m1} + x_2a_{m2} + \cdots + a_{mr})\xi_m.$$

Thus $\eta_1, \eta_2, \cdots, \eta_r$ are linearly dependent if there exists a nontrivial solution of the system of homogeneous linear equations

$$x_1a_{11} + x_2a_{12} + \cdots + x_ra_{1r} = 0$$
$$x_1a_{21} + x_2a_{22} + \cdots + x_ra_{2r} = 0$$
$$\cdots\cdots\cdots\cdots\cdots\cdots\cdots\cdots\cdots$$
$$x_1a_{m1} + x_2a_{m2} + \cdots + x_ra_{mr} = 0.$$

Since $r > m$, it follows by Theorem 10 that such a nontrivial solution exists.

Theorem 14. *Let* V *be a vector space of dimension* m *over* F *and suppose that the vectors* $\xi_1, \xi_2, \cdots, \xi_s$ *span* V. *Then* (1) s $\geq$ m; (2) *some* m *of the* s *vectors* $\xi_1, \xi_2, \cdots, \xi_s$ *are linearly independent; and* (3) *if* s $\geq$ t $>$ m, *any* t *of the* s *vectors* $\xi_1, \xi_2, \cdots, \xi_s$ *are linearly dependent.*

Let r be the greatest number of linearly independent vectors that can be chosen from among the vectors $\xi_1, \xi_2, \cdots, \xi_s$. Since we may renumber our vectors if we wish, there is no loss of generality if we assume that this maximal set is $\xi_1, \xi_2, \cdots, \xi_r$. Assume that $r < s$; then $\xi_1, \xi_2, \cdots, \xi_r$ are linearly independent but the sets of vectors $\xi_1, \xi_2, \cdots, \xi_r, \xi_{r+j}$ are linearly dependent for $j = 1, 2, \cdots, s - r$. Hence there exist scalars $c_1, c_2, \cdots, c_r, c_{r+j}$ not all zero such that

$$(3) \qquad c_1 \xi_1 + c_2 \xi_2 + \cdots + c_r \xi_r + c_{r+j} \xi_{r+j} = 0$$

for $j = 1, 2, \cdots, s - r$. Furthermore, $c_{r+j} \neq 0$. For if $c_{r+j} = 0$, our requirement that $c_1, c_2, \cdots, c_r, c_{r+j}$ be not all zero would imply, by equation (3), that there exist scalars $c_1, c_2, \cdots, c_r$ not all zero such that $c_1 \xi_1 + c_2 \xi_2 + \cdots + c_r \xi_r = 0$. But this is impossible since $\xi_1, \xi_2, \cdots, \xi_r$ are linearly independent. Hence we may solve for ξ_{r+j} in equation (3) to obtain ξ_{r+j} as a linear combination of $\xi_1, \xi_2, \cdots, \xi_r$ for $j = 1, 2, \cdots, s - r$. Hence $\xi_1, \xi_2, \cdots, \xi_r$ span V when $r < s$. By hypothesis, the same conclusion holds if $r = s$.

Now by Theorem 13, any set of more than r vectors of V is linearly dependent and since, by the definition of dimension, V contains m linearly independent vectors, we have $m \leq r$. But since V contains r linearly independent vectors we also have $r \leq m$. Hence $r = m$, which proves (2) of Theorem 14, and, since $s \geq r$, $s \geq m$, which is (1) of Theorem 14. Finally, (3) follows since we have shown that any one of the sets of $r + 1 = m + 1$ vectors $\xi_1, \xi_2, \cdots, \xi_r, \xi_{r+j}$ ($j = 1, 2, \cdots, s - r$) are linearly dependent.

DEFINITION.   A set of vectors $\xi_1, \xi_2, \cdots, \xi_r$ of a vector space V over F is called a *basis* of V of (1) the vectors $\xi_1, \xi_2, \cdots, \xi_r$ are linearly independent over V and (2) the vectors $\xi_1, \xi_2, \cdots, \xi_r$ span V.

Theorem 15.   If V *is a vector space of dimension* m *over* F, *any basis of* V *contains exactly* m (*linearly independent*) *vectors. Conversely, every set of* m *linearly independent vectors of* V *forms a basis of* V.

By Theorem 14, a basis contains m but not more than m linearly independent vectors. Since the vectors of a basis are linearly independent, a basis contains exactly m vectors in all.

Conversely, let $\xi_1, \xi_2, \cdots, \xi_m$ be any m linearly independent vectors of V and let ξ be any other vector of V. Since m is the dimension of V, the $m + 1$ vectors $\xi_1, \xi_2, \cdots, \xi_m, \xi$ are linearly dependent so that there are scalars $c_1, c_2, \cdots, c_m, c$ with $c \neq 0$ such that

$$c_1 \xi_1 + c_2 \xi_2 + \cdots + c_m \xi_m + c \xi = 0.$$

Hence every vector ξ of V is a linear combination of $\xi_1, \xi_2, \cdots, \xi_m$ and, thus, $\xi_1, \xi_2, \cdots, \xi_m$ span V. Since they are linearly independent, they also form a basis of V.

Exercises

1. Exhibit three different bases for $V_3(F)$, where F is the field of rational numbers.
2. Find a basis for $V_3(F)$, F being the field of rational numbers, which includes the vectors $(1, -1, 1)$ and $(2, 1, 1)$.

3. Show that no basis for $V_3(F)$, F being the field of rational numbers, can include both of the vectors $(1, -1, 1)$ and $(2, -2, 2)$.

4. Two vectors ξ and η are said to be *orthogonal* if $\xi \cdot \eta = 0$, and a vector ξ is said to be of *unit length* if $\xi \cdot \xi = 1$. A basis of a vector space that consists of mutually orthogonal vectors is called a *normal orthogonal basis*.

   a. Prove that the vectors $(2/3, -1/3, 2/3)$, $(2/3, 2/3, -1/3)$, and $(1/3, -2/3, -2/3)$ form a normal orthogonal basis of $V_3(F)$, F being the field of rational numbers.

   b. Find a normal orthogonal basis of $V_3(F)$, F being the field of real numbers, of which $(1/\sqrt{3}, 1/\sqrt{3}, -1/\sqrt{3})$ is one vector.

   c. Show that the vectors $\xi = (1, 1, -1)$ and $\eta = (2, -1, 1)$ are orthogonal and find a third vector orthogonal to both ξ and η.

8 Determinants and Matrices

1 · DEFINITION

Just as we associate a real number $\sqrt{a^2 + b^2}$ with every complex number $a + bi$, we may associate with every square matrix over a field F an element of the field, known as the determinant of the matrix. Let $A = [a_{ij}]$ be an $n \times n$ matrix. Then the determinant of A is denoted by $|A| = |a_{ij}|$ and is defined as follows.

Determinant

The determinant $|A|$ of the $n \times n$ matrix $A = [a_{ij}]$ over the field F is the polynomial in the elements a_{ij} of the matrix A obtained in the following way. Take the product $a_{11}a_{22} \cdots a_{nn}$ of the elements in the principal diagonal of A, and operate on the row subscripts of the elements by the $n!$ permutations

$$p = \begin{pmatrix} 1 & 2 & \cdots & n \\ i_1 & i_2 & \cdots & i_n \end{pmatrix}, \text{ where } i_1, i_2, \cdots, i_n \text{ are } 1, 2, \cdots, n \text{ in some order,}$$

thus obtaining $n!$ distinct terms. If p is an even permutation, prefix a plus sign to the term; if p is an odd permutation, prefix a minus sign to the term. The sum of these $n!$ signed terms is the determinant $|A|$.

Let sgn p, read sign p, denote the plus sign if the permutation p is an even permutation and denote the minus sign if p is an odd permutation. Thus the term obtained from $a_{11}a_{22} \cdots a_{nn}$ by operating on the row subscripts of these elements by the permutation p may be written sgn $p\ a_{i_1 1}a_{i_2 2} \cdots a_{i_n n}$.

EXAMPLE. Find the determinant of $A = \begin{bmatrix} a_{11} & a_{12} \\ a_{21} & a_{22} \end{bmatrix}$. The permutations on the symbols 1 and 2 are the identity $i = (1)(2)$ and $p = (12)$. Operating on the

128

row subscripts of the elements in $a_{11}a_{22}$ by the identity, we obtain $a_{11}a_{22}$, and, since the identity is an even permutation, this term is prefixed by a plus sign. Operating on the row subscripts of the elements in $a_{11}a_{22}$ by the permutation p, we obtain $a_{21}a_{12}$, and, since p is an odd permutation, this term is prefixed by a minus sign. Thus

$$\begin{vmatrix} a_{11} & a_{12} \\ a_{21} & a_{22} \end{vmatrix} = a_{11}a_{22} - a_{21}a_{12}.$$

Order

The order of a determinant of an $n \times n$ matrix is the integer n.

Exercises

1. Write out the determinant of the 3×3 matrix $A = [a_{ij}]$.
2. Write out the determinant of the 4×4 matrix $A = [a_{ij}]$.
3. Find the signs of the following terms in the determinant of the 5×5 matrix $A = [a_{ij}]$.

    a. $a_{51}a_{42}a_{23}a_{35}a_{14}$.
    b. $a_{15}a_{32}a_{43}a_{24}a_{51}$.
    c. $a_{21}a_{13}a_{42}a_{34}a_{55}$.

4. Prove that the product of the elements in the principal diagonal of a matrix is a term in its determinant.
5. Prove that one half the terms in the determinant of a matrix are prefixed by a plus sign and one half by a minus sign.

2 · COFACTORS

Note that each term in the determinant $|A|$ contains one and only one element from each row and each column of the matrix A. Thus a term containing a_{11} contains no further elements from the first row or the first column of A. Collect all the terms of $|A|$ containing the element a_{11} as a factor. Then the sum of these terms may be written $a_{11}C_{11}$. The factor C_{11} is called the *cofactor* of a_{11}. Note that the terms in C_{11} are composed of elements taken from the $(n-1) \times (n-1)$ submatrix of A, obtained by deleting the first row and the first column of A. Similarly the sum of all the terms of $|A|$ containing the factor a_{ij} may be written $a_{ij}C_{ij}$, where again the factor C_{ij} is called the cofactor of a_{ij}. The terms of C_{ij} are composed of elements from the submatrix M_{ij} of A, obtained by deleting the ith row and the jth column of A. Thus we may write the determinant $|A|$ as a linear homogeneous function of the elements of the ith row simply by collecting all the terms containing $a_{i1}, a_{i2}, \cdots, a_{in}$, respectively, and forming their sum. Thus

$$|A| = a_{i1}C_{i1} + a_{i2}C_{i2} + \cdots + a_{in}C_{in} = \sum_{j=1}^{n} a_{ij}C_{ij}.$$

Similarly we may write the determinant $|A|$ as a linear homogeneous function of the kth column by collecting all the terms containing $a_{1k}, a_{2k}, \cdots,$ a_{nk}, respectively, and forming their sum. Thus

$$|A| = a_{1k}C_{1k} + a_{2k}C_{2k} + \cdots + a_{nk}C_{nk} = \sum_{i=1}^{n} a_{ik}C_{ik}.$$

These two ways of writing the determinant $|A|$ are called the expansions of $|A|$ by the elements and cofactors of the ith row and kth column of $|A|$. We have thus proved the following theorem.

Theorem 1. $|A| = \sum_{j=1}^{n} a_{ij}C_{ij}$ *and* $|A| = \sum_{i=1}^{n} a_{ik}C_{ik}.$

The expansion of a determinant as a linear function of its cofactors enables us to prove the following property of determinants.

Theorem 2. If the elements of the ith row or the kth column of a matrix A are multiplied by an element c of the field, the determinant of the resulting matrix B equals c $|A|$.

Using the first formula in Theorem 1, we have $|B| = \sum_{j=1}^{n} ca_{ij}C_{ij} = c \sum_{j=1}^{n} a_{ij} C_{ij} = c |A|$. To prove the theorem for the kth column we use the second formula. (Note that we may take $c = 0$.)

Exercises

1. In the determinant of the 3×3 matrix $A = [a_{ij}]$ exhibit the cofactors C_{11}, C_{12}, C_{13}.

2. In the determinant $\begin{vmatrix} 5 & -2 & 1 \\ 3 & 0 & 2 \\ 4 & 1 & 5 \end{vmatrix}$ exhibit the cofactors C_{11}, C_{12}, C_{13}.

3. Show that $\begin{vmatrix} 2 & 3 & 4 \\ 5 & 15 & 5 \\ 2 & 9 & 0 \end{vmatrix} = 15 \begin{vmatrix} 2 & 1 & 4 \\ 1 & 1 & 1 \\ 2 & 3 & 0 \end{vmatrix}.$

3 · FURTHER PROPERTIES

Theorem 3. $|A^t| = |A|$ *where* A^t *is the transpose of the matrix* A.

Let $A = [a_{ij}]$ be an $n \times n$ matrix. Then $A^t = [a'_{ij}]$ where $a'_{ij} = a_{ji}$. Apply the definition of a determinant to the matrix A^t. The general term of $|A^t|$ may be written as $s = \operatorname{sgn} p \, a'_{i_1 1} a'_{i_2 2} \cdots a'_{i_n n}$ where

$$p = \begin{pmatrix} 1 & 2 & \cdots & n \\ i_1 & i_2 & \cdots & i_n \end{pmatrix},$$

and $i_1, i_2, \cdots, i_n$ are $1, 2, \cdots, n$ in some order. Substituting a_{ji} for a'_{ij} in s, we have $s = \operatorname{sgn} p \, a_{1i_1}, a_{2i_2}, \cdots, a_{ni_n}$. Except perhaps for sign, this is obviously a term in $|A|$ since $i_1, i_2, \cdots, i_n$ is a permutation of 1, 2, $\cdots, n$. We determine the permutation p' on the row subscripts of $d = a_{11} a_{22} \cdots a_{nn}$, which would produce this term. Thus the element a_{ki_k} in s is obtained from the element $a_{i_k i_k}$ in d by replacing the first i_k by k. Hence,

$$p' = \begin{pmatrix} i_1 & i_2 & \cdots & i_n \\ 1 & 2 & \cdots & n \end{pmatrix} = p^{-1}.$$

Now sgn p = sgn p^{-1}, for p^{-1} is an even or an odd permutation according as p is an even or odd permutation. Thus every one of the $n!$ terms of $|A^t|$ is a term of $|A|$, and, hence, $|A^t| = |A|$.

Theorem 3 thus enables us to replace any theorem concerning the rows of a determinant by a similar theorem concerning its columns, or vice versa.

Theorem 4.   If in the matrix A *two rows or two columns are interchanged, the determinant* $|B|$ *of the resulting matrix* B *equals* $-|A|$.

It is convenient to prove the theorem for the interchange of two columns. Then Theorem 3 proves the theorem for the interchange of two rows. Interchange the rth and sth columns of A, where $r < s$, obtaining the matrix B. The product of the elements in the principal diagonal of B is $a_{11} a_{22} \cdots a_{rs} \cdots a_{sr} \cdots a_{nn}$. Then the general term of $|B|$ is sgn $p \, a_{i_1 1} a_{i_2 2} \cdots a_{i_r s} \cdots a_{i_s r} \cdots a_{i_n n}$, where $p = \begin{pmatrix} 1 & 2 & \cdots & r & \cdots & s & \cdots & n \\ i_1 & i_2 & \cdots & i_r & \cdots & i_s & \cdots & i_n \end{pmatrix}$, and where $i_1, i_2, \cdots, i_n$ are $1, 2, \cdots, n$ in some order. This again, except perhaps for sign, is a term of $|A|$. To obtain this term by a permutation of the row subscripts of the elements in the principal diagonal of A, the permutation

$$q = \begin{pmatrix} 1 & 2 & \cdots & r & \cdots & s & \cdots & n \\ i_1 & i_2 & \cdots & i_s & \cdots & i_r & \cdots & i_n \end{pmatrix}$$

is used. Now $q = pt$, where $t = (i_r i_s)$. Since t is a transposition, sgn q = $-$sgn p. Moreover, if p runs through the $n!$ permutations of the symmetric group on n symbols, the permutations pt are these same permutations in some order; for recall that, if S is a group and t is an element of the group, $St = S$.

Corollary.   If a matrix A *has two identical columns or two identical rows, then* $|A| = 0$.

Interchange the two identical columns of A, obtaining the matrix B. Then $|B| = -|A|$ by the preceding theorem, but $B = A$, and hence $|A| = -|A|$, or $|A| + |A| = 0$. If the elements of A are in a field where $1 + 1 \neq 0$, then $|A| = 0$. The corollary also holds for fields in which $1 + 1 = 0$. For a suggestion for a proof see Exercise 3, p. 134.

Theorem 5. *Let C_{ij} be the cofactor of the element a_{ij} in the determinant $|A| = |a_{ij}|$ of order n, and let M_{ij} be the $(n - 1) \times (n - 1)$ submatrix of A obtained by deleting the ith row and the jth column of A. Then $C_{ij} = (-1)^{i+j} |M_{ij}|$.*

We prove first that $C_{11} = |M_{11}|$. Recall that the sum of the terms of $|A|$ which contain a_{11} as a factor may be written as $a_{11}C_{11}$, and that all of the elements of the terms of C_{11} are elements of the matrix M_{11}. Thus the general term of $a_{11}C_{11}$ is sgn $p \, a_{11} \, a_{i_2 2} a_{i_3 3} \cdots a_{i_n n}$, where

$$p = \begin{pmatrix} 1 & 2 & 3 & \cdots & n \\ 1 & i_2 & i_3 & \cdots & i_n \end{pmatrix}$$

and $i_2, i_3, \cdots, i_n$ are 2, 3, $\cdots$, n in some order. The permutation p may thus be regarded as a permutation on the symbols 2, 3, $\cdots$, n alone. Hence all the terms of $a_{11}C_{11}$ are obtained by allowing p to run through the $(n - 1)!$ permutations on the symbols 2, 3, $\cdots$, n, keeping 1 fixed. Thus the terms of C_{11} are obtained by operating on the row subscripts of the elements of the product $a_{22}a_{23} \cdots a_{nn}$ of the elements of the principal diagonal of M_{11}. Therefore $C_{11} = |M_{11}|$.

We now prove that $C_{ij} = (-1)^{i+j}|M_{ij}|$. Move the ith row of A into the first row by performing $i - 1$ successive interchanges of adjacent rows of A, and move the jth column of A to the first column by performing $j - 1$ successive interchanges of adjacent columns of A. Call the resulting matrix B. The element a_{ij} is thus in the first row and first column of B, and the submatrix of B obtained by deleting its first row and its first column is the submatrix M_{ij} of A. Thus the terms of $|B|$ containing a_{ij} are, according to the first part of our proof $a_{ij} |M_{ij}|$. But $|B| = (-1)^{i-1+j-1} |A| = (-1)^{i+j} |A|$, and thus $|A| = (-1)^{i+j} |B|$. Now the terms of $|A|$ containing a_{ij} as a factor are $a_{ij}C_{ij}$, and the terms of $|B|$ containing a_{ij} as a factor are $a_{ij} |M_{ij}|$. Therefore $C_{ij} = (-1)^{i+j} |M_{ij}|$.

The determinant $|M_{ij}|$ is called the *minor* of the element a_{ij} in the determinant $|A|$. Note that now Theorem 1 shows how a determinant of order n can be expanded as a linear function of determinants of order $n - 1$.

Theorem 6. *The zero formulas. Let C_{ij} denote the cofactor of the element a_{ij} in the determinant $|A| = |a_{ij}|$ of order n. Then $\sum_{j=1}^{n} a_{ij}C_{kj} = 0$ and $\sum_{j=1}^{n} a_{ji}C_{jk} = 0$, if $i \neq k$.*

The first formula becomes self-evident when we recall that the cofactors C_{kj}, with $j = 1, 2, \cdots, n$, are determinants of order $n - 1$ formed from the elements of $|A|$ that lie in all the rows of A except the kth row. Thus, if in the sum $\sum_{j=1}^{n} a_{kj} C_{kj}$ we replace the elements a_{kj} of the kth row of A by the elements a_{ij} of the ith row of A, when $i \neq k$, we obtain the desired sum. We now see, however, that this sum is the determinant of the matrix B obtained from A by replacing the kth row of A by its ith row. Thus the matrix B has two rows alike, and hence $|B| = 0$. Similarly the sum $\sum_{j=1}^{n} a_{ji} C_{jk}$, when $i \neq k$, represents the determinant of the matrix C obtained from A by replacing the kth column of A by its ith column. Since C has two columns alike, $|C| = 0$.

Theorem 7. *If in the* $n \times n$ *matrix* $A = [a_{ij}]$ *the* kth *row,* A_k, *of* A *is replaced by the row* $A_k + cA_i$, *with* $i \neq k$, *the determinant of the resulting matrix equals the determinant of* A.

Let B be the matrix obtained from A by replacing the kth row of A by $A_k + cA_i$, with $i \neq k$. Expand the determinant $|B|$ by the elements and the cofactors of its kth row. Thus

$$|B| = \sum_{j=1}^{n} (a_{kj} + ca_{ij}) C_{kj} = \sum_{j=1}^{n} a_{kj} C_{kj} + c \sum_{j=1}^{n} a_{ij} C_{kj}$$
$$= |A| + 0 = |A|$$

by Theorem 1 and Theorem 6. A similar theorem obviously also holds for the columns of a determinant.

The above theorems are used to simplify the labor of computing the value of a determinant. If for example, in a determinant of order n all the elements except one in a row or column are made zero, the determinant can be written as the product of this nonzero element times its cofactor, a determinant of order $n - 1$. Applying this rule successively to the determinant of a *diagonal* matrix, i.e., a matrix in which all the terms are zero except those in the principal diagonal, we see that the determinant of a diagonal matrix is the product of the elements in the principal diagonal.

EXAMPLE. We use the above theorems to evaluate Vandermonde's determinant of order 3.

$$|A| = \begin{vmatrix} 1 & 1 & 1 \\ x & y & z \\ x^2 & y^2 & z^2 \end{vmatrix} = \begin{vmatrix} 1 & 0 & 0 \\ x & y - x & z - x \\ x^2 & y^2 - x^2 & z^2 - x^2 \end{vmatrix}$$

$$= (y - x)(z - x) \begin{vmatrix} 1 & 0 & 0 \\ x & 1 & 1 \\ x^2 & y + x & z + x \end{vmatrix}$$

$$= (y - x)(z - x) \begin{vmatrix} 1 & 1 \\ y + x & z + x \end{vmatrix}$$

$$= (y - x)(z - x)(z - y).$$

However, we can evaluate this determinant more simply by noting that, if it is expanded in terms of the elements and cofactors of the first column, we may regard it as a polynomial in x. Thus, if $x = y$, we see that the determinant is zero, for it has two columns alike. Hence $x - y$ is a factor of the determinant. Similarly $x - z$ is a factor, and regarding the determinant as a polynomial in y, we see that $y - z$ is a factor. Thus $|A| = (x - y)(x - z)(y - z)b$, where b is to be determined. Since the product of the elements in the principal diagonal is a term in $|A|$, yz^2 is a term in $|A|$. The coefficient of yz^2 in our expansion is $-b$. Hence $b = -1$. Similarly, we can prove that Vandermonde's determinant of order n has the following factorization:

$$\begin{vmatrix} 1 & 1 & 1 & \cdots & 1 \\ x_1 & x_2 & x_3 & \cdots & x_n \\ x_1^2 & x_2^2 & x_3^2 & \cdots & x_n^2 \\ \cdots & \cdots & \cdots & \cdots & \cdots \\ x_1^{n-1} & x_2^{n-1} & x_3^{n-1} & \cdots & x_n^{n-1} \end{vmatrix} = \prod_{i>j}^{n} (x_i - x_j).$$

Exercises

1. Find the values of $\begin{vmatrix} 3 & 4 & -2 & 1 \\ 2 & 4 & 6 & 8 \\ 1 & 8 & 3 & 2 \\ 0 & 0 & 2 & 0 \end{vmatrix}$ and $\begin{vmatrix} 5 & 2 & -1 & 3 \\ 1 & 2 & 1 & 1 \\ -1 & 3 & 0 & 0 \\ 3 & 0 & 0 & 1 \end{vmatrix}$.

2. Let $|A| = |a_{ij}|$ be of order 4, and let C_{ij} be the cofactor of the element a_{ij}. Exhibit a matrix whose determinant equals $\sum_{j=1}^{4} x_j C_{3j}$. Exhibit a matrix whose determinant equals $\sum_{j=1}^{4} x_j C_{j2}$.

3. Prove by induction that the determinant of a matrix with two rows alike is zero. *Hint:* Check that this is true for a determinant of order 2. Use the cofactor expansion of a determinant.

4. Without expanding prove that the *skew-symmetric* determinant of odd order n over a field whose characteristic is not 2 equals zero; i.e., $|a_{ij}| = 0$, if $a_{ii} = 0$ and $a_{ij} = -a_{ji}$.

5. Prove that $\begin{vmatrix} a_1 + b_1 & c_1 & d_1 \\ a_2 + b_2 & c_2 & d_2 \\ a_3 + b_3 & c_3 & d_3 \end{vmatrix} = \begin{vmatrix} a_1 & c_1 & d_1 \\ a_2 & c_2 & d_2 \\ a_3 & c_3 & d_3 \end{vmatrix} + \begin{vmatrix} b_1 & c_1 & d_1 \\ b_2 & c_2 & d_2 \\ b_3 & c_3 & d_3 \end{vmatrix}$.

6. Write the following determinants as products of factors:

a. $\begin{vmatrix} 1 & x & 1 & y \\ x & 1 & y & 1 \\ 1 & y & 1 & x \\ y & 1 & x & 1 \end{vmatrix}$;

b. $\begin{vmatrix} b + c & a & a \\ b & c + a & b \\ c & c & a + b \end{vmatrix}$;

c. $\begin{vmatrix} x & a & b & c & 1 \\ d & x & e & f & 1 \\ d & g & x & h & 1 \\ d & g & k & x & 1 \\ d & g & k & m & 1 \end{vmatrix}$;

d. $\begin{vmatrix} a & x & y & a \\ x & 0 & 0 & y \\ y & 0 & 0 & x \\ a & y & x & a \end{vmatrix}$;

e. $\begin{vmatrix} a & b & b & b \\ a & b & a & a \\ a & a & b & a \\ b & b & b & a \end{vmatrix}$.

7. Let $A = [a_{ij}]$ be an $n \times n$ matrix, with $a_{ij} = 1$ when $i \neq j$, and $a_{ii} = 0$. Prove that $|A| = (n - 1)(-1)^{n-1}$.

4 · LAPLACE'S EXPANSION OF A DETERMINANT

DEFINITION.   Let D be an $r \times r$ submatrix of an $n \times n$ matrix A. The determinant of the submatrix D' of A obtained by deleting the r rows and r columns of A in which the elements of D lie is called the *complementary minor* of the minor $|D|$.

Theorem 8.   The determinant of the $n \times n$ *matrix* $A = [a_{ij}]$ *equals the sum of the signal products* $\pm|D_i| \cdot |D_i'|$, *where* $|D_i|$ *is an* $r \times r$ *minor of* A *formed from the elements of the first* r *columns of* A *and where* $|D_i'|$ *is its complementary minor. The plus sign or the minus sign is prefixed according as an even number or an odd number of interchanges of adjacent rows of* A *is necessary to bring the submatrix* D_i *into the first* r *rows of* A.

This is called Laplace's expansion by the minors of the first r columns. The proof will make it obvious that any r columns or any r rows of A can be used if proper account is taken of the signs of the products.

EXAMPLE.   Let $|A| = \begin{vmatrix} a_1 & a_2 & a_3 & a_4 \\ b_1 & b_2 & b_3 & b_4 \\ c_1 & c_2 & c_3 & c_4 \\ d_1 & d_2 & d_3 & d_4 \end{vmatrix}$.   Expand by the minors of the first two columns.   Thus

$$|A| = \begin{vmatrix} a_1 & a_2 \\ b_1 & b_2 \end{vmatrix} \cdot \begin{vmatrix} c_3 & c_4 \\ d_3 & d_4 \end{vmatrix} - \begin{vmatrix} a_1 & a_2 \\ c_1 & c_2 \end{vmatrix} \cdot \begin{vmatrix} b_3 & b_4 \\ d_3 & d_4 \end{vmatrix}$$

$$+ \begin{vmatrix} a_1 & a_2 \\ d_1 & d_2 \end{vmatrix} \cdot \begin{vmatrix} b_3 & b_4 \\ c_3 & c_4 \end{vmatrix} + \begin{vmatrix} b_1 & b_2 \\ c_1 & c_2 \end{vmatrix} \cdot \begin{vmatrix} a_3 & a_4 \\ d_3 & d_4 \end{vmatrix}$$

$$- \begin{vmatrix} b_1 & b_2 \\ d_1 & d_2 \end{vmatrix} \cdot \begin{vmatrix} a_3 & a_4 \\ c_3 & c_4 \end{vmatrix} + \begin{vmatrix} c_1 & c_2 \\ d_1 & d_2 \end{vmatrix} \cdot \begin{vmatrix} a_3 & a_4 \\ b_3 & b_4 \end{vmatrix} .$$

PROOF.　Let

$$|D_1| = \begin{vmatrix} a_{11} & \cdots & a_{1r} \\ \cdot & \cdots\cdots & \cdot \\ a_{r1} & \cdots & a_{rr} \end{vmatrix} \text{ and } |D_1'| = \begin{vmatrix} a_{r+1,r+1} & \cdots & a_{r+1,n} \\ \cdot & \cdots\cdots & \cdot \\ a_{n,r+1} & \cdots & a_{nn} \end{vmatrix}.$$

Apply the definition of a determinant to $|D_1|$ and to $|D_1'|$. The general term in $|D_1|$ is sgn $p\, a_{i_1 1} a_{i_2 2} \cdots a_{i_r r}$, where

$$p = \begin{pmatrix} 1 & 2 & \cdots & r \\ i_1 & i_2 & \cdots & i_r \end{pmatrix}$$

and where $i_1, i_2, \cdots, i_r$ are $1, 2, \cdots, r$ in some order. The general term in $|D_1'|$ is sgn $q\, a_{i_{r+1} r+1} \cdots a_{i_n n}$, where

$$q = \begin{pmatrix} r+1 & \cdots & n \\ i_{r+1} & \cdots & i_n \end{pmatrix}$$

and where $i_{r+1}, \cdots, i_n$ are $r+1, \cdots, n$ in some order. Clearly the general term in the product $|D_1| \cdot |D_1'|$ is (sgn p)(sgn q) $a_{i_1 1} \cdots a_{i_r r} a_{i_{r+1} r+1} \cdots a_{i_n n}$. This is a term in $|A|$, for it can be obtained from the principal diagonal of A by the permutation pq. Thus every term in $|D_1| \cdot |D_1'|$ is a term of $|A|$. Now consider the product $|D_i| \cdot |D_i'|$, with $i > 1$. Interchange adjacent rows of A so that the submatrix D_i occurs in the first r rows of the resulting matrix B. As in the first case discussed, the terms of $|D_i| \cdot |D_i'|$ are terms of $|B|$. If B has been obtained from A by making k interchanges of adjacent rows, then $|B| = (-1)^k |A|$, and hence the terms of $(-1)^k |D_i| \cdot |D_i'|$ are terms of $|A|$. Clearly the terms of $|D_i| \cdot |D_i'|$ and $|D_j| \cdot |D_j'|$, with $j \neq i$, are distinct. There are $C(n, r) = n!/[r!\,(n-r!)]$ products $|D_i| \cdot |D_i'|$, and each product contains $r!\,(n-r)!$ terms. Thus the sum of these signed products contains $C(n, r)r!\,(n-r)! = n!$ terms. Laplace's expansion has therefore been verified.

Exercises

1. Expand by Laplace's development by the minors of the first two columns and simplify the resulting sum:

$$\begin{vmatrix} a & 1 & 0 & 0 & 0 \\ b & a & 1 & 0 & 0 \\ 0 & b & a & 1 & 0 \\ 0 & 0 & b & a & 1 \\ 0 & 0 & 0 & b & a \end{vmatrix}.$$

2. Express as the product of two determinants of order 2:

$$\begin{vmatrix} 0 & 1 & x & y \\ 1 & 0 & y & x \\ z & w & 0 & 0 \\ w & z & 0 & 0 \end{vmatrix}.$$

3. Prove that:

$$\begin{vmatrix} a & b & c & d \\ e & f & g & h \\ 0 & 0 & j & k \\ 0 & 0 & l & m \end{vmatrix} = \begin{vmatrix} a & b \\ e & f \end{vmatrix} \cdot \begin{vmatrix} j & k \\ l & m \end{vmatrix}.$$

4. By the use of 2-rowed minors from the first two rows, show that:

$$\frac{1}{2}\begin{vmatrix} a & b & c & d \\ e & f & g & h \\ a & b & c & d \\ e & f & g & h \end{vmatrix} = \begin{vmatrix} a & b \\ e & f \end{vmatrix} \cdot \begin{vmatrix} c & d \\ g & h \end{vmatrix} - \begin{vmatrix} a & c \\ e & g \end{vmatrix} \cdot \begin{vmatrix} b & d \\ f & h \end{vmatrix} + \begin{vmatrix} a & d \\ e & h \end{vmatrix} \cdot \begin{vmatrix} b & c \\ f & g \end{vmatrix} = 0.$$

5 · PRODUCTS OF DETERMINANTS

We shall now develop some properties of the product of determinants. The determinant of the $n \times n$ identity matrix I is 1. Let E be a matrix obtained from the identity matrix by performing one elementary row operation. It is obvious from the properties of determinants that $|E| = -1, c,$ or 1 according as the first, second, or third elementary row operation has been performed on I. Now let A be an $n \times n$ matrix. Then $|EA| = -|A|, c|A|,$ or $|A|,$ and $|EA| = |AE|$. Hence we have proved the following theorem.

Theorem 9. If E *is an elementary matrix,* $|EA| = |AE| = |E| \cdot |A| = |A| \cdot |E|.$

We use this theorem to prove the following theorem.

Theorem 10. An n × n *matrix* A *is nonsingular if and only if* $|A| \neq 0.$

Let C be the canonical form of the matrix A. Then there exist nonsingular matrices S and T such that $SAT = C$. Hence $A = S^{-1}CT^{-1} = E_1 E_2 \cdots E_s C E_1' E_2' \cdots E_t'$, where the E_i and the E_i' are elementary matrices. Now, making successive applications of Theorem 9, we have $|A| = |E_1 E_2 \cdots E_s C E_1' E_2' \cdots E_t'| = |E_1| \cdot |E_2| \cdots |E_s| \cdot |C| \cdot |E_1'| \cdot |E_2'| \cdots |E_t'|.$ Since the determinants of the elementary matrices are not zero, we see that $|A| = 0$

if and only if $|C| = 0$. But $|C| = 0$ if and only if it has a row of zeros, i.e., if and only if A is of rank $< n$. Thus A is nonsingular if and only if $|A| \neq 0$.

The following theorem gives us a rule for multiplying together two determinants of order n to obtain a determinant of order n. We merely multiply together the matrices of the two determinants and find the determinant of the resulting matrix.

Theorem 11. $|AB| = |A| \cdot |B|$.

Let C_a and C_b be the canonical forms of the matrices A and B respectively Then $A = D_1 D_2 \cdots D_r C_a E_1 E_2 \cdots E_s$ and $B = F_1 F_2 \cdots F_t C_b G_1 G_2 \cdots G_u$, where the D_i, E_i, F_i, and G_i are elementary matrices. Thus

$$AB = D_1 D_2 \cdots D_r C_a E_1 E_2 \cdots E_s F_1 F_2 \cdots F_t C_b G_1 G_2 \cdots G_u,$$

and, using Theorem 9, we have

$$|AB| = |D_1 D_2 \cdots D_r| \cdot |C_a E_1 E_2 \cdots E_s F_1 F_2 \cdots F_t C_b| \cdot |G_1 G_2 \cdots G_u|$$

Now if A and B are nonsingular, C_a and C_b are identity matrices, and, using Theorem 9 again, we have

$$|AB| = |D_1 D_2 \cdots D_r C_a E_1 E_2 \cdots E_s| \cdot |F_1 F_2 \cdots F_t C_b G_1 G_2 \cdots G_u|$$
$$= |A| \cdot |B|.$$

If A is singular, C_a has a row of zeros, and hence $M = C_a E_1 E_2 \cdots E_s F_1 F_2 \cdots F_s C_b$ has a row of zeros. Thus $|M| = 0$ and $|AB| = 0$. If B is singular, C_b has a column of zeros, and hence M has a column of zeros, giving us again $|M| = 0$ and $|AB| = 0$. Now if either A or B is singular, $|A| \cdot |B| = 0$, and hence $|AB| = |A| \cdot |B|$.

Theorem 12. $|AB^t| = |A| \cdot |B|$, *where* B^t *is the transpose of the matrix* B.

Note that this theorem indicates a second way to multiply two determinants of order n: we merely find the determinant of the matrix AB^t. To state the result loosely, this theorem gives us a row-by-row rule for the multiplication of two determinants. The proof consists in observing that $|AB^t| = |A| \cdot |B^t| = |A| \cdot |B|$, for the determinant of the transpose of a matrix equals the determinant of the matrix.

EXAMPLE. $\begin{vmatrix} 1 & 2 \\ -1 & 3 \end{vmatrix} \cdot \begin{vmatrix} 0 & -1 \\ 2 & 1 \end{vmatrix} = \begin{vmatrix} 4 & 1 \\ 6 & 4 \end{vmatrix}$ if the multiplication has been performed by using the row-times-column rule, but the product $= \begin{vmatrix} -2 & 4 \\ -3 & 1 \end{vmatrix}$ if the multiplication has been performed by using the row-by-row rule.

Exercises

1. If $s_i = a^i + b^i + c^i$ for $i = 1, 2, 3$, and 4, prove that:

$$\begin{vmatrix} 1 & 1 & 1 \\ a & b & c \\ a^2 & b^2 & c^2 \end{vmatrix} \cdot \begin{vmatrix} 1 & a & a^2 \\ 1 & b & b^2 \\ 1 & c & c^2 \end{vmatrix} = \begin{vmatrix} 3 & s_1 & s_2 \\ s_1 & s_2 & s_3 \\ s_2 & s_3 & s_4 \end{vmatrix}.$$

2. Prove that:

$$\begin{vmatrix} aa' + bb' + cc' & ea' + fb' + gc' \\ ae' + bf' + cg' & ee' + ff' + gg' \end{vmatrix} =$$

$$\begin{vmatrix} a & b \\ e & f \end{vmatrix} \cdot \begin{vmatrix} a' & b' \\ e' & f' \end{vmatrix} + \begin{vmatrix} a & c \\ e & g \end{vmatrix} \cdot \begin{vmatrix} a' & c' \\ e' & g' \end{vmatrix} + \begin{vmatrix} b & c \\ f & g \end{vmatrix} \cdot \begin{vmatrix} b' & c' \\ f' & g' \end{vmatrix}$$

6 · ADJOINT AND INVERSE OF A MATRIX

DEFINITION. Let $A = [a_{ij}]$ be an $n \times n$ matrix. Let C_{ij} be the cofactor of the element a_{ij}. Then the matrix $[C_{ji}']$, where the element C_{ji}' in the jth row and the ith column equals C_{ij} is called the *adjoint* of A, often written adj A.

Theorem 13. $A(adj\ A) = |A|\ I$, *and* $(adj\ A)A = |A|\ I$.

The element in the kth row and the ith column of the product $A[C_{ji}']$ is $\sum_{j=1}^{n} a_{kj}C_{ji}' = \sum_{j=1}^{n} a_{kj}C_{ij}$, which by Theorem 6 equals zero if $k \neq i$, and which by Theorem 1 equals $|A|$ if $k = i$. Hence $A(adj\ A)$ is a diagonal matrix with diagonal elements equal to $|A|$. Thus $A(adj\ A) = |A|\ I$. Similarly the element in the jth row and the kth column of the product $[C_{ji}']A$ is $\sum_{i=1}^{n} C_{ji}'a_{ik} = \sum_{i=1}^{n} C_{ij}a_{ik}$, which equals zero if $j \neq k$, and which equals $|A|$ if $j = k$.

Hence from the definition of the inverse of a matrix, we have the following corollary.

Corollary. $A^{-1} = (adj\ A)/|A|$.

EXAMPLE. The adjoint of the matrix $A = \begin{bmatrix} 2 & -1 & 3 \\ 0 & 2 & 0 \\ 2 & 1 & 1 \end{bmatrix}$ is

$$\begin{bmatrix} \begin{vmatrix} 2 & 0 \\ 1 & 1 \end{vmatrix} & -\begin{vmatrix} -1 & 3 \\ 1 & 1 \end{vmatrix} & \begin{vmatrix} -1 & 3 \\ 2 & 0 \end{vmatrix} \\ -\begin{vmatrix} 0 & 0 \\ 2 & 1 \end{vmatrix} & \begin{vmatrix} 2 & 3 \\ 2 & 1 \end{vmatrix} & -\begin{vmatrix} 2 & 3 \\ 0 & 0 \end{vmatrix} \\ \begin{vmatrix} 0 & 2 \\ 2 & 1 \end{vmatrix} & -\begin{vmatrix} 2 & -1 \\ 2 & 1 \end{vmatrix} & \begin{vmatrix} 2 & -1 \\ 0 & 2 \end{vmatrix} \end{bmatrix} = \begin{bmatrix} 2 & 4 & -6 \\ 0 & -4 & 0 \\ -4 & -4 & 4 \end{bmatrix}$$

and $A(\text{adj } A) = \begin{bmatrix} -8 & 0 & 0 \\ 0 & -8 & 0 \\ 0 & 0 & -8 \end{bmatrix} = -8 \begin{bmatrix} 1 & 0 & 0 \\ 0 & 1 & 0 \\ 0 & 0 & 1 \end{bmatrix}$. The inverse of A is

$\begin{bmatrix} -1/4 & -1/2 & 3/4 \\ 0 & 1/2 & 0 \\ 1/2 & 1/2 & -1/2 \end{bmatrix}$.

Exercises

1. Perform the multiplication of the two determinants in two ways and exhibit the resulting determinants:

a. $\begin{vmatrix} 1 & -1 & 2 \\ 3 & 4 & 1 \\ 0 & 2 & 2 \end{vmatrix} \cdot \begin{vmatrix} 0 & 2 & 1 \\ 0 & 1 & 1 \\ 2 & -1 & 1 \end{vmatrix}$.

b. $\begin{vmatrix} a & 0 & a \\ b & 0 & b \\ c & c & c \end{vmatrix} \cdot \begin{vmatrix} 1 & 1 & -1 \\ 2 & 0 & 2 \\ 1 & 1 & 1 \end{vmatrix}$.

2. Find the adjoints and the inverses of the following matrices:

a. $\begin{bmatrix} 1 & 2 & 3 \\ 0 & 5 & 0 \\ 2 & 4 & 3 \end{bmatrix}$;   b. $\begin{bmatrix} 3 & -1 & 2 \\ 1 & 0 & 3 \\ 4 & 0 & 2 \end{bmatrix}$;   c. $\begin{bmatrix} 2 & 3 & -1 \\ 0 & 1 & -1 \\ 2 & 1 & 2 \end{bmatrix}$.

3. Find the product $A(\text{adj } A)$ if $A = \begin{bmatrix} 3 & 2 & -1 \\ 1 & -3 & 2 \\ 5 & -4 & 3 \end{bmatrix}$.

4. Let A be an $n \times n$ matrix. Prove that the determinant of the adjoint of A is $|A|^{n-1}$.

5. Let A be an $n \times n$ matrix. Prove that the adjoint of the adjoint of A is $|A|^{n-2}A$.

7 · CRAMER'S RULE

The last corollary proves Cramer's rule for solving n simultaneous linear equations in n unknowns.

Theorem 14. If the n simultaneous linear equations in n unknowns $\sum_{j=1}^{n} a_{ij}x_j = c_i$, with $i = 1, 2, \cdots, n$, have a nonzero determinant of coefficients $|A| = |a_{ij}|$ then the equations have the unique solutions $x_j = (C_{1j}c_1 + C_{2j}c_2 + \cdots + C_{nj}c_n)/|A|$, with $j = 1, 2, \cdots, n$, where C_{ij} is the cofactor of the element a_{ij} in $|A|$.

Letting $X^t = [x_1, x_2, \cdots, x_n]$ and $C^t = [c_1, c_2, \cdots, c_n]$, write the equations in matrix form as $AX = C$. Then the solution is, as we have seen, $X = A^{-1}C$. The form of the solution in the theorem is found by using $A^{-1} = (\text{adj } A)/|A|$. Thus the element in the jth row of the matrix solution is

$$x_j = \sum_{i=1}^{n} \frac{C_{ji}' c_i}{|A|} = \sum_{i=1}^{n} \frac{C_{ij} c_i}{|A|}.$$

Note that the numerator in the solution is

$$\begin{vmatrix} a_{11} & \cdots & a_{1,j-1} & c_1 & a_{1,j+1} & \cdots & a_{1n} \\ a_{21} & \cdots & a_{2,j-1} & c_2 & a_{2,j+1} & \cdots & a_{2n} \\ \cdots & \cdots & \cdots & \cdots & \cdots & \cdots & \cdots \\ a_{n1} & \cdots & a_{n,j-1} & c_n & a_{n,j+1} & \cdots & a_{nn} \end{vmatrix}$$

which is the determinant obtained by replacing the jth column of $|A|$ by the constants c_i, $i = 1, 2, \cdots, n$.

Exercises

Use Cramer's rule in finding the solutions of the following equations:

1. $2x + 3y - 4z = -8$,
   $3x + 2y + 4z = 3$,
   $5x - 4y + 5z = 18$.

2. $3x + y + z + w = 0$,
   $2x - y + 2z - w = 4$,
   $x + 2z + w = 3$,
   $2x + 3z + w = 1$.

3. $x + y + z = 11$,
   $2x - 6y - z = 0$,
   $3x + 4y + 2z = 0$.

4. $2x - y + 3z - 2w = 4$,
   $x + 7y + z - w = 2$,
   $3x + 5y - 5z + 3w = 0$,
   $4x - 3y + 2z - w = 5$.

8 · DETERMINANT RANK OF A MATRIX

DEFINITION. An $m \times n$ matrix A is said to be of *determinant rank d*, if there exists a $d \times d$ submatrix D of A whose determinant $|D| \neq 0$, and if the determinant of every $(d + 1) \times (d + 1)$ submatrix of A is zero.

Note that this definition implies that the determinant of any $r \times r$ submatrix of A, with $r > d + 1$, is zero, for a determinant is a linear homogeneous function of the cofactors of a row or a column, and the cofactors are determinants of order $r - 1$ if the determinant is of order r. Thus any determinant of order $r > d + 1$ can finally be expressed as a linear sum of determinants of order $d + 1$ and hence must be zero.

Theorem 15. The rank of a matrix equals its determinant rank.

Let d be the determinant rank of a matrix A, and let r be its rank. Thus A has a $d \times d$ submatrix D whose determinant $|D| \neq 0$. Consider those rows of A in which D lies. The rows of D are linearly independent since D is nonsingular. Hence the d rows of A which contribute elements to the rows of D are linearly independent, for a linear relation between the rows of A also provides a linear relation between the corresponding rows of D. Hence the maximum number r of linearly independent rows of A is at least d; i.e., $r \geq d$. We shall now prove that $r \leq d$. Consider r rows of A which are linearly independent, and denote by R the $r \times n$ submatrix of A formed by these r rows. Now since the row rank of R is r, its column rank is also r. Hence R has r linearly independent columns. Let R_1 be the $r \times r$ submatrix of R formed by these linearly independent columns. It is nonsingular, and hence $|R_1| \neq 0$. But R_1 is also a submatrix of A. Hence $r \leq d$. Recalling the previous inequality $r \geq d$, we conclude that $r = d$. Note that we have incidentally proved the following useful corollary.

Corollary. Any d *rows of a matrix which contain a* d × d *submatrix whose determinant is not zero are linearly independent.*

Exercises

Determine whether the rows of each of the following matrices are linearly dependent. If they are linearly dependent, find a maximum subset that is linearly independent.

a. $\begin{bmatrix} 1 & 0 & 1 & 1 \\ 1 & -1 & 1 & -1 \\ 2 & 1 & 0 & 2 \\ 4 & -1 & 2 & -4 \end{bmatrix}$;
b. $\begin{bmatrix} 3 & 4 & -1 & 1 \\ 1 & 1 & 1 & -1 \\ 2 & 3 & -2 & 2 \\ 5 & 7 & -3 & 3 \end{bmatrix}$;

c. $\begin{bmatrix} 2 & 3 & -4 & 5 \\ 1 & -1 & 2 & -1 \\ 4 & 1 & 0 & 3 \\ 7 & 3 & -2 & 7 \end{bmatrix}$;
d. $\begin{bmatrix} 2 & -1 & 3 & 2 \\ 1 & 7 & 1 & 1 \\ 3 & 5 & -5 & 0 \\ 4 & -3 & 2 & 1 \end{bmatrix}$.

9 · POLYNOMIALS WITH MATRIX COEFFICIENTS

Let $A_0, A_1, \cdots, A_r$ denote $n \times n$ matrices over a field F. Form the polynomial

$$f(x) = A_0 + A_1x + A_2x^2 + \cdots + A_rx^r$$

in the indeterminate x. The symbol x is to act as a scalar with respect to the matrix coefficients. Thus $f(x)$ may also be regarded as a matrix. For example, we may write

$$f(x) = \begin{bmatrix} 1 & 0 \\ 2 & -1 \end{bmatrix} + \begin{bmatrix} 1 & -1 \\ 0 & 0 \end{bmatrix} x + \begin{bmatrix} 3 & 1 \\ 0 & 1 \end{bmatrix} x^2$$

$$= \begin{bmatrix} 1 + x + 3x^2 & -x + x^2 \\ 2 & -1 + x^2 \end{bmatrix}.$$

If $g(x) = B_0 + B_1 x + \cdots + B_m x^m$, where $B_0, B_1, \cdots, B_m$ are also $n \times n$ matrices over the field F, we can define the sum and product of $f(x)$ and $g(x)$ as usual:

$$f(x) + g(x) = (A_0 + B_0) + (A_1 + B_1)x + \cdots$$
$$+ (A_m + B_m)x^m + A_{m+1}x^{m+1} + \cdots + A_r x^r, \quad r \geq m,$$
$$h(x) = f(x) \cdot g(x) = A_0 B_0 + (A_0 B_1 + A_1 B_0)x + \cdots$$
$$+ (A_0 B_k + A_1 B_{k-1} + \cdots + A_k B_0)x^k + \cdots + A_r B_m x^{r+m}$$

We are interested in defining a functional value of $f(x)$ when we substitute a matrix C for x. Since the multiplication of matrices is not commutative, the necessity for a definition is obvious, for we now see that x is replaced by a symbol that is no longer commutative with each matrix. For example, if

$$f(x) = \begin{bmatrix} 1 & 0 \\ -1 & 2 \end{bmatrix} + \begin{bmatrix} 2 & -1 \\ 3 & 2 \end{bmatrix} x = \begin{bmatrix} 1 & 0 \\ -1 & 2 \end{bmatrix} + x \begin{bmatrix} 2 & -1 \\ 3 & 2 \end{bmatrix},$$

and if we wish to substitute $\begin{bmatrix} 1 & 1 \\ 1 & -1 \end{bmatrix}$ for x, we note that the matrix

$$\begin{bmatrix} 1 & 0 \\ -1 & 2 \end{bmatrix} + \begin{bmatrix} 2 & -1 \\ 3 & 2 \end{bmatrix}\begin{bmatrix} 1 & 1 \\ 1 & -1 \end{bmatrix} \neq \begin{bmatrix} 1 & 0 \\ -1 & 2 \end{bmatrix}$$
$$+ \begin{bmatrix} 1 & 1 \\ 1 & -1 \end{bmatrix}\begin{bmatrix} 2 & -1 \\ 3 & 2 \end{bmatrix}.$$

Hence we define a *right functional value* $f_R(C)$ and a *left functional value* $f_L(C)$ as follows:

$$f_R(C) = A_0 + A_1 C + A_2 C^2 + \cdots + A_r C^r$$

and

$$f_L(C) = A_0 + CA_1 + C^2 A_2 + \cdots + C^r A_r.$$

It is easy to see that, if $f(x) \cdot g(x) = h(x)$, it does not necessarily follow that $f_R(C) \cdot g_R(C) = h_R(C)$. However, we can prove the following theorem.

Theorem 16. Let f(x) · g(x) = h(x), *where* f(x), g(x), *and* h(x) *are polynomials whose coefficients are* $n \times n$ *matrices over a field. Let* C *be an* $n \times n$ *matrix such that* $g_R(C) = 0$. *Then* $h_R(C) = 0$.

Using the notation for $f(x)$, $g(x)$, and $h(x)$ given above, we have

$$
\begin{aligned}
h_R(C) &= A_0B_0 + (A_0B_1 + A_1B_0)C + (A_0B_2 + A_1B_1 + A_2B_0)C^2 \\
&\quad + \cdots + A_rB_mC^{r+m} \\
&= A_0(B_0 + B_1C + B_2C^2 + \cdots + B_mC^m) \\
&\quad + A_1(B_0 + B_1C + \cdots + B_mC^m)C + \cdots \\
&\quad + A_k(B_0 + B_1C + \cdots + B_mC^m)C^k + \cdots \\
&\quad + A_n(B_0 + B_1C + \cdots + B_mC^m)C^r \\
&= A_0g_R(C) + A_1g_R(C)C + \cdots + A_rg_R(C)C^r.
\end{aligned}
$$

Thus, if $g_R(C) = 0$, $h_R(C) = 0$. Similarly it can be proved that, if $f_L(C) = 0$, then $h_L(C) = 0$.

From these remarks we observe that the theory of polynomials with matrix coefficients is more complicated than the theory of polynomials over a field.

Characteristic Polynomial of a Matrix

Let A be an $n \times n$ matrix over a field F. Form the matrix $A - xI$, where I is the $n \times n$ identity matrix and x is an indeterminate. The determinant $|A - xI| = b_0 + b_1x + \cdots + (-1)^n x^n = f(x)$ is called the characteristic polynomial of the matrix A.

EXAMPLE. Let $A = \begin{bmatrix} 2 & -1 \\ -6 & 1 \end{bmatrix}$. Then

$$
A - xI = \begin{bmatrix} 2 - x & -1 \\ -6 & 1 - x \end{bmatrix}
$$

and $|A - xI| = -4 - 3x + x^2 = f(x)$. A simple computation shows that $-4I - 3A + A^2$ is the zero matrix.

We shall now prove in general that, if a matrix A is substituted for x in its characteristic polynomial, and if the constant term in the polynomial is multiplied by the identity matrix, the resulting sum is the zero matrix. Thus a matrix A is said to be a zero of its characteristic polynomial.

Theorem 17. Cayley-Hamilton theorem. Let A *be an* $n \times n$ *matrix over a field and let* f(x) = $b_0 + b_1x + b_2x^2 + \cdots + (-1)^n x^n$ *be its characteristic polynomial. Then* $b_0I + b_1A + b_2A^2 + \cdots + (-1)^n A^n = 0$.

Now adj$(A - xI) \cdot (A - xI) = f(x)I$. The elements of adj$(A - xI)$ are polynomials in x of degree at most $n - 1$ with coefficients in the field F. Hence adj$(A - xI)$ may be regarded as a polynomial in x of degree at most $n - 1$ with matrix coefficients over F. Thus adj$(A - xI) \cdot (A - xI)$ is the product of two polynomials with matrix coefficients which equals a polynomial in x of degree n whose coefficients are scalar matrices over F. Note that $A - AI = 0$. Hence by the previous theorem $f_R(A)I = 0$, but since the coefficients of $f(x)I$ are scalar matrices the right and left functional values are the same. Hence we may write $f(A)I = 0$, which is the desired result.

DEFINITION. The zeros of the characteristic polynomial of a matrix over a field F are called the *characteristic roots** of the matrix. If the field F is the field of complex numbers, then the characteristic polynomial of an $n \times n$ matrix over F always has n zeros that are complex numbers.

The characteristic roots of the matrix A in the previous example are -1 and 4.

Exercises

Form the characteristic polynomial and find the characteristic roots of the following matrices over the field of complex numbers.

1. $\begin{bmatrix} 3 & 2 \\ -2 & 3 \end{bmatrix}$.   2. $\begin{bmatrix} 1 & -6 \\ 2 & -6 \end{bmatrix}$.

3. $\begin{bmatrix} 1 & 3 \\ -1 & 5 \end{bmatrix}$.   4. $\begin{bmatrix} i & -2i \\ 0 & -i \end{bmatrix}$.

5. $\begin{bmatrix} 3 & 0 & 0 \\ 0 & 1 & 0 \\ 0 & 0 & -1 \end{bmatrix}$.   6. $\begin{bmatrix} 3 & 2 & 2 \\ 1 & 4 & 1 \\ -2 & -4 & -1 \end{bmatrix}$.

7. Prove the Cayley-Hamilton theorem for 2×2 matrices by direct computation.
8. Find a necessary and sufficient condition that the characteristic roots of a 2×2 matrix be equal.
9. Find all 2×2 matrices with characteristic roots 1 and -1.

10 · SIMILAR MATRICES OVER A FIELD

DEFINITION. If a nonsingular matrix S exists such that $S^{-1}AS = B$, then A and B are said to be *similar*.

* Also called *eigenvalues*.

Note that similarity of matrices is a special case of the equivalence of matrices. We shall give some of the simpler properties of similar matrices.

Theorem 18.   The determinants of similar matrices are equal.

Let $B = S^{-1}AS$. Then $|B| = |S^{-1}AS| = |S^{-1}| \cdot |A| \cdot |S| = |A| \cdot |S^{-1}| \cdot |S| = |A| \cdot |S^{-1}S| = |A| \cdot |I| = |A|$.

Theorem 19.   Similar matrices have the same characteristic polynomial.

Let $B = S^{-1}AS$. Then

$$B - xI = S^{-1}AS - xI = S^{-1}AS - S^{-1}(xI)S$$

$$= S^{-1}(AS - xIS) = S^{-1}(A - xI)S.$$

Hence

$$|B - xI| = |S^{-1}| \cdot |A - xI| \cdot |S| = |A - xI|.$$

Diagonal matrices have particularly simple properties. For example, their determinants are the products of the elements in their principal diagonals, and the product of two diagonal matrices is a diagonal matrix. Moreover, the characteristic polynomial of a diagonal matrix whose diagonal elements are $d_1, d_2, \cdots, d_n$ is $(d_1 - x)(d_2 - x) \cdots (d_n - x)$, and hence its characteristic roots are $d_1, d_2, \cdots, d_n$. It is of interest to examine one simple example of a matrix that is similar to a diagonal matrix.

Theorem 20.   Let A be an n × n matrix over the field of complex numbers. If the characteristic roots of the matrix A are distinct, then A is similar to a diagonal matrix.

Let $|A - xI| = f(x)$ have the distinct zeros $r_1, r_2, \cdots, r_n$. We construct a nonsingular matrix S such that $S^{-1}AS$ is a diagonal matrix with diagonal elements $r_1, r_2, \cdots, r_n$. We first show that we can find nonzero $n \times 1$ matrices, or vectors, S_j, such that $AS_j = r_j S_j$ for $j = 1, 2, \cdots, n$. Denote the elements of S_j by $s_{1j}, s_{2j}, \cdots, s_{nj}$. Now $AS_j = r_j S_j$ may be written as $(A - r_j I)S_j = 0$, which for each $j = 1, 2, \cdots, n$, is a system of n linear homogeneous equations in the n unknowns s_{ij}, with $i = 1, 2, \cdots, n$. This system has a solution other than $(0, 0, \cdots, 0)$ if and only if the determinant $|A - r_j I| = 0$. But r_j is a zero of $f(x)$, and hence we have the desired nonzero solutions for each j. The columns of the matrix S are the n columns S_j.

We show next that the n vectors S_j are linearly independent. Suppose that a linear relation $\sum_{j=1}^{n} c_j S_j = 0$ exists. The method we use to show that

$c_1 = 0$, for example, may be used to prove that each $c_j = 0$ for $j = 1, 2, \cdots, n$. Multiply the matrix equation $\sum_{j=1}^{n} c_j S_j = 0$ on the left by the product

$$(A - r_2 I)(A - r_3 I) \cdots (A - r_n I),$$

obtaining

$$(A - r_2 I)(A - r_3 I) \cdots (A - r_n I)(c_1 S_1 + c_2 S_2 + \cdots + c_n S_n) = 0.$$

Note that the factors $(A - r_j I)$ are commutative with each other. Now

$$(A - r_j I)c_k S_k = (A S_k - r_j S_k)c_k = (r_k S_k - r_j S_k)c_k$$
$$= (r_k - r_j)S_k c_k,$$

so that

$$(A - r_j I)c_j S_j = 0.$$

Thus

$$(A - r_2 I)(A - r_3 I) \cdots (A - r_n I)(c_1 S_1 + c_2 S_2 + \cdots + c_n S_n)$$
$$= (A - r_2 I)(A - r_3 I) \cdots (A - r_n I)c_1 S_1$$
$$= (r_1 - r_2)(r_1 - r_3) \cdots (r_1 - r_n)c_1 S_1 = 0,$$

if and only if $c_1 = 0$. Hence the columns S_j are linearly independent so that S is nonsingular. Since $A S_j = r_j S_j$, where the S_j are the columns of S, we have

$$AS = S \begin{bmatrix} r_1 & 0 & 0 & \cdots & 0 \\ 0 & r_2 & 0 & \cdots & 0 \\ & & \cdots & & \\ 0 & 0 & 0 & \cdots & r_n \end{bmatrix}$$

and, finally, that $S^{-1}AS$ is a diagonal matrix.

EXAMPLE. Letting $A = \begin{bmatrix} 2 & -1 \\ -6 & 1 \end{bmatrix}$, we have $f(x) = |A - xI| = (x - 4)$ $(x + 1)$, which has the two zeros 4 and -1. We solve the two systems of equations $A S_1 = 4 S_1$ and $A S_2 = -S_2$. Thus we have $(A - 4I)S_1 = 0$ and $(A + I)S_2 = 0$, which, written out explicitly, are respectively

$$\begin{bmatrix} -2 & -1 \\ -6 & -3 \end{bmatrix}\begin{bmatrix} s_{11} \\ s_{21} \end{bmatrix} = 0 \quad \text{and} \quad \begin{bmatrix} 3 & -1 \\ -6 & 2 \end{bmatrix}\begin{bmatrix} s_{12} \\ s_{22} \end{bmatrix} = 0.$$

These equations give us $2s_{11} + s_{21} = 0$ and $3s_{12} - s_{22} = 0$. Choosing $s_{11} = 1$ and $s_{12} = 1$, we obtain $s_{21} = -2$ and $s_{22} = 3$. Thus $S = \begin{bmatrix} 1 & 1 \\ -2 & 3 \end{bmatrix}$ and $S^{-1}AS$ $= \begin{bmatrix} 4 & 0 \\ 0 & -1 \end{bmatrix}$.

Exercises

Find nonsingular matrices S such that $S^{-1}AS$ is a matrix in diagonal form for each of the following matrices A:

1. $\begin{bmatrix} 2 & -1 \\ 2 & 5 \end{bmatrix}.$
   2. $\begin{bmatrix} 2 & 5 \\ 4 & 1 \end{bmatrix}.$
   3. $\begin{bmatrix} 1 & 0 \\ 2 & 3 \end{bmatrix}.$

4. $\begin{bmatrix} 1 & 2 & 0 \\ 2 & 1 & 0 \\ 1 & 0 & -3 \end{bmatrix}.$
   5. $\begin{bmatrix} 1 & 0 & -1 \\ 2 & 3 & 1 \\ 1 & 0 & 2 \end{bmatrix}.$
   6. $\begin{bmatrix} 1 & 1 & -2 \\ 0 & 0 & 5 \\ 4 & 1 & 2 \end{bmatrix}.$

7. Show that any 2×2 matrix A such that $A^2 = -I$ is similar to the matrix $\begin{bmatrix} 0 & 1 \\ -1 & 0 \end{bmatrix}.$

9 Groups, Rings, and Fields

1 · NORMAL SUBGROUPS AND FACTOR GROUPS

Now that we have another example of a noncommutative operation, namely the multiplication of matrices, we shall turn to a further study of the properties of groups. The student should review the definitions of a group, a subgroup, and the left and right cosets of a subgroup in a group.

Normal or Invariant Subgroup

Let S be a subgroup of a group G. Then, if $aS = Sa$ for every a in G, S is said to be a normal or invariant subgroup of G. Note that, if S is a normal subgroup of G, the right and left cosets of S in G coincide, so that we may speak of cosets without ambiguity.

EXAMPLES. Every subgroup of an abelian group is a normal subgroup. The subgroup S with elements $i = (1)(2)(3)$, (123), (132) is a normal subgroup of the symmetric group on three symbols. The right and left cosets of this subgroup in the symmetric group on three symbols are i, (123), (132), and (12), (13), (23), and hence $aS = Sa$ for every a in G.

Note that, when we write $aS = Sa$, we do not mean that we must have $as = sa$ for all elements s of S. Rather we mean that, if we are given an element s_1 of S, there exists an element s_2 of S such that $as_1 = s_2a$; s_2 may or may not be equal to s_1. Thus we have $(12)(123) = (13) = (132)(12)$, where (123) and (132) are both in S.

DEFINITION. If S_1 and S_2 are two subsets of a group G, we define the *product* S_1S_2 to be the set consisting of all products s_1s_2 for s_1 in S_1 and s_2 in S_2.

Theorem 1. *If* S *is a normal subgroup of a group* G, *then the product,* (aS)(bS), *of two cosets,* aS *and* bS, *of* S *in* G *is the coset* (ab)S.

If x is in $(ab)S$, then $x = (ab)s$, where s is in S. Hence $x = (ai)(bs)$, where i is the identity element of S. Thus x is in $(aS)(bS)$. Conversely, if x is in $(aS)(bS)$, $x = (as_1)(bs_2) = a(s_1b)s_2$, where s_1 and s_2 are in S. Since S is a normal subgroup of G, $s_1b = bs_3$, where s_3 is in S. Hence $x = a(bs_3)s_2 = (ab)(s_2s_3)$. But S is a subgroup of G so that $s_2s_3 = s_4$ in S. Thus $x = (ab)s_4$ and, hence, x is in $(ab)S$.

Theorem 2. *If* S *is a normal subgroup of a group* G, *then the cosets of* S *in* G *form a group with respect to coset multiplication.*

We have just proved that the product of two cosets of S is a coset of S. We can easily show that $(aS)[(bS)(cS)] = [(aS)(bS)](cS)$. The identity element is $iS = S$, for $S(aS) = (Sa)S = (aS)S = a(SS) = aS$, and the inverse of aS is $a^{-1}S$, for $(a^{-1}S)(aS) = (a^{-1}a)(SS) = iS = S$.

EXAMPLE. The two cosets of the subgroup $i = (1)(2)(3)$, (123), (132) in the symmetric group on three symbols form a group of order 2.

Quotient or Factor Group

The group of cosets of a normal subgroup S of a group G under coset multiplication is called a quotient group or a factor group of the given group G. It is denoted by G/S or, in the case of Abelian groups, customarily by $G - S$.

Only normal subgroups can be used to define a factor group of a group G. For, in order that the left cosets or the right cosets of a subgroup S in G form a group, we must demand either that the product of two left cosets of S in G is a left coset of S or that the product of two right cosets of S is a right coset of S. The following theorem shows that this condition implies that S is a normal subgroup.

Theorem 3. *If the product of two left cosets of a subgroup* S *in a group* G *is a left coset of* S *in* G, *then* S *is a normal subgroup.*

We wish to show that $aS = Sa$ for every a in G. We first show that every element of Sa is an element of aS. Since the product of two left cosets is a left coset, we have $S(aS) = (iS)(aS) = bS$. But $a = i(ai)$ is in $S(aS)$ and, since two cosets are either identical or disjoint, $bS = aS$. Hence $(Sa)S = aS$. Now i is in S and thus, if $x = sa$ is in Sa, we have $xi = (sa)i = s(ai) = as'$ where s' is in S, i.e., every element of Sa is an element of aS.

On the other hand, suppose that as is any element of aS, where s is in S. Form the product $(as)(a^{-1}s^{-1}) = a(sa^{-1}s^{-1})$. Since we have just shown that Sa is contained in aS, we have $sa^{-1} = a^{-1}s_1$, where s_1 is in S. Hence

$(as)(a^{-1}s^{-1}) = a(a^{-1}s_1 s^{-1}) = a(a^{-1}s_2) = s_2$ in S since S is a subgroup of G. It follows that $as = s_2(sa) = (s_2 s)a = s_3 a$, where s_3 is in S. Thus every element, as, of aS is equal to an element, $s_3 a$, of Sa and hence $aS = Sa$ for every a in G.

Exercises

1. Prove that the following matrices form a group G with respect to matrix multiplication:

$$i = \begin{bmatrix} 1 & 0 \\ 0 & 1 \end{bmatrix}, \quad a = \begin{bmatrix} 0 & 1 \\ -1 & 0 \end{bmatrix}, \quad b = \begin{bmatrix} -1 & 0 \\ 0 & -1 \end{bmatrix}, \quad c = \begin{bmatrix} 0 & -1 \\ 1 & 0 \end{bmatrix},$$

$$d = \begin{bmatrix} 1 & 0 \\ 0 & -1 \end{bmatrix}, \quad e = \begin{bmatrix} 0 & 1 \\ 1 & 0 \end{bmatrix}, \quad f = \begin{bmatrix} -1 & 0 \\ 0 & 1 \end{bmatrix}, \quad g = \begin{bmatrix} 0 & -1 \\ -1 & 0 \end{bmatrix}.$$

2. In the following four exercises let G denote the group in Exercise 1.

   a. Prove that the subgroup S consisting of the elements i, b is a normal subgroup of G.
   b. Prove that the factor group G/S of G is not cyclic.
   c. Show that the elements i, a, b, c form a normal subgroup of G.
   d. Show that the elements i, d do not form a normal subgroup of G.

3. Let k denote the number of left cosets of a subgroup S in a group G. Prove that, if $k = 2$, the subgroup S is a normal subgroup.
4. Prove Theorem 3 for right cosets.
5. Prove: If G is an abelian group and S is a subgroup of G, then G/S is abelian.
6. List all of the normal subgroups of the symmetric group on three symbols.

2 · CONJUGATES

DEFINITION. Let x and a be any elements of a group G. Then the element $x^{-1}ax$ is said to be *conjugate* to a under G, and $x^{-1}ax$ and a are called *conjugate elements* under G. The element $x^{-1}ax$ is also called the *transform* of the element a by x.

Theorem 4. The elements of a group can be separated into mutually exclusive classes of conjugate elements.

To prove this theorem we need merely show that the relation b conjugate to a under a group G is an equivalence relation. The three properties of an equivalence relation can be checked as follows. The element a is conjugate to a, for $i^{-1}ai = a$, where i is the identity. If a is conjugate to b, then b is conjugate to a, for if $a = x^{-1}bx$, then $b = xax^{-1} = (x^{-1})^{-1}ax^{-1}$. If a is conjugate to b, and if b is conjugate to c, then a is conjugate to c, for if $a = x^{-1}bx$ and $b = y^{-1}cy$, then $a = x^{-1}(y^{-1}cy)x = (yx)^{-1}c(yx)$. Thus the elements of a group can be separated into mutually exclusive classes of conjugate elements.

EXAMPLE. The student can check that the elements of the symmetric group on three symbols can be separated into the following three classes of conjugate elements. The first class consists of the identity $i = (1)(2)(3)$; the second class consists of (123) and (132); and the third class consists of the elements (12), (13), and (23).

Theorem 5. Those elements x *of a group* G *such that* $x^{-1}ax = a$ *form a subgroup* N *of* G, *called the **normalizer** of the element* a.

Note that this theorem says that all the elements of G which are commutative with a given element of G form a group. It is obvious that the normalizer contains the cyclic group generated by the given element. We proceed to the proof. Consider the set N of elements that are commutative with the element a. In order to prove that N is a subgroup, we need merely prove that the set N is closed and that if it contains x it contains x^{-1}. Let $x^{-1}ax = a$ and $y^{-1}ay = a$. Then $a = x^{-1}ax = y^{-1}(x^{-1}ax)y = (xy)^{-1}a(xy)$. Thus the set N is closed. Now if x is in N it is obvious that x^{-1} is in N, for if $x^{-1}ax = a$, $a = xax^{-1} = (x^{-1})^{-1}ax^{-1}$.

Theorem 6. Let N *be the normalizer of an element* a *of a group* G. *Then all the elements of the right coset* Nb *of* N *transform the element* a *into the same conjugate* $b^{-1}ab$. *Moreover, if* $b^{-1}ab = c^{-1}ac$, *then* Nb = Nc. *Thus there is a one-to-one correspondence between the right cosets of* N *in* G *and the elements conjugate to* a *under* G.

Any element nb of Nb transforms a into $b^{-1}ab$, for $(nb)^{-1}a(nb) = b^{-1}(n^{-1}an)b = b^{-1}ab$. Now if $b^{-1}ab = c^{-1}ac$, then $(bc^{-1})^{-1}a(bc^{-1}) = a$ and bc^{-1} is in N. Since bc^{-1} is in N, $N = N(bc^{-1})$ so that $Nc = N(bc^{-1})c = Nb(c^{-1}c) = Nb$.

Corollary. If G *is a finite group, the number of elements in a given class of conjugates is a divisor of the order of the group.*

By Theorem 6 the number of distinct right cosets of the normalizer of an element a in G is the number of conjugates in a class. Now we apply the theorem of Lagrange which states that the number of right cosets of a subgroup in a group is a divisor of the order of the group.

Transform of a Permutation

It is of interest to find a simple way to transform any permutation by any other permutation. Let $a = (1\ 2\ 3 \cdots n)$ be any cycle of n symbols, and let $x = \begin{pmatrix} 1\ 2\ 3 \cdots n \\ i_1\ i_2\ i_3 \cdots i_n \end{pmatrix}$ be any permutation on these n symbols. Then $x^{-1} = \begin{pmatrix} i_1\ i_2\ i_3 \cdots i_n \\ 1\ 2\ 3 \cdots n \end{pmatrix}$, and it is easily seen that $x^{-1}ax = (i_1\ i_2\ i_3 \cdots i_n)$.

Thus, to transform the permutation a by any other permutation, we replace the symbols in a by the symbols that follow them in the transforming permutation. Let $a = (123)(456)$ and $x = (2143)(56)$, for example. Then $x^{-1}ax = (412)(365)$.

Conjugate Subgroups

The relation of being conjugate is not restricted to the elements of a group. If x is an element of a group G and if S is a subgroup of G, then $x^{-1}Sx$ is a subgroup of G and is called a conjugate of S under G. It is easily seen that $x^{-1}Sx$ is a subgroup, for the product of two elements of the set $x^{-1}Sx$, $(x^{-1}sx)(x^{-1}s'x) = x^{-1}(ss')x$ is again an element of the set $x^{-1}Sx$. Moreover, if $x^{-1}sx$ is in $x^{-1}Sx$, then its inverse, $x^{-1}s^{-1}x$, is in $x^{-1}Sx$. Thus it is seen that the word subgroup can be substituted for element throughout the preceding theorems on conjugate elements.

Note that our definition of a normal subgroup, i.e., a subgroup S of G such that $aS = Sa$ for every a in G, can be restated to read: S is a normal subgroup of G if $a^{-1}Sa = S$ for every a in G. We say, then, that a normal subgroup is *self-conjugate* under G.

Exercises

1. Separate the elements of the octic permutation group $i = (1)(2)(3)(4)$, (1234), $(13)(24)$, (1432), (13), (24), $(12)(34)$, $(14)(23)$ into classes of conjugate elements.
2. Find the normalizer of the element $(14)(23)$ in the octic group.
3. Find the normal subgroups of the octic group.
4. Find the classes of conjugate elements of the cyclic group of order 5.

3 · AUTOMORPHISMS OF A GROUP

DEFINITION. An isomorphism of a group with itself is called an *automorphism*.

We want to define the product of two automorphisms of a group. To do this, it is convenient to write $a \leftrightarrow \mathbf{f}(a)$ rather than, as previously, $a \leftrightarrow a'$. Thus $\mathbf{f}$ is an automorphism of a group G if and only if $a \leftrightarrow \mathbf{f}(a)$ is a one-to-one correspondence of G with itself and $\mathbf{f}(ab) = \mathbf{f}(a)\,\mathbf{f}(b)$ for all elements a and b in G.

DEFINITION. The *product*, $\mathbf{f} \cdot \mathbf{g}$, of two automorphisms $\mathbf{f}$ and $\mathbf{g}$ of a group G is the correspondence $\mathbf{h}$ defined by $a \leftrightarrow \mathbf{h}(a) = \mathbf{f}[\mathbf{g}(a)]$.

We will now demonstrate that the product of two automorphisms is an automorphism and, in fact, show that we have a group of automorphisms.

Theorem 7. The set of all automorphisms of a group forms a group under the product operation for automorphisms.

Let G be a group and $\mathbf{f}$, $\mathbf{g}$, and $\mathbf{h}$ be automorphisms of G. Then certainly $a \leftrightarrow \mathbf{f} \cdot \mathbf{g}(a) = \mathbf{f}[\mathbf{g}(a)]$ is a one-to-one correspondence between the elements of G since $a \leftrightarrow \mathbf{g}(a) = a'$ and $a' \leftrightarrow \mathbf{f}(a')$ are one-to-one correspondences. Also $\mathbf{f} \cdot \mathbf{g}(ab) = \mathbf{f}[\mathbf{g}(ab)] = \mathbf{f}[\mathbf{g}(a)\,\mathbf{g}(b)] = \mathbf{f}[\mathbf{g}(a)]\mathbf{f}[\mathbf{g}(b)] = [\mathbf{f} \cdot \mathbf{g}(a)][\mathbf{f} \cdot \mathbf{g}(b)]$ so that the correspondence $a \leftrightarrow \mathbf{f} \cdot \mathbf{g}(a)$ is preserved under the group operation. Hence we have closure. Obviously, if $\mathbf{i}(a) = a$, the correspondence $a \leftrightarrow \mathbf{i}(a)$ yields the identity automorphism $\mathbf{i}$. If $\mathbf{f}$ is the one-to-one correspondence $a \leftrightarrow \mathbf{f}(a)$ and $\mathbf{g}$ is the one-to-one correspondence $\mathbf{f}(a) \leftrightarrow \mathbf{g}[\mathbf{f}(a)] = a$, then $\mathbf{g} \cdot \mathbf{f} = \mathbf{i}$ and $\mathbf{g}$ is a left inverse of $\mathbf{f}$. Finally, $[(\mathbf{f} \cdot \mathbf{g}) \cdot \mathbf{h}](a) = [\mathbf{f} \cdot \mathbf{g}]\mathbf{h}(a) = \mathbf{f}\{\mathbf{g}[\mathbf{h}(a)]\} = \mathbf{f}[\mathbf{g} \cdot \mathbf{h}(a)] = [\mathbf{f} \cdot (\mathbf{g} \cdot \mathbf{h})](a)$ so that $(\mathbf{f} \cdot \mathbf{g}) \cdot \mathbf{h} = \mathbf{f} \cdot (\mathbf{g} \cdot \mathbf{h})$.

Theorem 8. *For any fixed element* x *of a group* G, *the correspondence* $a \leftrightarrow x^{-1}ax$ *is an automorphism of* G.

If $a \leftrightarrow x^{-1}ax$ and if $b \leftrightarrow x^{-1}bx$, then $ab \leftrightarrow (x^{-1}ax)(x^{-1}bx) = x^{-1}(ab)x$. Automorphisms that may be established by transforming the elements of a group G by a fixed element x of G are called *inner* automorphisms of G. All other automorphisms are called *outer* automorphisms of G.

Theorem 9. *The inner automorphisms of a group* G *form a normal subgroup* I *of the group* A *of automorphisms of* G.

Let $\mathbf{f}(a) = x^{-1}ax$ and $\mathbf{g}(a) = y^{-1}ay$. Then $\mathbf{f} \cdot \mathbf{g}(a) = \mathbf{f}(y^{-1}ay) = x^{-1}(y^{-1}ay)x = (x^{-1}y^{-1})\, a(yx) = (yx)^{-1}\, a(yx)$. Hence $\mathbf{f} \cdot \mathbf{g}$ is an inner automorphism if $\mathbf{f}$ and $\mathbf{g}$ are inner automorphisms. The identity automorphism $\mathbf{i}$ has the property that $\mathbf{i}(a) = a = i^{-1}ai = x$ (where i is the identity of G) and, hence, $\mathbf{i}$ is an inner automorphism. Finally, if $\mathbf{f}(a) = x^{-1}ax$, then $\mathbf{f}^{-1}(a) = (x^{-1})^{-1}ax^{-1} = xax^{-1}$ since $\mathbf{f}^{-1} \cdot \mathbf{f}(a) = \mathbf{f}^{-1}(x^{-1}ax) = x(x^{-1}ax)x^{-1} = a = \mathbf{i}(a)$. Hence if $\mathbf{f}$ is an inner automorphism, so is $\mathbf{f}^{-1}$. Thus the inner automorphisms form a subgroup I of the group A of automorphisms of G.

It remains to be proved that I is a normal subgroup of A, i.e., we must show that, if $\mathbf{f}$ is any automorphism and $\mathbf{j}$ is any inner automorphism, then $\mathbf{f}^{-1} \cdot \mathbf{j} \cdot \mathbf{f}$ is an inner automorphism. Suppose that $\mathbf{j}(a) = x^{-1}ax$. Then

$$[\mathbf{f}^{-1} \cdot \mathbf{j} \cdot \mathbf{f}](a) = [\mathbf{f}^{-1} \cdot \mathbf{j}]\mathbf{f}(a) = \mathbf{f}^{-1}[x^{-1}\mathbf{f}(a)x]$$
$$= \mathbf{f}^{-1}(x^{-1})\mathbf{f}^{-1}[\mathbf{f}(a)]\mathbf{f}^{-1}(x) = [\mathbf{f}^{-1}(x)]^{-1}a[\mathbf{f}^{-1}(x)] = y^{-1}ay$$

where $y = \mathbf{f}^{-1}(x)$. (Note that we use the fact that, in an isomorphism, if the image of a is b, the image of a^{-1} is b^{-1}.)

EXAMPLES

1. The cyclic group of order four, a, a^2, a^3, $a^4 = i$, has no inner automorphism except the identity, but it has the following outer automorphism:

$$i \leftrightarrow i \qquad a^2 \leftrightarrow a^2$$
$$a \leftrightarrow a^3 \qquad a^3 \leftrightarrow a$$

Thus the group of automorphisms is of order 2.

2. The group of automorphisms of the symmetric group on three symbols consists only of inner automorphisms. We list the automorphisms, and under each automorphism we give the transforming permutation x used to establish the automorphism:

a	b	c
$i \leftrightarrow i$	$i \leftrightarrow i$	$i \leftrightarrow i$
$(123) \leftrightarrow (123)$	$(123) \leftrightarrow (132)$	$(123) \leftrightarrow (132)$
$(132) \leftrightarrow (132)$	$(132) \leftrightarrow (123)$	$(132) \leftrightarrow (123)$
$(12) \leftrightarrow (12)$	$(12) \leftrightarrow (13)$	$(12) \leftrightarrow (12)$
$(13) \leftrightarrow (13)$	$(13) \leftrightarrow (12)$	$(13) \leftrightarrow (23)$
$(23) \leftrightarrow (23)$	$(23) \leftrightarrow (23)$	$(23) \leftrightarrow (13)$
$x = i$	$x = (23)$	$x = (12)$

d	e	f
$i \leftrightarrow i$	$i \leftrightarrow i$	$i \leftrightarrow i$
$(123) \leftrightarrow (132)$	$(123) \leftrightarrow (123)$	$(123) \leftrightarrow (123)$
$(132) \leftrightarrow (123)$	$(132) \leftrightarrow (132)$	$(132) \leftrightarrow (132)$
$(12) \leftrightarrow (23)$	$(12) \leftrightarrow (23)$	$(12) \leftrightarrow (13)$
$(13) \leftrightarrow (13)$	$(13) \leftrightarrow (12)$	$(13) \leftrightarrow (23)$
$(23) \leftrightarrow (12)$	$(23) \leftrightarrow (13)$	$(23) \leftrightarrow (12)$
$x = (13)$	$x = (123)$	$x = (132)$

We now give the multiplication table for the group of automorphisms where **a** is the identity automorphism.

	a	b	c	d	e	f
a	a	b	c	d	e	f
b	b	a	f	e	d	c
c	c	e	a	f	b	d
d	d	f	e	a	c	b
e	e	c	d	b	f	a
f	f	d	b	c	a	e

For example:

$$\mathbf{b} \cdot \mathbf{c}(i) = \mathbf{b}[\mathbf{c}(i)] = \mathbf{b}(i) = i = \mathbf{f}(i);$$
$$\mathbf{b} \cdot \mathbf{c}(123) = \mathbf{b}[\mathbf{c}(123)] = \mathbf{b}(132) = (123) = \mathbf{f}(123);$$
$$\mathbf{b} \cdot \mathbf{c}(132) = \mathbf{b}[\mathbf{c}(132)] = \mathbf{b}(123) = (132) = \mathbf{f}(132);$$
$$\mathbf{b} \cdot \mathbf{c}(12) = \mathbf{b}[\mathbf{c}(12)] = \mathbf{b}(12) = (13) = \mathbf{f}(12);$$
$$\mathbf{b} \cdot \mathbf{c}(13) = \mathbf{b}[\mathbf{c}(13)] = \mathbf{b}(23) = (23) = \mathbf{f}(13);$$
$$\mathbf{b} \cdot \mathbf{c}(23) = \mathbf{b}[\mathbf{c}(23)] = \mathbf{b}(13) = (12) = \mathbf{f}(23).$$

Thus $\mathbf{b} \cdot \mathbf{c}(a) = \mathbf{f}(a)$ for all elements a of the symmetric group on three symbols and, hence, $\mathbf{b} \cdot \mathbf{c} = \mathbf{f}$.

Exercises

1. Find the order of each of the automorphisms of the symmetric group on three symbols.
2. Find the group of automorphisms of the group of the five fifth roots of unity. Is it cyclic? Are any of these automorphisms inner automorphisms?
3. Find the group of automorphisms of the octic group.
4. Find the group of automorphisms of the cyclic group of order 6.
5. Find the group of automorphisms of the four group $i = (1)(2)(3)(4)$, $(12)(34)$, $(13)(24)$, $(14)(23)$.
6. Find the group of automorphisms of the alternating group on four symbols. Are any of the automorphisms outer automorphisms?
7. How many automorphisms has a cyclic group of order p? One of order pq? (p and q distinct primes).

4 · HOMOMORPHISMS OF GROUPS

DEFINITION.   Let $a, b, c, \cdots$, denote the elements of a group G, and let $a', b', c', \cdots$ denote the elements of a group G'. The group G' is said to be a *homomorphic* image of the group G if a correspondence $a \rightarrow a'$ can be set up from the elements of G onto the elements of G' such that:

1. every element a in G' has exactly one image a' in G';
2. every element of G' occurs at least once as an image;
3. if $a \rightarrow a'$ and $b \rightarrow b'$, then $ab \rightarrow a'b'$.

The correspondence is called a *homomorphism* of G onto G'.

Note the omission of the double arrow to indicate that the mapping is from G onto G'. A homomorphism is not in general a one-to-one correspondence but a many-to-one correspondence. If the correspondence is one-to-one, a homomorphism reduces to an isomorphism.

EXAMPLE.   Let G be the symmetric group on n symbols, and let G' be the multiplicative group of order 2 consisting of the elements 1 and -1. A homomorphism can be set up by letting every even permutation have the image 1 and every odd permutation the image -1.

Theorem 10.   Let a group G′ *be the homomorphic image of a group* G. *Then the image of the identity in* G *is the identity in* G′, *and, if* a $\rightarrow$ a′, *then* a^{-1} $\rightarrow$ (a′)$^{-1}$.

This theorem is proved in the same way in which we proved the corresponding theorem for an isomorphism between two groups. Let the identity i of G have the image a' in the homomorphism, and let x' be any element of G'. Let x be an element of G which has x' as its image in G'. Then $ix \rightarrow a'x'$. However, $ix = x$, and so $a'x' = x'$ for any element x' of G. Hence a' is the identity of G'. Similarly, if $x^{-1} \rightarrow b'$, then $x^{-1}x \rightarrow b'x'$.

However, $x^{-1}x = i$, and so $b'x' = i'$, the identity of G'. Thus b' is the inverse of x'.

Now put into one class all those elements a of G which have the same image a' in G'. The following theorem describes these classes.

Theorem 11. Let a group G' *be a homomorphic image of a group* G. *Then those elements* a *of* G *whose image is the identity in* G' *form a normal subgroup* S *of* G, *and those elements of* G *which have the same image in* G' *form a coset of* S *in* G. *The factor group* G/S *is isomorphic to* G'.

Consider the elements in G which have the identity i' as an image in G'. Denote this set by S. If $a \to i'$ and $b \to i'$, then $ab \to i'i' = i'$. Thus the set S is closed. Further, if $a \to i'$, then by the previous theorem $a^{-1} \to (i')^{-1} = i'$, and so the inverse of each element in S is in S. Hence S is a subgroup of G.

We next prove that S is a normal subgroup of G. Now all the elements of the left coset xS have the same image in G', for, if $x \to x'$ and s is in S, then $xs \to x'i' = x'$. Moreover, if $y \to x'$, then, as we shall prove, y lies in xS. Now $x^{-1}y \to (x')^{-1}x' = i'$. Hence $x^{-1}y$ is in S and y is in xS. Similarly we can prove that all the elements of G whose image is x' in G' form the right coset Sx. Hence $Sx = xS$ and S is a normal subgroup of G.

Note that we have established a one-to-one correspondence between the cosets of S in G and the elements a' of G'. Hence if $aS \to a'$ and $bS \to b'$, then $(aS)(bS) = (ab)S \to a'b'$. Hence the factor group G/S and G' are isomorphic.

DEFINITION. The subgroup S is called the *kernel* of the homomorphism.

Now combining our previous discussion of a factor group of G with the definition of homomorphism, we have the following theorem.

Theorem 12. Let S *be a normal subgroup of a group* G. *Then the factor group* G/S *is a homomorphic image of* G.

EXAMPLE. We may set up a homomorphism of the alternating group on four symbols onto the cyclic group of order 3 as follows:

$$i = (1)(2)(3)(4) \to i' = a^3$$
$$(12)(34) \to i'$$
$$(13)(24) \to i'$$
$$(14)(23) \to i'$$
$$(123) \to a$$
$$(243) \to a$$
$$(142) \to a$$
$$(134) \to a$$
$$(132) \to a^2$$
$$(143) \to a^2$$
$$(234) \to a^2$$
$$(124) \to a^2.$$

Exercises

1. Set up a homomorphism of the octic group onto the cyclic group of order 2.
2. Set up a homomorphism of the octic group onto the permutation group
   $i = (1)(2)(3)(4)$, $(12)(34)$, $(13)(24)$, $(14)(23)$.
3. Set up a homomorphism of the cyclic group of order 8 onto the cyclic group of order 4.
4. Set up a homomorphism of the symmetric group on four symbols onto the symmetric group on three symbols.
5. Set up a homomorphism of the additive group of integers onto the additive group of residue classes modulo 3.
6. Set up a homomorphism of the additive group of integers onto the additive group of residue classes modulo m.
7. Prove that the homomorphic image of a cyclic group is a cyclic group.

5 · IDEALS IN COMMUTATIVE RINGS

We shall now apply the theory of factor groups and homomorphisms of groups to commutative rings. In order to do this we must define a new concept, namely, that of an ideal in a commutative ring. An ideal in a ring is a certain kind of subring which plays a role analogous to that played by a normal subgroup in a group. Hence we first need necessary and sufficient conditions that a nonempty subset S of elements of a ring R be a subring. These are:

1. The elements of S form an additive subgroup of the additive group of R.
2. The set S is closed with respect to multiplication, i.e., if a and b are in S, then ab is in S.

Condition (1) is often phrased as follows: if a and b are in S, then $a - b$ is in S. The student should check that this is a necessary and sufficient condition that a nonempty subset of an additive group be a subgroup. We shall use this formulation of condition (1) in our definition of an ideal in a commutative ring and will, as is customary, denote ideals by German letters.

Definition of an Ideal

A nonempty subset of elements $\mathfrak{m}$ of a commutative ring R is an ideal if the following two conditions are satisfied:

1. If a and b are in $\mathfrak{m}$, then $a - b$ is in $\mathfrak{m}$.
2. If a is in $\mathfrak{m}$ and if r is in R, then ra is in $\mathfrak{m}$.

EXAMPLES
1. The even integers form an ideal S in the ring of integers, for, if $2n$ and $2m$ are in S, then $2n - 2m = 2(n - m)$ is in S. Moreover, if r is any integer, then $r(2n) = 2(rn)$ is an even integer.
2. The ring R itself is an ideal called the *unit ideal* of the ring.

3. The zero element of a ring is an ideal in the ring called the *zero ideal*. It is denoted by (0).

4. Let $R[x]$ be the ring of polynomials with integral coefficients. The polynomials of degree zero (i.e., the integers) together with the zero polynomial form a subring of $R[x]$. However this subring is not an ideal, for, if $f(x)$ is any polynomial in $R[x]$ of degree greater than zero, and if a is any integer, $af(x)$ is not an integer.

5. The ideal generated by an element a of a ring R consists of all elements of the form $ra + na$, where r is in R and n is an integer. This ideal is called a *principal* ideal and is denoted by (a). We prove that the set of elements of the given form $ra + na$ form an ideal. First, if $r_1a + n_1a$ and $r_2a + n_2a$ are in the set, then $r_1a + n_1a - (r_2a + n_2a) = (r_1 - r_2)a + (n_1 - n_2)a$ is of the given form. Next let r be any element of R. Then $r(r_1a + n_1a) = (rr_1 + n_1r)a = r'a + 0 \cdot a$, where r' is in R. Note that, when R has a unity element u, every element of the principal ideal (a) can be written as ra, where r is an element of R. For an element $r'a + na$, where n is an integer, can be written as $r'a + n(ua) = r'a + (nu)a = (r' + nu)a = ra$ when nu is an element of R.

6. Similarly, we define the ideal $(a_1, a_2, \cdots, a_n)$ in a ring R generated by the finite number of elements $a_1, a_2, \cdots, a_n$ of R as the set of elements of the form $\sum_{i=1}^{n} r_ia_i + \sum_{j=1}^{n} n_ja_j$, where the r_i are in R and the n_j are integers. The elements $a_1, a_2, \cdots, a_n$ are said to form a *basis* of the ideal.

Exercises

1. Prove that the integral multiples of any fixed integer m in the ring of integers form an ideal.
2. In the ring of integers prove that the ideal $(6, 4) = (2)$.
3. In the ring of integers prove that the ideal $(9, 25)$ is the ring of integers.
4. In the ring of polynomials $R[x]$, where R is the ring of integers, prove that all polynomials whose constant term is zero form an ideal. Is this a principal ideal? If so, what is its generator?
5. Using the fact that every subgroup of a cyclic group is cyclic, prove that every ideal in the ring of integers is a principal ideal.
6. Prove that the only ideals in the field of rational numbers are the zero ideal (0) and the field itself.
7. Prove that the only ideals in any field are the zero ideal and the field itself.
8. Find all the ideals in the ring of residue classes modulo 10.
9. Show that in the polynomial ring $R[x]$, where R is the field of rational numbers, the ideal $(x^2 + 5x + 6, x + 3) = (x + 3)$.
10. Show that every ideal in the polynomial ring $F[x]$, where F is a field, is a principal ideal. *Hint:* Show that the ideal either consists of the zero ideal or contains a polynomial $r(x)$ of least degree such that every polynomial in the ideal is a polynomial times $r(x)$.

6 · RESIDUE CLASS RINGS

Ideals enable us to construct rings from a given ring in the same way we constructed factor groups by means of normal subgroups. Since an ideal

$\mathfrak{m}$ in a commutative ring R is a normal subgroup of the additive group of the ring, the elements of the ring can be separated into cosets of $\mathfrak{m}$ in R. These cosets are called residue classes of R modulo the ideal $\mathfrak{m}$. Thus a residue class modulo $\mathfrak{m}$ is the set of elements $\mathfrak{m} + a$, where a is any element of the ring R. Recall that a necessary and sufficient condition for the equality of two cosets Sa and Sb of a subgroup S in a group G is that ab^{-1} be in S. (See p. 55, Exercise 6.) This condition translated into the additive notation and applied as a criterion for the equality of two residue classes $\mathfrak{m} + a$ and $\mathfrak{m} + b$ is that $a - b$ be in the ideal $\mathfrak{m}$. We now define $a \equiv b \pmod{\mathfrak{m}}$ if and only if $a - b$ is in $\mathfrak{m}$. Thus we have a generalization of the idea of congruences of integers. We prove the following rules governing congruences modulo an ideal $\mathfrak{m}$.

Theorem 13. Let R *be a commutative ring and* $\mathfrak{m}$ *an ideal in* R. *If* a $\equiv$ b *(mod* $\mathfrak{m}$*) and if* a' $\equiv$ b' *(mod* $\mathfrak{m}$*), then* a + a' $\equiv$ b + b' *(mod* $\mathfrak{m}$*),* aa' $\equiv$ bb' *(mod* $\mathfrak{m}$*), and* ra $\equiv$ rb *(mod* $\mathfrak{m}$*), where* r *is in* R.

Since $a - b$ and $a' - b'$ are both in $\mathfrak{m}$, then $(a - b) + (a' - b') = (a + a') - (b + b')$ is in $\mathfrak{m}$, and $a + a' \equiv b + b' \pmod{\mathfrak{m}}$. Further, since $a - b$ is in $\mathfrak{m}$, $a'(a - b)$ is in $\mathfrak{m}$, and since $a' - b'$ is in $\mathfrak{m}$, $(a' - b')b$ is in $\mathfrak{m}$. Therefore $a'(a - b) + (a' - b')b = a'a - b'b$ is in $\mathfrak{m}$, and $a'a \equiv b'b \pmod{\mathfrak{m}}$. Obviously, if $a - b$ is in $\mathfrak{m}$, $r(a - b)$ is in $\mathfrak{m}$, and $ra \equiv rb$ (mod $\mathfrak{m}$).

Definition of Addition and Multiplication of Residue Classes

Let a be an element of the residue class $\mathfrak{m} + a$ and let b be an element of the residue class $\mathfrak{m} + b$. The *sum* of the two residue classes $\mathfrak{m} + a$ and $\mathfrak{m} + b$ is defined as the class containing the element $a + b$. The *product* of the two residue classes $\mathfrak{m} + a$ and $\mathfrak{m} + b$ is defined as the residue class containing the product ab. Note that by the previous theorem the sum residue class and the product residue class are independent of the particular representatives chosen from the given residue classes.

Theorem 14. Let R *be a commutative ring and* $\mathfrak{m}$ *an ideal in* R. *The residue classes modulo* $\mathfrak{m}$ *form a ring with respect to addition and multiplication.*

The ring formed by the residue classes modulo $\mathfrak{m}$ is called a *residue class ring* denoted by $R/\mathfrak{m}$ or a *difference ring* denoted by $R - \mathfrak{m}$.

From the theory of groups we know that the residue classes form an additive abelian group, for they are the cosets of a normal subgroup $\mathfrak{m}$ in an additive abelian group R. The above definition of product of two residue classes gives us the closure with respect to multiplication. It is left to the student to prove the associative laws for multiplication and the distributive law.

EXAMPLES

1. Let R be the ring of integers and let $\mathfrak{m} = (m)$. Then $R/(m)$ is the ring of residue classes modulo the integer m.

2. Let $R[x]$ be the polynomial ring, where R is the ring of integers and $\mathfrak{m}$ the ideal $(x - 3)$. The ideal $(x - 3)$ consists of all elements of the form $f(x)(x - 3)$, where $f(x)$ is a polynomial in $R[x]$. Now any polynomial $g(x)$ in $R[x]$ can be written as $g(x) = q(x)(x - 3) + g(3)$. Therefore $g(x) \equiv g(3) (\bmod (x - 3))$. That is to say, any residue class can be represented by an integer. Now if two integers a and b lie in the same residue class, $a - b$ is in the ideal $(x - 3)$ that is, $a - b = q(x)(x - 3)$. Now unless $q(x) = 0$, the degree of the right-hand side is greater than zero. Hence $q(x) = 0$ and $a = b$. Thus every integer determines a different residue class. Hence we can set up a one-to-one correspondence between the residue classes of $R[x]$ modulo $(x - 3)$ and the integers a by letting $(x - 3) + a \leftrightarrow a$. The student can easily check that this correspondence is an isomorphism.

3. Let R be the ring of complex numbers $a + bi$, where a and b are integers, and let $\mathfrak{m} = (2)$. Then, since 2 and $2i$ are elements of $\mathfrak{m}$, any number $a + bi = 2k + r + (2k' + r')i$, where $0 \le r < 2$ and $0 \le r' < 2]$. Thus $a + bi \equiv r + r'i \,(\bmod (2))$. Hence we have the four distinct residue classes: $(2), (2) + 1, (2) + i, (2) + 1 + i$.

Exercises

1. Determine whether the residue classes in Example 3 form an integral domain.
2. Exhibit the residue class ring of the ring of complex numbers of the form $a + bi$, where a and b are integers, modulo the ideal (3). Is this residue class ring a field?
3. Exhibit the residue class ring of the ring $R[x]$, where R is the ring of integers, modulo the ideal (x).
4. Exhibit the residue class ring of the ring $R[x]$, where R is the ring of integers modulo the ideal $(x^2 + 1)$.
5. Prove the associative laws for multiplication and the distributive law in $R/(m)$.

7 · HOMOMORPHISMS OF RINGS

The definition of a homomorphism of a ring is an extension of the definition of a homomorphism of a group. The correspondence merely preserves two operations instead of one.

DEFINITION. Let $a, b, c, \cdots$ denote the elements of a ring R, and let $a', b', c', \cdots$ denote the elements of a ring R'. The ring R' is said to be a *homomorphic image* of the ring R if a correspondence $a \to a'$ can be set up from the elements of R onto the elements of R' such that:

1. Every element a in R has exactly one image a' in R';
2. Every element of R' occurs at least once as an image;
3. If $a \to a'$ and $b \to b'$, then $a + b \to a' + b'$ and $ab \to a'b'$.

Again we note that a homomorphism is a many-to-one mapping of the

162 HIGHER ALGEBRA FOR THE UNDERGRADUATE

elements of R onto the elements of R'. We show the intimate relation between ideals and the homomorphism of rings in the following theorem.

Theorem 15. If a ring R' is a homomorphic image of a commutative ring R, those elements of R whose image is the zero element of R' form an ideal $\mathfrak{m}$, and the residue class ring $R/\mathfrak{m}$ is isomorphic to R'.

We first show that those elements of R whose image is the zero element of R' form an ideal $\mathfrak{m}$. Denote the zero element of R' by $0'$. Then, if $a \rightarrow 0'$ and $b \rightarrow 0'$, we have $a - b \rightarrow 0' - 0' = 0'$. Further, if r is any element of the ring R whose image is r' in R', $ra \rightarrow r' \cdot 0' = 0'$. Thus those elements of R whose image is the zero element of R' form an ideal $\mathfrak{m}$ in R. Now separate the elements of R into residue classes modulo $\mathfrak{m}$. If $a \rightarrow a'$, all the elements of the residue class $\mathfrak{m} + a$ have the image a', for any element $m + a$, where m is in $\mathfrak{m}$, of this class is mapped onto $0' + a' = a'$. Moreover, if $b \rightarrow a'$, then $a - b \rightarrow a' - a' = 0'$, and $a - b$ is in $\mathfrak{m}$. If now we regard the residue classes of R modulo $\mathfrak{m}$ as elements, the correspondence $\mathfrak{m} + a \rightarrow a'$ is obviously an isomorphism, for if $\mathfrak{m} + b \rightarrow b'$, then $\mathfrak{m} + a + b \rightarrow a' + b'$, and $\mathfrak{m} + ab \rightarrow a'b'$.

Now, combining our previous discussion of residue class rings of a ring R with our definition of homomorphism, we can see that any residue class ring of R is a homomorphic image of R. Let $\mathfrak{m}$ be an ideal in R, then the correspondence $a \rightarrow \mathfrak{m} + a$ gives us the homomorphism. Hence we have the following theorem.

Theorem 16. Every ideal $\mathfrak{m}$ in a commutative ring R determines a homomorphism of R onto its residue class ring $R/\mathfrak{m}$.

Exercises

1. Prove that a homomorphic image of a commutative ring is a commutative ring.
2. Prove that, if R' is a homomorphic image of a ring R with unity element, R' has a unity element.
3. What are the possible homomorphic images of a field?
4. The polynomial ring $F[x]$, where F is the field of rational numbers, is mapped homomorphically onto the ring of complex numbers $a + bi$, where a and b are rational, by the correspondence $f(x) \rightarrow f(i)$. What is the ideal that determines the homomorphism?
5. Find all the ideals in the residue class ring of integers modulo 12. Hence find all the homomorphic images of this residue class ring.

8 · AUTOMORPHISMS OF FIELDS

Automorphism of a Field

An automorphism of a field F is a one-to-one correspondence of F with itself which is preserved under addition and multiplication.

In terms of the notation introduced in connection with automorphisms of groups, $\mathbf{f}$ is an automorphism of a field F if it is a one-to-one correspondence of F with itself such that $\mathbf{f}(a + b) = \mathbf{f}(a) + \mathbf{f}(b)$ and $\mathbf{f}(ab) = \mathbf{f}(a)\,\mathbf{f}(b)$.

EXAMPLES

1. If $a \leftrightarrow a$, we have the *identity* automorphism.

2. Let F be the field consisting of all numbers of the form $a + b\sqrt{2}$, where a and b are rational numbers. Then $a + b\sqrt{2} \leftrightarrow a - b\sqrt{2}$ is an automorphism of F. For if $a + b\sqrt{2} \leftrightarrow a - b\sqrt{2}$ and $c + d\sqrt{2} \leftrightarrow c - d\sqrt{2}$, then $(a + b\sqrt{2}) + (c + d\sqrt{2}) = (a + c) + (b + d)\sqrt{2} \leftrightarrow (a + c) - (b + d)\sqrt{2} = (a - b\sqrt{2}) + (c - d\sqrt{2})$, and $(a + b\sqrt{2})(c + d\sqrt{2}) = (ac + 2bd) + (ad + bc)\sqrt{2} \leftrightarrow (ac + 2bd) - (ad + bc)\sqrt{2} = (a - b\sqrt{2})(c - d\sqrt{2})$.

3. If F is the field of real numbers, the correspondence $a \leftrightarrow -a$ is one-to-one, and is preserved under addition but is not preserved under multiplication. For $a + b \leftrightarrow -(a + b) = (-a) + (-b)$ but $ab \leftrightarrow -(ab) \neq (-a)(-b)$. Hence this correspondence is not an automorphism.

4. We may use the concept of an automorphism of a field to provide an alternate proof of Theorem 12 of Chap. 5. If $a_0 x^n + a_1 x^{n-1} + \cdots + a_n$, where $a_0, a_1, \cdots, a_n$ are real numbers, has the zero $a + bi$, (a and b real numbers) we have $a_0(a + bi)^n + a_1(a + bi)^{n-1} + \cdots + a_n = 0$. Now consider the automorphism $\mathbf{f}$ of the field of complex numbers defined by $\mathbf{f}(a + bi) = a - bi$ for a and b real numbers. Then

$$\mathbf{f}[a_0(a + bi)^n + a_1(a + bi)^{n-1} + \cdots + a_n]$$
$$= \mathbf{f}(a_0)[\mathbf{f}(a + bi)]^n + \mathbf{f}(a_1)[\mathbf{f}(a + bi)]^{n-1} + \cdots + \mathbf{f}(a_n)$$
$$= a_0(a - bi)^n + a_1(a - bi)^{n-1} + \cdots + a_n = \mathbf{f}(0) = 0.$$

The proofs of the following theorems closely parallel the proofs of the corresponding theorems for groups, and we leave them as exercises for the student.

Theorem 17. If $\mathbf{f}$ is an automorphism of a field F with additive identity 0 and multiplicative identity 1, $\mathbf{f}(0) = 0$ and $\mathbf{f}(1) = 1$.

Theorem 18. Let $\mathbf{f}$ and $\mathbf{g}$ be automorphisms of a field F. Then the correspondence $\mathbf{k}$ given by $a \leftrightarrow \mathbf{k}(a) = \mathbf{f}[\mathbf{g}(a)]$ is an automorphism of F.

EXAMPLE. Let F be the field consisting of the numbers $a + b\sqrt{2} + ci + d\sqrt{2}i$, where a, b, c, and d are rational numbers. Then if $\mathbf{f}(a + b\sqrt{2} + ci + d\sqrt{2}i) = a - b\sqrt{2} + ci - d\sqrt{2}i$ and $\mathbf{g}(a + b\sqrt{2}i + ci + d\sqrt{2}i) = a + b\sqrt{2} - ci - d\sqrt{2}i$, $\mathbf{f}$ and $\mathbf{g}$ are automorphisms of F. Then $\mathbf{k}$ is defined by $\mathbf{k}(a + b\sqrt{2} + ci + d\sqrt{2}i) = \mathbf{f}[\mathbf{g}(a + b\sqrt{2} + ci + d\sqrt{2}i) = \mathbf{f}(a + b\sqrt{2} - ci - d\sqrt{2}i) = a - b\sqrt{2} - ci + d\sqrt{2}i$ and is another automorphism of F,

DEFINITION. If $\mathbf{f}$ and $\mathbf{g}$ are automorphisms of a field F, $\mathbf{f} \cdot \mathbf{g}$ is the automorphism $\mathbf{k}$ defined by $a \leftrightarrow \mathbf{k}(a) = \mathbf{f}[\mathbf{g}(a)]$.

Theorem 19.   The set of all automorphisms of a field F *form a group called the automorphism group of* F.

We return to the example following Theorem 18. It may be shown that the only automorphisms of this field are the identity automorphism **e** and the automorphisms **f**, **g**, and **k**. The automorphism group of *F* has the multiplication table.

	e	f	g	k
e	e	f	g	k
f	f	e	k	g
g	g	k	e	f
k	k	g	f	e

Exercises

1. Prove Theorem 17.
2. Prove Theorem 18.
3. Prove Theorem 19.
4. Consider the field F consisting of all numbers of the form $a + br + cr^2 + dr^3 + ei + fir + gir^2 + hir^3$, where $a, b, \cdots, h$ are rational numbers and $r = \sqrt[4]{3}$. Find all the automorphisms $\mathbf{f}$ of F such that $\mathbf{f}(i) = i$.

Bibliography

GENERAL REFERENCES

Albert, A. A., *Introduction to Algebraic Theories*, Chicago, University of Chicago Press, 1941.

Albert, A. A., *Modern Higher Algebra*, Chicago, University of Chicago Press, 1937.

Andree, R. V., *Selections from Modern Abstract Algebra*, New York, Henry Holt and Co., 1958.

Birkhoff, G., and S. MacLane, *A Survey of Modern Algebra*, revised edition, New York, The Macmillan Co., 1953.

Johnson, R. E., *First Course in Abstract Algebra*, Englewood Cliffs, N. J., Prentice-Hall, 1953.

McCoy, N. H., *Introduction to Modern Algebra*, Boston, Allyn and Bacon, 1960.

MacDuffee, C. C., *An Introduction to Abstract Algebra*, New York, John Wiley and Sons, 1940.

van der Waerden, B. L., *Modern Algebra*, vols. 1 and 2, translated from the German by Fred Blum, New York, Frederic Unger Publishing Co., 1953.

NUMBER THEORY

Dickson, L. E., *Modern Elementary Theory of Numbers*, Chicago, University of Chicago Press, 1939,

Ore, O., *Number Theory and Its History*, New York, McGraw-Hill Book Co., 1952.

Niven I. and H. S. Zuckerman, *Introduction to the Theory of Numbers*, New York, John Wiley and Sons, 1960.

Stewart, B. M., *Theory of Numbers*, New York, The Macmillan Co., 1952.

Uspensky, J. V., and M. H. Heaslet, *Elementary Number Theory*, New York, McGraw-Hill Book Co., 1939.

GROUP THEORY

Carmichael, R. D., *Introduction to the Theory of Groups of Finite Order*, New York, Dover Publications, 1956.

Hall, M., Jr., *The Theory of Groups*, New York, The Macmillan Co., 1959.

Kurosh, A. G., *The Theory of Groups*, vol. 1, translated from the Russian by K. A. Hirsch, New York, Chelsea Publishing Co., 1955.

Zassenhaus, H., *The Theory of Groups*, translated from the German by Saul Kravetz, New York, Chelsea Publishing Co., 1949.

VECTORS AND MATRICES

Halmos, P. R., *Finite Dimensional Vector Spaces*, 2d edition, Princeton, N. J., D. Van Nostrand Co., 1958.

Hohn, F. E., *Elementary Matrix Algebra*, New York, The Macmillan Co., 1958.

MacDuffee, C. C., *The Theory of Matrices*, 2d edition, New York, Chelsea Publishing Co., 1946.

MacDuffee, C. C., *Vectors and Matrices*, Carus Mathematical Monograph No. 7, Buffalo, N. Y., The Mathematical Association of America, 1943.

Murdoch, D. C., *Linear Algebra for Undergraduates*, New York, John Wiley and Sons, 1957.

Perlis, S., *Theory of Matrices*, Cambridge, Mass., Addison-Wesley Press, 1952.

Stoll, R. R., *Linear Algebra and Matrix Theory*, New York, McGraw-Hill Book Co., 1952.

Thrall, R. M., and L. Tornheim, *Vector Spaces and Matrices*, New York, John Wiley and Sons, 1957.

RINGS AND IDEALS

Artin, E., C. J. Nesbitt, and R. M. Thrall, *Rings with Minimum Condition*, Ann Arbor, University of Michigan Press, 1944.

Jacobson, N., *The Theory of Rings*, Mathematical Surveys, No. 2, New York, American Mathematical Society, 1943.

McCoy, N. H., *Rings and Ideals*, Carus Mathematical Monograph No. 8, Buffalo, N. Y., The Mathematical Association of America, 1948.

Index

This book, a revision of the original edition by Marie Weiss, is intended as an introductory text in abstract algebra for the undergraduate. It covers the major elementary aspects of the subject: integral domains, rings, fields, groups, vector spaces and matrices. In preparing the revision Roy Dubisch has preserved the organization and spirit of the original text. However he has added many constructive and explicit illustrations of definitions and greatly added to the number of exercises. Also, previously omitted topics such as linear independence and dependence of vectors, the inner products of vectors, and the concept of basis and dimension of a vector space are now covered, with the addition of two new chapters (6 and 7). Sophisticated approaches are avoided and simple examples are used to illustrate the concepts introduced.

This text provides a smooth and gradual transition from the predominantly problem solving courses to a postulational approach, providing the student with a firm foundation for further work in other fields of mathematics.

H.G.-H.P. 162-2207